PMR Conversion Handbook

Chris Lorek, G4HCL

Radio Society of Great Britain

Published by the Radio Society of Great Britain, Cranborne Road, Potters Bar, Herts EN6 3JE.

First published 1997

ISBN 1 872309 40 2

Cover design: Jennifer Crocker.
New illustrations: Bob Ryan.
Design and production: Ray Eckersley, Seven Stars Publishing.

Printed in Great Britain by Bell & Bain Ltd, Glasgow.

I wish to dedicate this book to my family. Not just my wife Sheila and children Steven, David and Carolyn for their patience with "Dad tapping at the keyboard until the middle of the night", but also to my parents Karl and Diane for their never-ending support, for without their continual help I would have had even less opportunity to enjoy family life.

Disclaimer

The information given in this publication has, due to very nature of the subject, been compiled from a wide range of sources. All reasonable care has been taken to ensure accuracy, but equipment build standards do change, neither are we humans infallible and even PMR manufacturers make mistakes in their technical manuals despite much proof reading. Thus, regrettably neither the author nor the publisher can be held liable or responsible for any errors that may occur in the information given in this book.

Acknowledgements

This book, besides containing information which I've sometimes learned the hard way by trial and error, could not have been possible without the help of, and information from, a number of equipment manufacturers and a far larger number of fellow radio amateurs.

My thanks in particular go to the Publications and Publicity Department of Philips Telecom (now owned by Simoco) for their permission, a number of years ago, to reproduce information from their early equipment manuals. My thanks also go to the South Midlands Communications Group for their help and supply of ex-PMR equipment and information. At least one other PMR equipment manufacturer I've found appears to have a much less amenable approach to amateurs seeking information from them, even to the extent of actively discouraging young enthusiasts, who are sometimes the PMR engineers of tomorrow, from modifying their ex-PMR equipment for amateur use. It's good to see *some* manufacturers *do* care.

The individual amateurs who have provided me with much information I have also thanked, wherever possible, throughout this book in the appropriate sections. However, to those I may have missed I apologise in advance – it wasn't intentional. I've chatted with several hundred amateurs and listeners at rallies, lectures, via packet, e-mail and 'snail mail', all of whom have provided me with an incentive and significant encouragement for this book, as well as giving extremely useful feedback on what's needed within it. To all of you I express my thanks.

A significant amount of the modification information here has been provided to me by the UK PMR User Group, which is made up of individual amateurs, all of whom wish to freely share their knowledge and information with others. I hope that I've helped a little in this aim through this book.

Contents

Preface

EIGHT years ago as I write this, I set off on a move from one part of the UK to another with my career, and I had the fortune to find that I had a couple of months of paid time 'on my hands'. Following a series of my articles on ex-PMR conversions in *Ham Radio Today* magazine, I'd had my arm twisted by many amateurs to collate a book on the subject. I thought this was the ideal opportunity! The result was indeed a book on converting surplus two-way radio equipment, consisting of details on modifying a number of Pye equipments to the amateur bands.

Since then, many, many amateurs have asked me "When's the next book coming out?", but shortage of time has always been the limiting factor. However, my arm was finally twisted again, this time by the Radio Society of Great Britain, and agreeing on a deadline to meet was quite an inducement. If it were not for Marcia, 2E1DAY, at the RSGB HQ continually asking me "Where's my book?" and the RSGB then giving me a contract to write it, you may not be reading this now. Yes, I *did* make it by the agreed date, and I left for two overseas business trips the day after I personally handed it to Marcia!

In these pages, I hope you'll find help and guidance, maybe even encouragement, in 'having a go' at getting on the air at low cost. My experience of answering many amateurs' questions in the past years have guided me greatly in the book's content, and I thank you all for helping me with this. Even though you may feel you were asking my advice, I have learnt a number of valuable lessons in preempting what would be asked, and hopefully now include many of the answers to these questions in this book.

In this respect, you *won't* find a massive volume of step-by-step conversion instructions for virtually every ex-PMR radio to be found either now or in the future. To do that would require a book at least a hundred times the size, and even then it wouldn't cover everything.

Instead, I've tried to concentrate a little more on *teaching* readers what they will find in typical ex-PMR gear, with guidance on alignment, what to do with the signalling equipment you'll possibly find in the set that renders it unusable at first, information on channel spacing and frequency bands, and, most importantly, on what will easily 'convert' to the amateur bands and what, without a great deal of work, will not.

OK, I give in. Yes, I've also included step-by-step instructions on getting a range of typically found ex-PMR mobile, portable, and base station gear going onto the 4m, 2m and 70cm amateur bands as well!

Please read, enjoy, and take this book with you when searching for equipment at a rally to help you identify what's what, and have fun with your converted ex-PMR gear on the bands.

Chris Lorek, G4HCL

1 Private mobile radio systems

PRIVATE mobile radio, or 'PMR' for short, refers to mobile radio communications in the private sector as opposed to military communications etc. However, much of the equipment covered in this book has typically also found service in the government sector, particularly in the emergency services such as the police, ambulance, and fire and rescue services.

In the UK, PMR has developed substantially over the years, the first 'private' use being by a taxi firm in Cambridge on a single, crystal-controlled channel. Nowadays, the use of trunked multiple-channel systems with synthesised transceivers under microprocessor control, with intelligent channel allocation from off-air received signalling, is commonly used in both the private and public-access mobile radio sectors.

Private mobile radio (PMR) is a little different to public-access mobile radio (PAMR). PMR is normally used by individual fleets of users, such as a taxi firm, delivery firm or a police force, with communications limited to their own users on their own government-allocated channels.

PAMR covers public-access communications, including those with PSTN (Public Switched Telephone Network) access, cellular telephones being a typical example. Another development on both a national and regional scale in the UK, which is particularly significant to readers of this book, is that of the growing use of trunked radio, such as that on Band III. In these services, both cellular and Band III, a 'pool' of channels are shared between many users, sophisticated digital signalling circuits within the radio equipments being used to control communication and channel access.

A SCARCE RESOURCE

The radio frequency spectrum is a limited resource and, to cope with the ever-growing need for PMR communication in the UK, spectrum conservation techniques such as trunking are being used more and more in the PMR as well as in the PAMR fields. What does this mean to us? For one, it often means that users of existing radio systems need to upgrade their sets to meet newly introduced requirements. For example, the UK public utilities, ie the water, electricity and gas boards, relinquished their 'mid-band' radios and went to a trunked radio system. Transport organisations such as bus and rail companies are another example, many of these now using the

Band III spectrum. London Underground is one example of a user which disposed of its channelised UHF FM communication system and replaced it with a fully trunked radio system, this time also on UHF FM. What happened to its 'old' radios? Well, my local 70cm repeater benefited from this, with the repeater itself and the standby unit both using Pye F490 wall-mounting base station repeaters which had previously seen years of service beneath the city streets of our capital. I'm sure plenty of amateurs have also benefited from the UHF portable radios that became subsequently obsolete.

SIMPLEX

The simplest form of PMR communication is by using a single frequency for both transmit and receive, each user 'taking turns' to press their PTT (push-to-talk) button and speak. This is very common to virtually every amateur radio non-repeater contact we have, where everyone in range of each station, and on that frequency and mode can listen in and join in with the contact. You'll typically find that some 'on-site' PMR equipment uses this, particularly in the 169MHz range where sets are used for short-term hire purposes.

HALF AND FULL DUPLEX

Half duplex still uses a PTT principle in the mobile and portable equipments, but here they transmit and receive on different frequencies, in a similar way to the 'repeater split' that we use on 2m and 70cm. The users typically communicate with a base station which operates in full-duplex mode, where the operator can 'listen in' to the receive channel whilst transmitting to allow users to interrupt if needed. Emergency services, such as the police, ambulance, and fire and rescue service, commonly use this. Others use sets through a well-sited repeater, often on a hilltop or tall building in a city, again as we do with amateur repeaters. However, in large systems the 'radio console' operator at the office site has either a direct landline or UHF / microwave radio link to the remote duplex radio base station, using what is effectively an audio interface with microphone and speaker rather than a complete radio transceiver at their console. 600Ω twisted-pair lines are used for the link at either end, with either DC or tone / FFSK-controlled signalling for various functions, such as PTT, talkthrough enable, channel change, receiver squelch etc.

This explains why many ex-PMR base station equipments for system use are usually designed for rack mounting, and invariably have an internally fitted interface unit giving 600Ω line audio input / output control and audio lines, but often with very few, if any, manual user controls on the front panel. Don't despair, as these control facilities *are* available; you'll find more details in Chapter 5 – 'Base stations' later in this book.

In the commercial field with smaller groups of users (a delivery firm, for example) usually only a few radios will be in use. Here, a 'shared' or 'common base station' repeater is used, which is in permanent talkthrough operation. CTCSS or five-tone (more about these later in this chapter) is used in the mobile and portable equipment, together with PTT time-out timers, to give the users a degree of privacy and an equal chance of using the shared repeater.

As well as providing a little background to the way the set or sets you might have in front of you right now *did* work in the past, this brief section has hopefully explained why many ex-PMR mobile and portable sets you'll find operate on different frequencies for transmit and receive. This is why they won't usually 'talk' to each other set-to-set unless they're also equipped with one or more single-frequency simplex channels, and why they may be also fitted with a variety of signalling systems and transmission controls, which will need to be considered before modifying them for amateur use (see later).

Table 1.1. Pye/Philips/Simoco band designators

Band	Frequency range (MHz)
A, A0	146–174
A1	148–162
A2	160–174
B, B0	132–156
B1	132–146
B2	142–156
D1	88–100
D2	98–108
D3	86–100
E, E0	68–88
E1	68–79
E2	77–88
K1	174–208
K2	192–225
P	79–101
T1	405–440
U0	440–470
TP	405–447
UP	438–472
WP	466–512

FREQUENCY BANDS

Private mobile radio equipment usually operates in the VHF and UHF bands, commonly between 68–88MHz, 138–174MHz, and 405–470MHz, with trunked PAMR (public access mobile radio) as well as some transport-related mobile radio in the Band III segment at 174–225MHz. There are other frequency allocations coming into use as I write this, for example within the old TV Band I spectrum around 45MHz. Although sets for this band are still to become available as this is book being prepared, in years to come surplus sets from this band many be quite suitable for use in the amateur 6m (50MHz) band.

PMR manufacturers typically produce a number of frequency band variants of their equipment, usually with band designator letters and possibly also number sub-divisions. For example, the Pye/Philips/Simoco system includes the designators shown in Table 1.1 in sets you'll see in the surplus PMR market.

Tuning range

You'll find that a set which operates at any frequency, or frequencies, within the given manufacturer's sub-band should also be capable of operation, following realignment, on *any* channel frequency in that band. You may, however, find that the 'spread' of the available frequency coverage isn't the entire band, but rather a sub-section of it. This can, for crystalled equipment, typically be around ±0.25% to ±0.5% of the centre ('alignment') frequency, ie between 0.5% to 1% total for both the transmitter and receiver, although the centre frequencies of these ranges can be different. Thus, you can usually expect a set aligned correctly for a centre frequency of 145.400MHz to operate perfectly on the 2m repeater and simplex channels between 145.000 and 145.775MHz, but not very well down at the non-amateur 143MHz 'space segment', eg for orbiting space station reception, or extremely poorly, if at all, around 137MHz for weather satellite reception.

Synthesised sets usually tend to have a wider tuning range, these typically using a final-frequency VCO (voltage-controlled oscillator), thus overcoming the limitation of narrow-bandwidth crystal multiplier stages. Instead the tuning range is primarily limited by the VCO range, together with the bandwidth of the receiver front-end tuned stages, which may even be varicap controlled to track the receiver tuning range, and on transmit by the transmitter PA stages, which could even be a wide-band PA module type.

Channel spacing

In earlier days, PMR systems in the UK used AM with 50kHz channel spacing. This was the technology of the time, and a narrower channel spacing wasn't required as there was no great shortage of channels. Time went on, and FM also came into use, again with a channel spacing of 50kHz. You may indeed still come across the occasional UHF base station 'relic' with 50kHz channel spacing filters, and a transmit deviation set up for a peak of 10–15kHz.

Nowadays, however, you'll mainly find 12.5kHz channel spacing equipment on the ex-PMR market. 25kHz channel spacing equipment can, however, still often be found, especially in ex-government UHF transceivers which in 1996 continue to use 25kHz channel spacing in the 450–453MHz range throughout the UK.

Channel spacing identification

You might find the channel spacing is indicated on the serial number or frequency identification label of the equipment. If, for example, the frequency is an obvious 12.5kHz increment, ie something like 165.2375MHz or 170.0375MHz, it's a reasonably sure bet that the filters within the set are those for 12.5kHz spacing also. Manufacturers usually also have the channel spacing as part of the 'equipment code' which again is marked on the identification label. Pye/Philips/Simoco codes, for example, are:

S – 12.5kHz channel spacing, for 2.5kHz transmit deviation
R – 20kHz channel spacing, mainly found outside the UK
V – 25kHz channel spacing, for 5kHz transmit deviation
N – 50kHz channel spacing, for 15kHz transmit deviation (quite rare, this one, but still occasionally found)

If all else fails, then take a look inside the box at the set's receiver IF circuitry. Here, you'll find either a multi-pole crystal filter (in a small box-shaped metal case) or possibly two monolithic dual-pole crystal filters (which each look like a small metal-cased crystal, but with three connection leads instead of two), plus one or two plastic-cased ceramic filters (see photos). The ceramic filters are usually the easiest to identify – the bandwidth is commonly marked on these as either 'LF8' (8kHz total bandwidth, for 12.5kHz channel spacing),

Left: **ceramic filters**

Right: **crystal filters – two eight-pole types and a two-pole type are shown here**

or 'LF15' (15kHz total bandwidth, for 25kHz channel spacing). You may instead find these are marked with an indication of the centre frequency, ie 'CFU455', indicating a ceramic filter unit for 455kHz, followed by a code letter. Typical codes are shown in Table 1.2.

If the set uses a multi-pole crystal filter at the first IF, and if this has a type number on it which can be traced to a supplier's catalogue, it's sometimes a better identification. Typical filter types you may find are given in Table 1.3.

Crystal and ceramic filters in a typical ex-PMR rig, the SMC545L1. The crystal ones are top left; the ceramic ones are bottom centre

AM or FM?

As I briefly mentioned earlier, the first PMR rigs in the UK used AM (amplitude modulation) as their mode of operation. As time went by, users of these PMR systems replaced and upgraded their sets, but in order not to have a complete changeover, AM often remained as the mode of operation, and to this day is still used by many PMR users in the UK. AM will also continue to be used for the foreseeable future for some VHF two-way radio systems, due to the absence of the 'capture effect' as found on FM. On FM, a PMR signal, say, 5–10dB stronger than a weaker signal will often completely override the weaker one without any heterodyne or other noises to be heard. The result is usually a higher grade of communication. However, AM has the benefit of the operator being aware if a weaker signal from another user is trying to 'get through', and is still used around the world for airband communication and by emergency services in the UK.

You will thus also see AM equipment offered for sale on the surplus PMR market as well as FM gear. My advice, unless you're prepared for a lot of hard work, is to pass AM equipment by in favour of FM equipment, which, albeit at a higher price (usually, but not always!), is normally also readily available. The added cost of components and boards in 'converting' an AM set to FM is often outweighed by the relative

Table 1.2. Ceramic filter codes

Code	Bandwidth (kHz)	Indicated channel spacing (kHz)
CFU455D2	20	25
CFU455E2	15	25
CFU455F2	12	12.5
CFU455G2	9	12.5
CFU455H2	6	12.5
CFW455E	14	25
CFW455F	12	12.5
CFW455G	9	12.5
CFW455HT	6	12.5

Table 1.3. Crystal filter codes

Code	IF (MHz)	Bandwidth (kHz)	Indicated channel spacing (kHz)
Two-pole crystal filters			
10M08A	10.7	8	12.5
10M08AH	10.7	8	12.5
10M15A	10.7	15	25
21M30A	21.4	8	12.5
45U8AF	10.7	8	12.5
45U15AF	10.7	8	12.5
Eight-pole crystal filters			
10M08DZ	10.7	8	12.5
10M15DZ	10.7	15	25
21S08DZ	21.4	8	12.5
21S15DZ	21.4	15	25

cost of buying similar FM equipment in the first place. It *can* be done but is usually subject to specific and detailed modification for each particular type of equipment.

SIGNALLING

With the frequency spectrum being a limited and necessarily shared resource, it's rare that the 'typical' PMR user (with, say, a few sets and a base station back at the office) will be able to get a licence for a frequency for their exclusive use in a given area. They usually find they need to share their channel with others. The Radiocommunications Agency, whose local offices have a 'hands-on' approach to frequency allocation from their local knowledge, do take steps to ensure that heavy daytime radio users share with heavy night-time users. For example, a local delivery or service company, having most calls during the day, could share with a night-time security service without too many instances of the channel being 'blocked'.

However, despite all the steps taken, channel sharing is invariably required during heavy airtime usage periods of the day, and to help with this, some form of selective signalling is commonly used in each user's radio system. The usual aim of this is to keep the set's speaker muted not only until a signal is received on the channel (ie the receiver squelch lifts), but also one that is from a valid user on that channel, ie one in the same 'fleet' and one who wants to communicate with that particular user. At the time of writing, the Radiocommunications Agency won't take any action of reported 'interference' to a user's PMR system from other radio system users unless a selective calling system like CTCSS is being used in the fleet's radios.

To do this, sets are usually internally (or occasionally externally) equipped with circuitry to provide this 'signalling', which can have a number of forms, the most common of which I've detailed below. So, don't be surprised if your ex-PMR set, straight out of service and having been bought as 'guaranteed working', can't hear anything at all on the channel even though your scanner on the same frequency can. Your ex-PMR set might just also need the off-air signal to have the correct signalling tone or tone sequence.

CTCSS

Probably the most commonly used signalling system in ex-PMR equipment you'll find from small- to medium-sized fleets is CTCSS (Continuous Tone Controlled Squelch System), or 'sub-tone' as it's commonly called. Motorola call this 'PL' (Private Line) in their range of PMR equipment, but it's exactly the same thing.

Here a sub-audible tone of between 67Hz and 250.3Hz is

automatically generated in the set's transmitter (Fig 1.1). This is typically at around 10–15% of the peak system deviation, ie for a 12.5kHz channel spacing set with 2.5kHz peak deviation, you'll find the CTCSS tone at around 250–375Hz deviation.

In each receiver a decoder circuit, which is usually combined with the encoder, is used to identify that the correct CTCSS tone accompanies the received signal. If it does, the receiver squelch is lifted and the radio user hears the message.

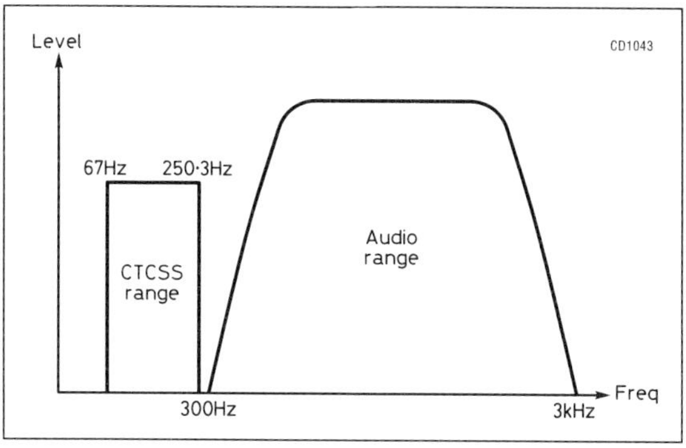

Fig 1.1. CTCSS signalling

CTCSS is now commonly used as an alternative access method to a 1750Hz toneburst for amateur repeaters, so don't just discard the unit! You'll find details of the required CTCSS tones for repeaters around the UK, as well as details for adding a one-IC CTCSS encoder to your set, in the appendices to this book.

You'll often encounter a CTCSS unit in ex-PMR transceivers, and it's important to note that, with the unit in circuit, the set won't receive anything unless it's accompanied by the correct CTCSS tone. An indication of the set's internal squelch having lifted (but without the speaker enabled) is usually that a 'busy' LED is lit on the set's front panel, showing that the channel is in use by others.

CTCSS is often used with fleet users in conjunction with a 'common base station', which introduces other control features to the set. You'll find more information on this topic later in this chapter.

Table 1.4. CTCSS frequencies (in hertz)

67.0	107.2	167.9
71.9	110.9	173.8
74.4	114.8	179.9
77.0	118.8	186.2
79.7	123.0	192.8
82.5	127.3	203.5
85.4	131.8	210.7
88.5	136.5	218.1
91.5	141.3	225.7
94.8	146.2	233.6
97.4	151.4	241.8
100.0	156.7	250.3
103.5	162.2	

Sequential tone signalling

This signalling method, again very commonly used in the PMR field in the UK and Europe but mainly by larger fleets, uses a sequential series of tones for selective calling, or 'Selcall' for short. Each mobile radio is typically assigned a multi-digit ID, eg '12345', as its 'calling address', and a decoder circuit is fitted to detect and act on the correct sequence of tones received which corresponds to its individual ID. Five tones are commonly used, to give a five-digit ID, and from this the system has gained the commonly used name of 'five-tone' (see Fig 1.2). Motorola call it 'Select 5' in their PMR equipment, but again it's the same thing. Unfortunately there's no 'standard' set of tones used, instead there's a number of 'standards', usually dependent upon what the manufacturer has had experience of in their early equipment, although many standard plug-in five-tone encoder/decoder boards are now programmable for a number of systems.

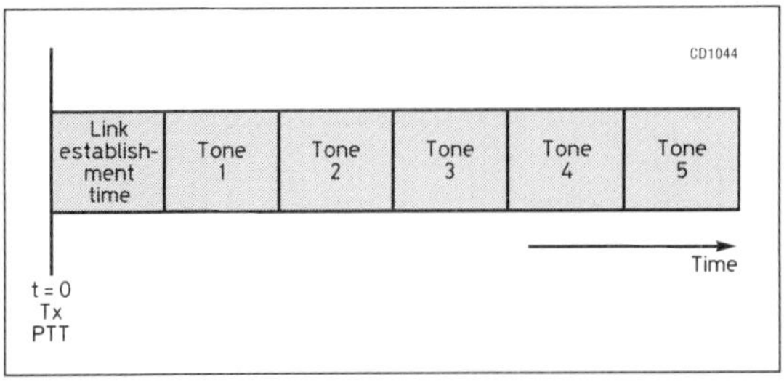

Fig 1.2. Five-tone signalling

Let's take an example of the use of this system. From Table 1.5, an ID of 12345 with EEA tones would correspond to an initial burst of 1124Hz, immediately followed by a burst of 1197Hz, then of 1275Hz, then of 1358Hz, and finally of 1446Hz. Each digit's tone is a predetermined length, eg for EEA each is 40ms long, although the length of the first tone in any system is invariably lengthened to allow for the time delays of transmitter key-up and the remote receiver squelch opening time.

On transmit, the set can also automatically transmit its Selcall ID each time the PTT is keyed. A 'universal' decoder with digital display (this sometimes incorporating an automatic conversion of numbers into user names etc) would be fitted at the radio base station operator's console, to provide a visual ID of who was transmitting at any time. Some sets have this enabled to send an ID when the radio is first switched on, as a 'starting work' indication in a mobile fleet to show who's available on the radio. *With this in mind, be very careful if your ex-PMR has a five-tone unit built in. Plug it into a dummy load, not your signal generator, when first switching on after purchasing it – you could easily find it will automatically transmit a burst of RF power for half a second or so!*

Table 1.5. Sequential tone signalling frequencies (in hertz)

Standard:	EEA	ZVEI	DZVEI	CCIR	CCITT
Digit 1:	1124	1060	970	1124	697
Digit 2:	1197	1160	1060	1197	770
Digit 3:	1275	1270	1160	1275	852
Digit 4:	1358	1400	1270	1358	941
Digit 5:	1446	1530	1400	1446	1209
Digit 6:	1540	1670	1530	1540	1335
Digit 7:	1647	1830	1670	1640	1477
Digit 8:	1747	2000	1830	1747	1633
Digit 9:	1860	2200	2000	1860	1800
Digit 0:	1981	2400	2200	1981	400
Repeat:	2110	2600	2400	2110	2300
Tone length:	40ms	70ms	70ms	100ms	100ms

A further enhancement is where the final, or final two, Selcall digits that are transmitted can be manually changed from the set's front panel, to act as a 'user status' indication as well as an ID, eg the first four digits being the ID and the fifth digit being the status. For example, a final '1' could mean 'On duty and awaiting work', '2' could mean 'at customer's premises', '3' could mean 'at lunch' and so on.

These status digits can be thumbwheel switches, up/down push buttons linked to a digital display, or similar. They're *not* always a channel change – so even if your set has a control that apparently looks like it changes between 99 different 'channels', inside it could still be a single-channel, crystal-controlled set. Don't be fooled when examining sets at a rally stand.

Each mobile or portable unit's ID would be stored in the set's five-tone Selcall unit, which would typically mute the set's speaker until the correct five-tone sequence is decoded. Each user's transceiver can, in advanced systems, also have more than one decode sequence, a common application being a 'transpond' system. Here, the radio user's 'normal' Selcall is used to call the radio for speech communication, but a slightly different Selcall number is used to automatically 'interrogate' the set. When it's received, the set transmits its ID plus any status indication the user has entered. This way, the radio base station console operator can check to see if Joe Smith firstly has his radio switched on and is in range, and secondly by the received status whether he's available for the work required or whatever. Sometimes, for example in a very busy radio system, the radio's PTT is intentionally inhibited and the only transmission capable is that of a status. In these cases, one pre-determined status sequence is usually a 'request for speech', where upon receipt by the base station system, the set is automatically acknowledged over the air with a five-tone sequence and is placed in a 'queue' for the manual operator, who then, when able to respond in voice, sends yet another five-tone ID to 'open up' the mobile's PTT facility.

So your ex-PMR set may well not be able to transmit with the microphone PTT when you first try it into your power meter and dummy load, even though there's nothing wrong with it. If this is the case, you can of course just try pressing the 'status send' button, you may just see a brief burst of RF power, showing all is well.

A further feature which again you should be aware of, when using an ex-PMR set with a five-tone unit, is that of a possible 'alarm' facility. Here, by pressing a given button, or a button sequence, the set can automatically transmit an 'emergency' ID, with this sometimes being repeated every few seconds until cancelled by an over-the-air five-tone command from the base station. Another 'added feature' is where the emergency ID is followed by a short period of continuous transmission with a 'live microphone'. I'm sure you can think of uses, for example lone bus or taxi drivers. But again, beware when testing your set equipped with a five-tone unit for the first time, for example when connected to a signal generator – a wrong button and *pop* goes your transmitter PA or maybe, even worse, the receiver test equipment you have the set's antenna connector attached to.

The above goes to show that a five-tone unit can act to inhibit transmission, automatically enable transmission, and disable reception. In other words, a lot of problems for the typical amateur who's trying to see if the set works! My advice is thus to always remove it, either electrically (by linking or programming it out of circuit) or by physically removing it and making the appropriate receiver and transmitter audio plus PTT links, *before* attempting to realign it to the amateur bands.

Free 1750Hz toneburst?

A five-tone unit may, however, have an 'offshoot' use, but I'd suggest trying this *after* you're happy that you can get the set aligned onto the frequency or frequencies you want.

You'll see from Table 1.5 that, in the case of both EEA and CCIR selective calling systems, digit '8' is 1747Hz, which should be close enough to 1750Hz to open up virtually any repeater requiring a 1750Hz toneburst. So, if your set is fitted with a tone signalling unit, of which there are many types, check the links on these. If it's not a type that needs remote programming, eg from a PC or dedicated programmer, then you'll usually see the sequential digit links, which may be either wire links, diodes, or solder pads. By setting these to '8 8 8 8 8' you'll get either a 250ms (EEA) or 500ms (CCIR) burst of 1747Hz. A word or warning here though. If an ID of '8 8 8 8 8' is employed in PMR use, it isn't a repeated tone corresponding to the '8' digit. Instead, it comprises of '8', 'Repeat', '8', 'Repeat', '8'. This is because, besides the need for timing, if the mobile radio encounters a brief 'fade' in signal, then the '8' digit could get broken momentarily and result in a falsely decoded signal. So, if you program an '8R8R8' as you would correctly for an ID of 88888, you'll get a pretty sounding alternating tone as a result, with only small parts of it being 1747Hz! In PMR use, the receiving decoder always knows that, in every five-tone system, each sequential digit is a *different* tone.

This 'fading' problem is one reason why DTMF (touch-tone) signalling is rarely used over the air in professional mobile radio use in the UK.

FFSK and MPT1327

FFSK, which stands for 'fast frequency-shift keying', might be familiar to VHF/UHF 1200 baud packet radio users. FFSK is commonly used in PMR equipment for more complex signalling requirements than five-tone, and for brief data messages. Unfortunately for amateurs, the tones used are 1200Hz and 1800Hz (one cycle of 1200Hz or one-and-a-half cycles of 1800Hz) for each binary 1 or 0. Also, a completely different protocol is used. Besides the occasional simple 'one-burst' data type of signalling, which can be used just like five-tone above but in 'digital' form, the most common use you'll probably find in ex-PMR equipment is the vastly more complex MPT1327 signalling system. In practical terms, in the radio system it's a complete control system, including frequency and channel change, automatic scanning, and so on.

It's commonly used in the UK's Band III spectrum, where continuous or time-shared control channels transmit their constant 1200bps data 'burble', which is in fact the CCSC (Control Channel System Codeword), plus various data commands and acknowledgements to mobiles on the system.

In use, when the mobile radio is switched on, it 'hunts' in its prestored channels for a valid CCSC, scanning around on receive as needed. When it find the control channel it's looking for, ie it's detected a valid system which the set is allowed to operate on, it transmits a brief 'RQR' data burst as a 'ReQuest for Registration'. When the system receives this (if it doesn't, the set keeps retrying for a pre-determined number of times), and finds the set is indeed authorised to use the system (eg the user or fleet have paid their bill!), the set receives a brief registration acknowledgement 'OK' and the set's front panel indicates the set is 'In Service'.

Of course, all this is done silently – the radio user doesn't hear any off-air received data signals or whatever. Until the transceiver has achieved a valid service status, it *can't* transmit or place a call from the front panel at all. Also, it can't receive anything unless it's actually called by someone over the system, or if the set has successfully established a call to another user.

So don't be surprised if your set, if fitted with an MPT1327 signalling board, refuses to transmit or receive at all. It's quite normal, but you can usually easily link out the controller to make the set operate as a 'normal' set. The exception to this is if the radio's synthesiser programming information is contained within the MPT1327 control unit itself. Some sets, like the MX290 series, have all the frequencies stored in a plug-in PROM (programmable read only memory) IC, which you can replace – you'll find the details elsewhere in this book. However, other sets, such as the SMC2520, have the information within the controller, and for most purposes *aren't* 'convertible' at all for amateur use without a lot of work, unless of course you're a software genius. It *does* happen – I know one amateur who's successfully rewritten software for a CX290 controller (used with the MX290 series) to give direct channel readout, channel scanning, and so on from the controller itself. It took him a long time to do it. I'm still busy trying to 'twist his arm' to publish the information!

Common base station PMR use

A community repeater or CBS (common base station) is very commonly used in PMR service. This acts in many ways in a similar manner to an amateur repeater, where such a repeater is placed in a well-sited location to cover a particular area and is shared by a number of users. These repeaters are usually privately owned, with airtime, and often the sets themselves, rented or leased to small fleets of PMR users.

But of course, the radio users of Joe Blogg's delivery firm don't want to listen in to messages for those of Bill Bailey the agricultural merchants, or Fred Smith the motor mechanics. Each of these usually want, and need, some degree of privacy in their communications, as well as not often wanting to have to listen to all the other activity on the channel.

So, the community repeater uses signalling, typically CTCSS but occasionally other means such as five-tone or FFSK, for control and access authorisation. For this, it incorporates a 'control panel' connected to the repeater itself, which typically contains a number of CTCSS tone decoders and re-encoders together with time-out circuits to prevent individual user fleets 'hogging' the repeater. Each mobile radio encodes and decodes only its own fleet's CTCSS tone, the community repeater regenerating this along with the user's transmitted speech.

Timeout and busy channel lockout

Several fleets of users can all employ the same community repeater, with some degree of time sharing being enforced to prevent a given user fleet from monopolising the available airtime. For this, the repeater's control panel incorporates a timer system, which typically gives each fleet (*not* each individual radio user) a given amount of time, as a 'timeout'. So, when a mobile radio user calls his base station operator, and the CBS isn't otherwise being used, a timer is started in the CBS's control panel. While the conversation is taking place, the fleet's CTCSS tone is regenerated on the output frequency of the CBS to allow all in the fleet to 'listen in' and join in with the conversation if required. However, after this has gone on for a given time period, typically between 30 seconds and a couple of minutes, a series of warning 'time-out' bleeps are transposed on the repeater output audio signal, and after the final time-out, that fleet's CTCSS tone isn't recognised any more, usually for a short 'penalty' period, to allow users of other fleets to get a chance to use the CBS.

To prevent interference when the repeater is in use by another fleet, mobile radios detect when their receiver squelch is raised, and when the signal isn't accompanied by their CTCSS tone a 'busy' LED usually lights on the set's front panel, warning the user that they can't transmit at the moment. But even if they tried to, and *this* is the important part as far as any amateurs are concerned who are attempting to tune an ex-PMR set, a 'busy channel lockout' comes in which automatically disables the microphone PTT whenever the squelch is raised without a valid CTCSS tone being present. If the squelch is closed, no problem, you can transmit. But, when you're trying to get the set going on an amateur frequency, typically with the receiver squelch open for alignment purposes, don't be surprised if you find the transmitter doesn't work! This, of course, would rule the set out for most amateur use on a typical amateur repeater for example. So, although CTCSS encode can be quite useful for UK amateur repeater access, make sure any busy channel lockout is *disabled* on your set's CTCSS unit if fitted.

2 Choosing and buying ex-PMR equipment

KNOW WHAT YOU'RE BUYING

Jim (radio club chairman): *"Hi Chris, can you help us? Our club have just bought 20 synthesised ex-PMR rigs for our members. Can you tell us how to convert them to 70cm?"*

Chris: *"Which rigs are they?"*

Jim: *"They look just like the one you helped Bill, the new 2E1, to get going last week on all the 70cm simplex and repeater channels. He bought his for £15 but these only cost the club £5 each out of our funds."*

Chris: *"Which rigs are they, in other words, what's the model number?"*

Jim: *"They look just like Bill's."*

Chris: *"What's the model number?"*

Jim: *"It's an MX290 series."*

Chris: *"What's the model number? It's on the serial number plate of the set."*

Jim: *"Oh, hang on, let's see, ah, they're MX293 sets."*

Chris: *"Well, they're synthesised all right, but they're AM sets and they've on VHF, not UHF."*

Jim: *"Oh dear – maybe I should have checked first!"*

The above is an all-too-common story. I see many packet messages asking if anyone has conversion details on a rig model number that's actually a *series* of rigs, just because that's what's on the front panel label. What is an MX290 set, for example? At the last count there were over 20 different types of these in the series, covering VHF AM through to UHF FM with varying front-panel control options.

PMR manufacturers, in general, often design a *range* of sets which are similar in appearance from the outside. This way, besides having the same outer case which cuts down on manufacturing costs, several common accessories can be used, eg for portables, the same batteries, chargers, antennas, speaker-mics, protective cases etc. For mobiles, as well as the similar outer case moulding, the same series of differing 'control units', ie the front part with all the knobs and buttons, can be used between the models in a range, depending upon their control and selecting calling needs for any given user.

From this you may see that, firstly, several sets which are very different inside can look identical from the outside. Also that,

Yes sir, which band would you like to get going on?

typically in the case of mobile equipment, sets of the same band and mode, ie the same 'RF deck', can look very different from the front.

Moral number one: *To know what you're buying, look at the set's actual model number, which is usually on the serial number plate. Don't just rely on what the front panel looks like.*

BARGAINS

"Where can I get the best bargains?" is another common question. Here, my usual answer is to say "Often at radio rallies", although there *are* notable exceptions to this, which I'll detail a little later. Why rallies? The typical amateur radio rally is, or was, a large field or hall, packed with a diverse array of traders selling everything from boxes of what is commonly described as 'junk' but is deemed 'surplus' wire, chassis, equipment and components by many, through to gleaming new oriental rigs, with a lot in between the two extremes. In the ex-PMR field, you may find anything from a trader with a solitary set at the end of his table of 'junk', to a small team with a large van packed full of ex-PMR equipment, which they have bought as a large job lot from a fleet user who'd 'traded up' to new gear. I've seen both extremes at rallies. When I asked one of the latter type of traders one fine sunny day, in a field at a rally by his table, how many more similar MX294 rigs for 2m he had available, he replied by asking me how many did I want? He had over 200 more sets in his large van at the rally, and still more at his base.

WHAT TO LOOK FOR AND WHAT TO AVOID

Whatever happens, you need to know *what* you're buying. Many traders are honest, and if you see their name and address clearly

An ex-PMR rig is a perfect companion to a packet TNC

displayed on their rally stand or table they've usually little to hide. If, however, they refuse to give you their details or a receipt for the equipment you're interested in buying, then take care because there must be *some* reason for them acting like this. A common excuse that's given is they don't want the tax man to find out, which of course then clearly identifies them as a thief, ie someone who blatantly admits they're dishonest and admits they want to, and intend to, steal from you and I (ie honest taxpayers). So you're buying from a thief. Harsh words, but I've seen sets offered on rally stands with their serial number plates forcibly removed. One set on the top of a large pile of similar rigs had a large fluorescent label saying '70cm FM' prominently stuck on the top of it. On asking if I could take a look under the cover of that set, and after being given the 'OK', I found inside some lovely looking circuitry, very nice and clean, but it was an 108MHz/140MHz VHF AM transceiver. The trader said he didn't know, but I wonder how he knew enough to describe it as a 70cm FM set. Maybe it was because it looked just like the similar 70cm FM variant in that set's equipment range from the outside?

Moral number two: *If it hasn't got a serial number, be very, very careful. If you see it's been physically removed, then maybe the rally organiser or even the police would be likely to take a professional interest in what's being offered for sale at this trader's stand.*

BARGAINING

Bargaining is often expected at rallies. Indeed some traders consider it part of the fun and experience of selling – it sometimes brightens their otherwise dull day. I know because they've told me! But don't, however, offer a daft price. If a trader has an asking price for a set, then he's expecting to get at least *somewhere* near that, and possibly for the sale of a single set he may not be able to afford to accept a lower price. Also the seller may need payment by cash for the advertised price. If you come along with a cheque or credit card (if the trader takes them) for the purchase of a rig costing just a few pounds, then don't be surprised if the price goes up. It's not usually because the trader is 'fiddling' the accounts, it's because a cheque paid into a business account (rather than a personal account) costs

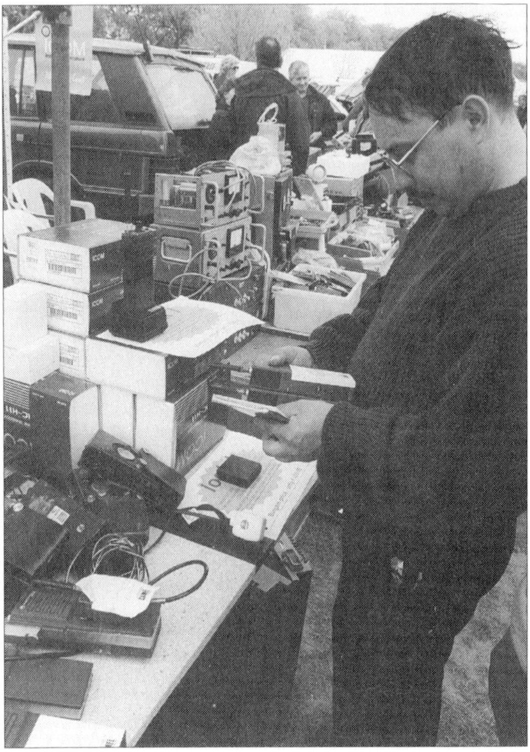

This wise buyer is checking the type number of the two PF-85s he's holding

the trader *money*. Also, as many of us know, each credit card company places a 'levy' on each transaction.

The way to get a good deal is usually to see if you can buy a batch of items in one go, or maybe even the trader's entire stock of sets if there's a group of you together at the event. As well as the ex-PMR rigs themselves, there may be accessories on offer, for example batteries, chargers, leather cases and speaker-mics for portable sets – all useful accessories which may even be 'thrown in' if you take the lot off the trader's hands. If you *do* bargain, then keep things good-natured. Even if the rigs *are* tatty and worn, which will probably reflected in the asking price in any case, don't denigrate the equipment on offer. If you don't like it, don't buy it. The objective is to come to a price that both of you are happy with.

Finally, if you go home and you're happy with your purchase, you'll often find your friends asking you where you bought it from, because they'd like to get some of the same. It's little use saying "The third table in the fourth row of the flea market area at last week's rally". If you feel you've got a bargain, and the seller deals in such equipment regularly, then ask him for some contact details so you can put more business his way. Or at least to see if he'll be at the rally you're 'tossing up' as to whether to visit next weekend in the hope of buying more similar ex-PMR gear. His attendance could sway your decision. Many reputable traders will have a printed card they'll be happy to give you. If they refuse to tell you who they are and are offering you ex-PMR gear for sale, in my opinion they're worth steering *very* clear of.

Moral number three: *Get the seller's details.*

UNKNOWN RIGS

As various types of ex-PMR equipment become available on the surplus market, amateurs naturally become interested in getting it going on their band of interest. You see it on sale, the label or sign says "Can convert to 2m" or whatever, so you buy it and then try to find the information to do so.

Now, I tell myself, if the person selling the set knows it's 'convertible', he should *also* know, or have the information on, *how* to do it, either from an article or from his own modification work. If he

Which ex-PMR portable rig would you like?

doesn't, he shouldn't be advertising the fact that it's convertible to such-and-such a band in the first place. Before you buy *anything* that you *don't* have the conversion details for, either in your hand or back at your home, ask for a copy of the conversion information to accompany the rig as a condition of the purchase. If the seller can't provide these, or at least show you the details (such as a magazine article) which if you wanted to you could copy down 'longhand' on a piece of paper even if it takes you a while to do so, then *go away and don't bother buying it.* I've seen 24V to 12V DC to DC converters on sale, advertised as "Convertible to 2m". They probably were, with a lot of work and a significant amount of added circuitry. *Nothing's* impossible, *everything's* 'convertible', it's just the differing degree of difficulty involved!

Moral number four: *Make sure you have the details to convert the set before you buy it.*

REPUTABLE DEALERS

OK, from the above you'll see how you can possibly get bargains at a rally if you 'take a chance', although hopefully if you follow my advice you'll be taking rather less of a chance than you otherwise would have done.

There are also a number of established dealers who take great pains to source ex-PMR equipment for amateurs, and to advertise this in magazines to attract sales. They may, or may not, visit rallies, often preferring to provide a good mail-order service. The things to bear in mind are that this level of service, ie stockholding, sorting, advertising, and all the other overheads, must be paid for somehow. That's why the equipment will usually be priced a little higher than you otherwise could have 'bargained down' for. Your assurance is that you know *what* you're buying, you know *who* you're buying from, and for the firm to survive in the marketplace they can't afford to get a bad reputation for selling 'duff gear'. You'll

Bargain ex-PMR rigs – these 2m 25W FM sets were just £2 each

also often find they may provide a photocopied sheet, or sheets, of all the information you need to convert the set to the band you're interested in.

Very often, if the dealer is within travelling distance of your home, you may find it very worthwhile to pay them a visit. You'll probably also see a lot of gear at their premises that isn't advertised, which you'll also be interested in. Such dealers usually must have a large quantity of a given model of set in order to advertise it in the amateur press, as the subsequent response often 'clears their shelves' in a short time. If instead they have, say, 10 or 20 items of a given set and they advertised these, they often wouldn't be able to supply all the order requests. I speak through experience in talking to these people!

I fondly remember visiting one ex-PMR dealer several years ago, and seeing three container lorries arriving in the dealer's large yard. The manager told me they were all full of low-band VHF ex-PMR gear from a government user, with portables, mobiles, and base stations in the consignment. He said they'd be sold within eight weeks. On looking around his shelves, I saw piles and piles of other rigs. "Not worth advertising", he said. I went away with a car full of bargains, including a large box of 70cm portable rigs, batteries, speaker microphones etc for the young prospective amateurs I was teaching at my local secondary school Novice class.

Moral number five: *If you don't see it advertised or displayed, go hunting – you may be pleasantly surprised.*

3 Alignment techniques

THE commonest thought by amateurs considering getting an ex-PMR rig 'going' is that they need a whole stack of expensive radio communications test equipment to accurately align the set. If you *do* have access to such, and I must confess that I'm fortunate in this position at the moment, then it's all well and good. You probably won't need me to tell you how to use it!

However, a quick word of caution. If you are offered the loan of such expensive test gear, then *do* make sure you know what you're doing with it. For example *don't* transmit straight into a frequency counter or a signal generator – the owner of the said equipment will not be a very happy person to discover it doesn't work any more. If in doubt, seek the help of someone who is familiar with the gear, preferably the owner.

Note also my comments in Chapter 1 regarding automatic signalling circuits, which in some cases could cause your set to automatically and unexpectedly transmit briefly, even if you don't have a microphone connected.

Throughout this book I've necessarily referred to alignment steps as simply telling you to adjust for 'maximum power', 'accurate frequency', 'best received signal' etc without expanding each time on the details of how these are actually measured. This is because amateurs will no doubt be using a number of differing methods, depending upon the type of equipment to hand or the lack of it. So read on – I hope you'll find a few useful hints and ideas.

NO TEST GEAR?

Don't worry. My first ex-PMR rig was an AM25B Pye Vanguard, which I bought at the Leicester Show for a few pounds back in the early 'seventies. In my shack I had a simple multimeter, absorption wavemeter, SWR meter, and an amateur bands receiver but fortunately I had the help of an experienced amateur (thanks Greg), who helped me get the transceiver going on 2m. I was elated when I made my first QSO with the set! Some time later, when I moved away to study, my two amateur flatmates and I all managed to get our UHF PF1 transmitter/receiver units going on air using similar equipment (but no power meter) plus the help of a few filed-down matchsticks as 'trimming tools'. I've been through a large number of ex-PMR conversions since then, having learned how to cope with what was to hand at many times.

Use an analogue meter, not a digital type. This AVO cost the author just £10

BASIC EQUIPMENT

To align most of the equipment detailed in this book, a reasonably sensitive DC voltmeter, eg a multimeter, is virtually a 'must'. You *can* get by without one, but you'll find things are a lot easier if you have one by your side. This is not just to help you tune the set up with, but also for minor details like checking the condition of the nicads supplied for your portable ex-PMR rig. If you're going to source a meter for alignment purposes, then I'd recommend *against* buying a digital multimeter. Not that there's anything wrong with them, but you'll find that you'll be adjusting the various coils and capacitors in your set for a *change* in voltage and current level, rather than measuring an unchanging value at any time. It's a lot easier to see this change on a moving coil meter needle than trying to determine the change on a digital voltage readout. Also, and this is a sad fact with many early plastic-cased digital meters, the close proximity of RF from, say, a PMR handheld antenna can cause them to misread, sometimes indicating a decrease in level as your RF power is actually increasing. I've seen it happen several times, and it doesn't help in getting your set aligned!

If you're selecting a meter to use, then *don't* choose one of the many cheap 1kΩ per volt meters which you'll often see for sale at the 'budget' level. I've found many times that they will load the ex-PMR set's measuring point under test so much that it's impossible to get *any* reading at all for alignment. Use a meter with at least 20kΩ per volt sensitivity if you want it to be of any help to you. If you have a reasonably sensitive microammeter lying around in your junk box or you come across one at a rally or surplus equipment sale (make sure it's in working order!) at a 'next-to-nothing' price, then remember that by adding a series resistor of a suitable value you will have a nice DC voltmeter, and with a low-value shunt resistor you've a DC ammeter in your hands, even if it isn't in a pretty-looking box.

TRANSMIT POWER

You may be fortunate in having some form of in-line power meter in your existing station equipment. Providing this is suitable for use at the frequency band your ex-PMR set will be operating on, then it'll be very useful indeed for transmitter alignment purposes. I personally find the very first SWR meter I bought works very well, this having a 'sensitivity' knob for setting the forward power. This type of meter can be set for a high sensitivity, ie low power reading, when initially tuning and looking for a tiny amount of power, then 'backed off' in the later stages of alignment when finally tuning for absolute maximum power. The meter doesn't need to be perfectly accurate, because you're essentially looking to use it for tuning for maximum indicated power, rather than knowing to a high degree of accuracy what your exact transmit power is when the set is finally aligned. A home-made power meter is quite sufficient here, and you can easily make one with a resistor, diode and a capacitor or two together with a surplus meter movement, or by using your DC multimeter as the indicating meter.

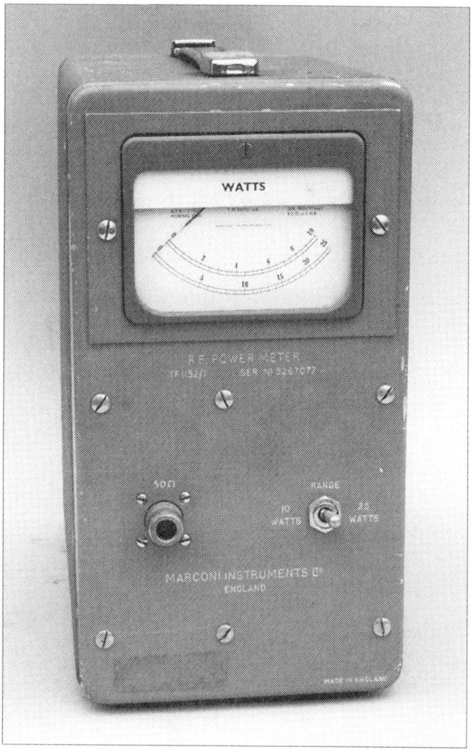

Surplus RF power meters can be found at rallies, this one cost £2

Remember that you *must* tune up into a 50Ω load, preferably a dummy load. If you don't already have one in your shack, you can easily make one from non-inductive carbon resistors. Indeed, for portable rigs, a single 0.5W or 1W 47Ω carbon composition resistor will often be quite adequate. For higher-powered sets, a 'cage' of resistors soldered together around the end of a short length of coaxial cable can be made, eg from ten 470Ω 1W resistors in parallel for a 10W load. Remember that you must use non-inductive resistors for this – for example don't use wirewound types. Even though these types are usually the cheapest readily available types for high wattage, you'll end up with a non-resistive load due to the resistors acting as short helical antennas.

In the case of portable equipment without an external antenna socket, you may be able to substitute a short length of coaxial cable onto the set's antenna connection point, with the antenna itself disconnected, for use with a power meter. Alternatively you can just tune for maximum radiated power from the set-top antenna by monitoring this with a field-strength meter. A tuneable meter is the preferred option, ie an absorption wavemeter, as this shows that you've actually tuned to the correct crystal multiplication. If your portable set uses a helical antenna that's resonant on a PMR band, you'll probably find quite an improvement in effective radiated power by substituting an antenna that's correctly resonant. In either case, a slight retune of the portable radio's final PA circuitry for maximum radiated power will provide the best match between the set and the possibly non-50Ω antenna impedance.

In the initial stages of transmitter alignment, you'll probably find no RF indication whatsoever, and you may sometimes be tuning 'blind'. Here, a receiver or further amateur transceiver, tuned to the frequency you're aligning on, is a very useful tool, especially if it

A dummy load should be used for transmitter alignment

has an S-meter. A hint here is that a wide-band scanner receiver comes in handy, which you can also use for receive alignment (you'll see how a little later). You can then initially tune the set for the strongest signal strength on the adjacently positioned receiver, removing the antenna from the receiver as needed. Also, in the case of crystal-controlled sets, you can check that the crystal itself is oscillating by tuning to the crystal frequency and holding the receiver antenna near to the oscillator stage, likewise with the various frequency multiplier stages. As you progress with the transmitter tuning, you might find it useful to place a DC current meter in line with the voltage supply to the set, initially tuning for an increase in current drawn before you see any RF power, then tuning for maximum power output. When the PA is producing power, or the set has started to draw additional current, then in all cases make sure that you only key the transmitter PTT for as long as needed to make the adjustment – give the set's PA a rest in between transmit periods. This is especially important in the alignment and tuning stages, because an initially misaligned PA can overheat a lot more than a correctly tuned circuit, with greater possibility of damage.

TRANSMIT FREQUENCY

If you don't have access to a frequency counter, then again an adjacent receiver can be very helpful, especially if it has the facility of a centre-zero discriminator meter. Unfortunately, few modern sets nowadays have such a meter, this being a relic of the times when manually tuneable FM receivers were the 'norm'. If you can access your monitor receiver's discriminator output, directly via a DC path from the output itself rather than through a coupling capacitor, you may find you can effectively use your voltmeter at this point. The DC offset voltage here will swing positive and negative as the receive frequency is varied, ie your transmitter frequency varies, a zero DC voltage giving you a 'centre tuned' indication. If this isn't feasible, then by setting your receiver's step size to 5kHz, disconnecting the receiver's antenna and tuning a few steps either side of your set's transmit frequency, providing the receiver's IF filters are symmetrical, you can usually get fairly close. An SSB receiver with the BFO switched on (remember, many scanners have SSB receive now as well as AM and FM) will let you 'zero in' for a zero audio beat note very accurately. If you have access to a HF receiver with SSB, but not a VHF/UHF receiver, then in the case of a crystal-controlled rig you can instead tune to one of the crystal multiples for netting purposes; you'll just need to be that bit more accurate in your tuning here though.

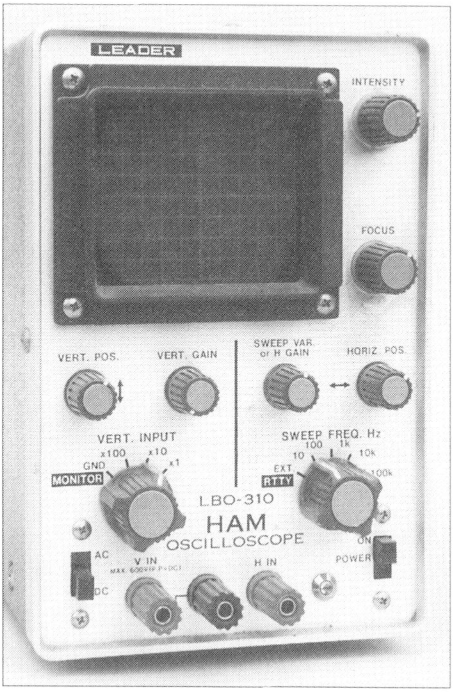

An oscilloscope is useful but not always essential

DEVIATION

This one's a little more difficult. Again, a separate receiver is very useful, and you can compare the level of your transmitted audio with that of other signals of known accuracy, preferably with an AC voltmeter or oscilloscope connected to the discriminator output (or the speaker output as a 'second best'). You'll find amateur repeaters are usually very accurately set for 5kHz peak deviation, but virtually every new Japanese amateur transceiver I've tested has been in excess of 5kHz. If an aural check is used, it's best done by someone else listening to and comparing your audio, rather than yourself – in any case don't expect accurate results doing it in this way! Some repeaters have a useful overdeviation indicator, which lets you or your QSO partner know if your deviation is some way 'over the top' of 5kHz whilst you're transmitting on the repeater input. This overdeviation threshold is usually set at around 6kHz or so, but it can vary depending upon the individual repeater's setting. So, by slowly increasing your deviation, shouting a loud 'four' into your microphone until you hit the overdeviation indicator, then 'backing off' the deviation setting by an appropriate amount, you should be able to get fairly close. Do respect other repeater users of course, ie make sure you choose a quiet time for testing in this way, rather than a morning or evening mobile rush hour for example.

RECEIVER SENSITIVITY

Here you'll need some form of signal of a variable level (high at first, then decreasing as you tune the set for maximum sensitivity) at the frequency you want to receive. If you've a further transmitter at that frequency, you can terminate this into a dummy load and use that for initial alignment, locating the transmitter further and further away, maybe even eventually down at the bottom of the garden or at the other end of your house or flat with it switched to low power, to give you a progressively weaker signal. Some amateur handhelds have a switchable 'EL' power level of just 10mW, which can be especially useful for this.

Alternatively, if you know a local signal is definitely on the air, ie a local active repeater (check by listening on a further receiver), then this can also be used, first with an outdoor antenna, then substituting an indoor whip and so on. Maybe you have a friendly local

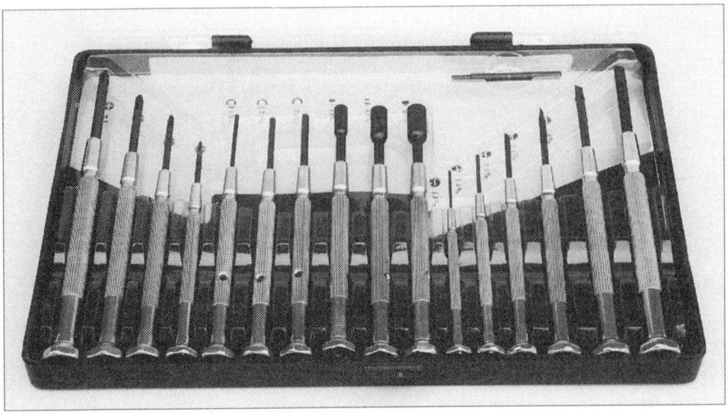

Nice to look at, but these can ruin an ex-PMR rig

amateur who'll help you by transmitting a signal, again first at high power with an outdoor antenna, then switching down in power and possibly also into different antennas such as a horizontal beam pointed away from you.

If you have a scanner receiver, this can also be the source of a weak signal for receiver alignment. The scanner's first local oscillator will be at the scanner's receive frequency plus or minus the set's first IF. For example, if the IF is 10.8MHz (commonly used IFs are 10.7MHz, 10.8MHz, 21.4MHz and 21.6MHz), and your ex-PMR rig needs to receive a signal on 145.5MHz, then tap in 156.300MHz (145.500 + 10.8) or 134.700MHz (145.500 – 10.8) or similar. You can first connect the scanner's antenna connector directly to your ex-PMR rig (make sure the set doesn't transmit!), then use the much weaker radiated signal from the scanner's antenna at varying distances from the rig's antenna.

Your ex-PMR rig's receiver must usually have its 'front end' retuned to the amateur band and, in the case of crystal rigs, the local oscillator multiplier stages as well. However, if the rig came out of working PMR service, then the IF stages and the discriminator coil will already be aligned – you won't need to adjust these. So if you don't have any tuning instructions, don't go in and madly adjust everything – go about it logically! You'll typically find that the RF front end and crystal multiplier stages use readily adjustable coils or occasionally trimmer capacitors, whereas the IF will use 10.7MHz and 455kHz transformers, often similar to the type you find in broadcast radio receivers. Finally, it may sound obvious but, before you attempt to tune the front end, then in the case of crystal-controlled sets try first adjusting the receiver crystal oscillator trimmer until you can hear something on a very strong local signal such as an adjacent transmit rig on the correct frequency. This way, you know you won't be tuning, or more likely mistuning, the front end for reception of a signal that won't be there.

TOOLS

Apart from the usual tools which you'll need to open the set's case with, ie cross-head and flat-bladed screwdrivers, you'll invariably also need some form of tool, or tools, to actually align the set's circuitry. *Don't* use your metal screwdrivers! The capacitor slots on the transmitter PA may suit your small flat-bladed screwdriver very nicely, but that trimmer adjustment screw may also very well be 'live' with RF, especially if it's a series coupling capacitor. Your

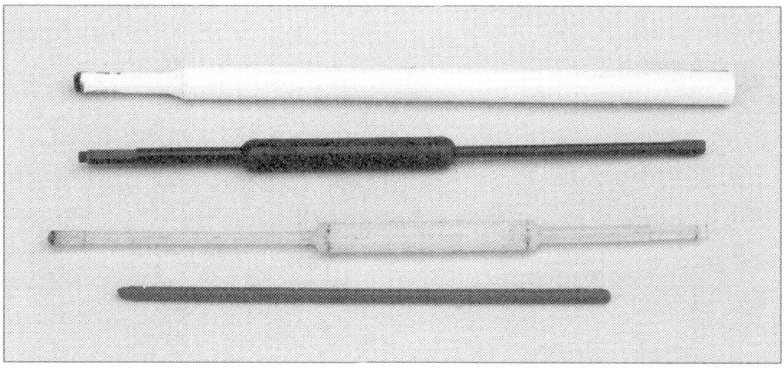

Use the correct type of non-metallic trimming tool

screwdriver will then act as a very effective antenna, and will provide a mismatch to what the poor set thinks it should be 'seeing' at that stage. In the case of higher-power sets you could also get a nasty RF burn if you touch the metal adjuster. By now you might be thinking that you shouldn't use the all-metal 'jeweller's screwdrivers' for tuning the transmitter. That's right. *Don't* be tempted to use them for the receiver either – and *especially* not for adjusting ferrite cores. The brittle ferrites usually have a small slot in them, and if they're stiff to turn and you use a metal implement, you'll crack the ferrite and thus jam the core in the former. It's better to bend or break the end of a small replaceable plastic trimming tool than to make an ex-PMR rig absolutely useless. I really have lost count of the number of amateurs who've asked me where they can get replacement cores from after disregarding this advice. The answer is usually from the PMR rig manufacturer, if they're still going, and then you'll find the minimum order is usually around £10 plus VAT.

Always use a non-metallic trimming tool of the correct size and shape for the adjustments required in your particular rig. You can usually buy these adjusting tools, either individually or in a set, from a number of component suppliers. Alternatively, you can file a plastic knitting needle or similar implement down to shape – even matchsticks can sometimes be useful for a temporary adjustment tool.

If an undamaged ferrite core is stiff and won't turn, *don't* force it. Instead, try heating it up using the end of a fine-pointed soldering iron – this will usually loosen any linseed oil or similar (which is often used on these cores) that's hardened with age. If you find you have cracked a core, or if someone before you has, then you'll often find the ferrite core has a similar slot at the other end. If this isn't accessible via a hole in the PCB, then first unsolder and remove the coil former assembly, making sure you remember which way it's orientated for correct replacement. Using a correct trimming tool, remove the core completely out from the lower side of the former, then thoroughly clean the inevitable ferrite 'grit' in the former before replacing the core, this time with the core 'upside down' for adjustment through the top of the former.

FINAL CHECK

After you've aligned the set the best you can with available non-professional test equipment, then bear in mind that, at a number of rallies and especially repeater and packet group events, a 'rig check' facility is sometimes offered. Here, specialised radio communication test gear is available for your use on a dedicated stand, with a

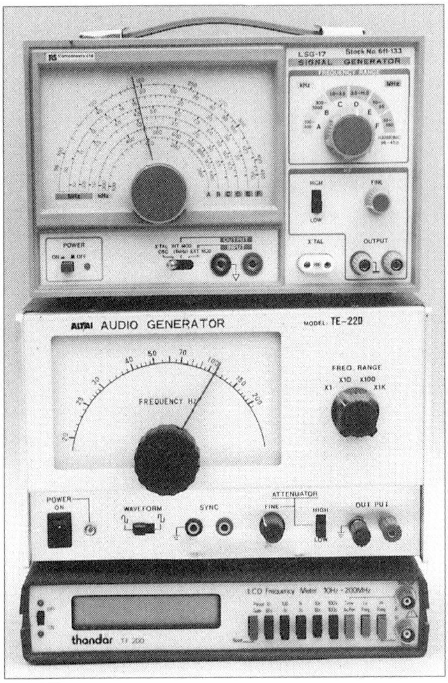

Left: **Amateur test equipment is useful for radio club or individual use.**

Right: **Surplus test equipment can often be bought at rallies**

similarly dedicated and experienced engineer (who's usually an amateur as well) on the stand to do the testing for you! Do take advantage of these opportunities – you'll often find the person or group on the stand is more than willing to help you set your frequency, deviation etc up accurately if you go along 'armed' with the required adjustment information and the correct trimming tools. However, *don't* expect a full alignment service 'from scratch' – it's up to you to get the set at least in an operational state.

Alternatively, if you're friendly with the owner of your local PMR workshop (he or she will often also be an amateur!) there's nothing to be lost by asking if you could go along for a few minutes one evening or lunchtime for a 'rig check' – taking along a small token of appreciation usually goes down very well.

Finally, if you do feel like 'taking the plunge' and putting together some items of test gear, eg a simple deviation meter, power meter etc, maybe for use in a club or group conversion project, you'll find surplus test gear is again readily available at rallies. I've purchased a number of items this way, calibrating them myself against known and accurate standards.

You can of course make your own test equipment, maybe again as a club project, and for this the RSGB's book *Test Equipment for the Radio Amateur* is a valuable source of information.

4 Mobile equipment

PYE/PHILIPS M290 AND MX290 SERIES

From walking around rallies in the UK, the M290 and MX290 series of rigs must be about the most commonly found set on the surplus market at the time of writing, just like the Westminster and Europa series of sets were a number of years ago. I've seen at least one model of the M290 range available at virtually every rally I've visited – one trader even had a van load of them! However, it *is* a range, and identification of the set is the first thing that's important before considering any conversion attempt.

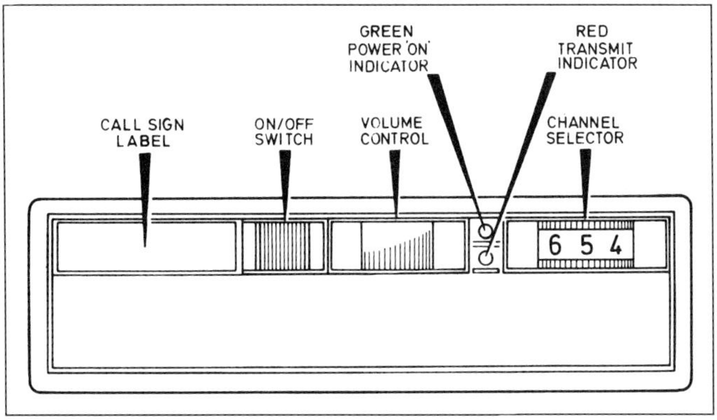

Fig 4.1. M/MX290 series front-panel controls

The M290 series are crystal-controlled sets, and come in single-channel and six-channel versions. A later set, using chip components, is the M294E, which comes with three switchable crystal channels.

The MX290 series are synthesised sets, which you'll read about a little later, but it's important to note that at first glance they may look the same as the M290 series as they share a common front panel and a similarly sized chassis.

Front panel

The front panel of the set (Fig 4.1) is secured by two screws, one on either side of the front sides of the case. The panel itself can either be a plain internally metallised plastic cover, or also have a PCB attached to it with CTCSS, five-tone selective call, or (in the case of the MX series) digital trunking circuitry. If it does contain this, you'll find the front-panel module with its attached PCB can usually slide out of the front of the set, which disconnects it from the front 'facility' connector on the RF deck of the transceiver itself (this connector is on the front right of each of the set's motherboards, viewed from the component side with the set's controls towards you). In the case of trunking radio controllers, the front panel can also control the actual channel addressing of the set via a connector on the front left of the

Table 4.1. M290 and MX290 series facility module connector pins

A	Gnd
B	Mic mute
C	In-band TX encode
D	Sub-audio TX encode
E	RX audio for decoders
F	RX squelched audio
G	Undedicated
H	10V
J	TX 10V
K	10V via TX PTT
L	Key TX
M	Undedicated
N	Batt sw input 13.2V
P	Undedicated
Q	Undedicated/sq defeat

Table 4.2. M290 and MX290 series mic socket connections

1	Mic live
2	Ground
3	10V PTT line
4	RX low level audio
5	10V output

RF deck. In either case, you'll often find that the transceiver RF motherboard might not function 'on it's own', and you'll need to make a few links – the information you need in each case is given in the actual set conversion and alignment instructions which follow. The multi-way board-mounted plug which is used for interfacing the selective calling modules has the connections shown in Table 4.1.

Microphone connections

Each set, apart from the M294E which has a wired-in microphone, uses a five-pin 270° DIN socket for the microphone connector. See Table 4.2.

The transceiver needs a switched 10V positive voltage for PTT, *not* a switched line to 0V. For use with a packet TNC with 0V switching, a simple PNP transistor interface can be used, as shown in Fig 4.19 later on.

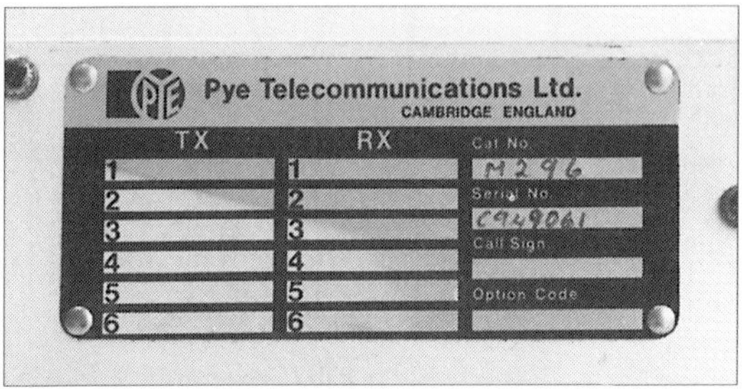

Check the rear panel for identification

M290 SERIES – M294 AND M296

The M290 series outer case is a black-painted extruded alloy section. There are no upper or lower lids (unlike the MX290 series which have these), and the RF section is a single PCB which slides out of the rear of the set, complete with the attached alloy rear-panel section which also acts as a transmitter PA heatsink. It's secured to the extrusion with four screws, one at each corner of the rear panel, and a metal cover with a riveted-on serial number plate is again attached to the rear panel, again with four screws – this covers the various mic/speaker leads and their feed-through capacitor connections. See Fig 4.2.

Your first look should thus be at the serial number plate to identify

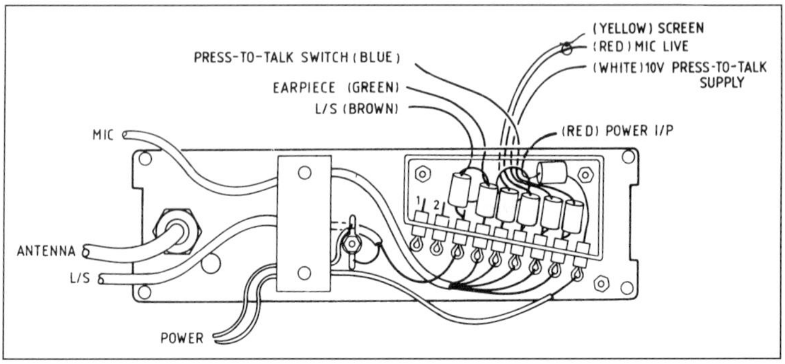

Fig 4.2. Rear-panel connections on the M294 and M296

You'll often find circuitry for selective calling or trunking attached to the front panel of the set

the set. This will have the *real* model of the equipment marked to identify which of the M290 series it is. The front panel of the set can vary depending upon which, if any, selective calling options have been fitted. These are common to all of the series, VHF or UHF, AM or FM, and can be either a standard front panel with no selective call options, a TED1 or TED2 (Tone Encoder Decoder 1 or 2, for CTCSS), or a TED6 (Tone Encoder Decoder 6, for five-tone selective calling and CTCSS).

The RF variants available are:

M293	VHF AM, 1–6 channels
M294	VHF FM, 1–6 channels
M294E	VHF FM, 1–3 channels
M296	UHF FM, 1–6 channels

The M293 is not covered here, as amateur radio usage is now invariably FM on VHF/UHF, unlike the 'early days'. The M294E uses broadly similar circuitry to the M294, as well as using the same crystal type and multiplication formulae, thus it won't be dealt with separately.

Bands

The set is available in the bands shown in Table 4.3.

Table 4.3. M290 series bands

M294	
A0:	148–174MHz
B0:	132–156MHz
E0:	68–88MHz
M1:	105–108MHz (TX)
P5:	79–88MHz (TX)
P8:	96–106MHz (RX)
M296	
T1:	405–440MHz
U0:	440–470MHz

The crystals fit in a compartment with a hinge-up lid

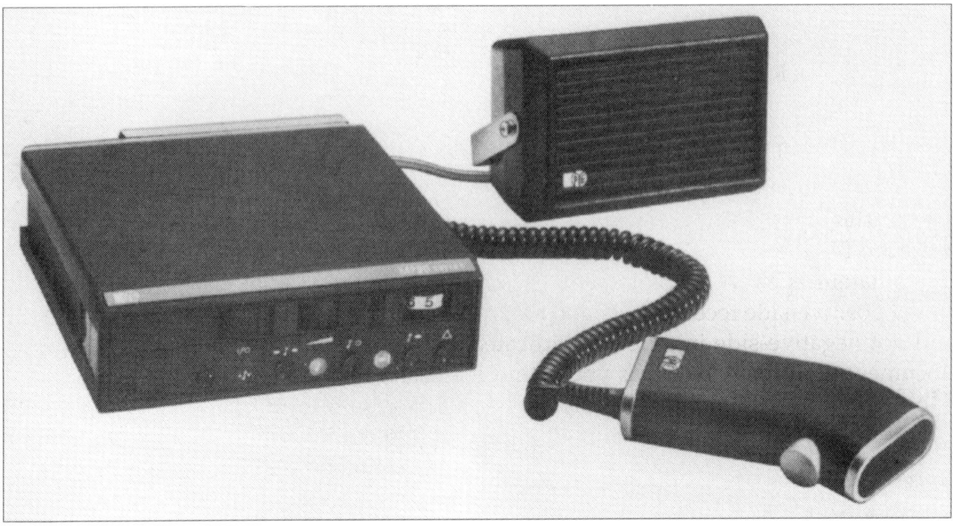

The M294/M296, shown here fitted with a TED6 selective calling front panel

Identification codes

The rear panel 'code' label will give you details on what the set actually is, the alphanumeric codes being in the order shown in Table 4.4.

M294

Crystals

The crystal frequencies needed are:

A and B band:

$$\text{RX xtal freq} = \frac{\text{RX freq} + 10.7\text{MHz}}{3}$$

$$\text{TX xtal freq} = \frac{\text{TX freq}}{16}$$

Table 4.4. M290 series identification codes

Equipment type:	M294, M296
Market code:	01 (standard production)
Installation items:	0–4
Number of crystalled channels:	0–6
Transmit power:	1 (25W), 2 (15W), 3 (10W), 4 (6W), or 5 (1W)
Function:	1, 2 (No tone options), 3 (Fitted TED1 or TED2), 4 (fitted TED6)
Channel spacing:	S (12.5kHz), V (25kHz), R (20kHz)
Transmit freq band:	A0, E0 etc
Receive freq band:	A0, E0 etc
Number of channels:	1 or 6
Primary options:	00 (no options), 20 (fist mic), 90 (fist mic with built-in TX timer)
Secondary options:	00 (no options), 42 (standard), 43 (fitted in AC PSU), 44 (fitted in transportable case)

E band:

$$\text{RX xtal freq} = \frac{\text{RX freq} + 10.7\text{MHz}}{2}$$

$$\text{TX xtal freq} = \frac{\text{TX freq}}{16}$$

The crystals are HC-25/U types – the commercial specifications for these are T71 for the receiver and T93RX for the transmitter, requesting 'amateur spec' versions to keep the cost down. Note that I've stated positive-side receiver injection for 2m on both A and B bands, and not negative-side injection as indicated in the manufacturer's documentation for A band, as you'll find it's easier to tune the A band receiver oscillator multiplier stages down to a 2m receive frequency if positive-side injection is employed.

Receiver alignment

A component layout and alignment diagram are shown in Figs 4.3 and 4.4. You'll first need an external speaker of 3–8Ω impedance connected to the blue and brown speaker leads (these are terminated in a small white plastic connector in the original set). If your set has been fitted with a selective calling module, check that pin F1 is connected via a wire link to pin G (some sets may have pin G1 connected to S, which disables the direct receive audio path). For transmit PTT keying, the lead from mic socket pin 3 should go to pin L2. You may find it's linked instead to pin K3 to give transmit inhibit. Further links are required from pin K1 to pin K2 and from pin L1 to pin L2.

The crystals fit into the compartment with a hinge-up lid, which you'll probably find is held down with a small screw. Switch on, and adjust the squelch preset RV4 to 'open' the squelch and set the volume control to a suitable level, making sure you've selected the appropriate channel on the channel switch. With your multimeter set to the 2.5V DC range, connect the negative lead to the set's chassis. Connect the positive lead to TP1 and adjust L15 for maximum voltage reading, then adjust L16 for a 'dip' in voltage. Switch your multimeter to read 10V and transfer the positive lead to TP7. Adjust L16 and then L17 for maximum, then L15, L16 and L17 in that order again for maximum reading. Now, with a received off-air signal, initially adjust the cores of L1–L5 downwards from the top of the coil former by around three turns each, then adjust the receiver crystal tuning coil for the correct frequency. Adjust L1, L2, L3, L4 and L5 in that order for best reception. You shouldn't need to adjust L6 and L7 – these are the IF coils and should already be correctly tuned. Finally adjust any other crystalled channels for correct frequency and reset the squelch preset potentiometer.

Transmitter alignment

For transmit PTT, you'll need to link pins 3 and 5 on the mic plug. Note that the PTT uses positive voltage switching – *don't* short the

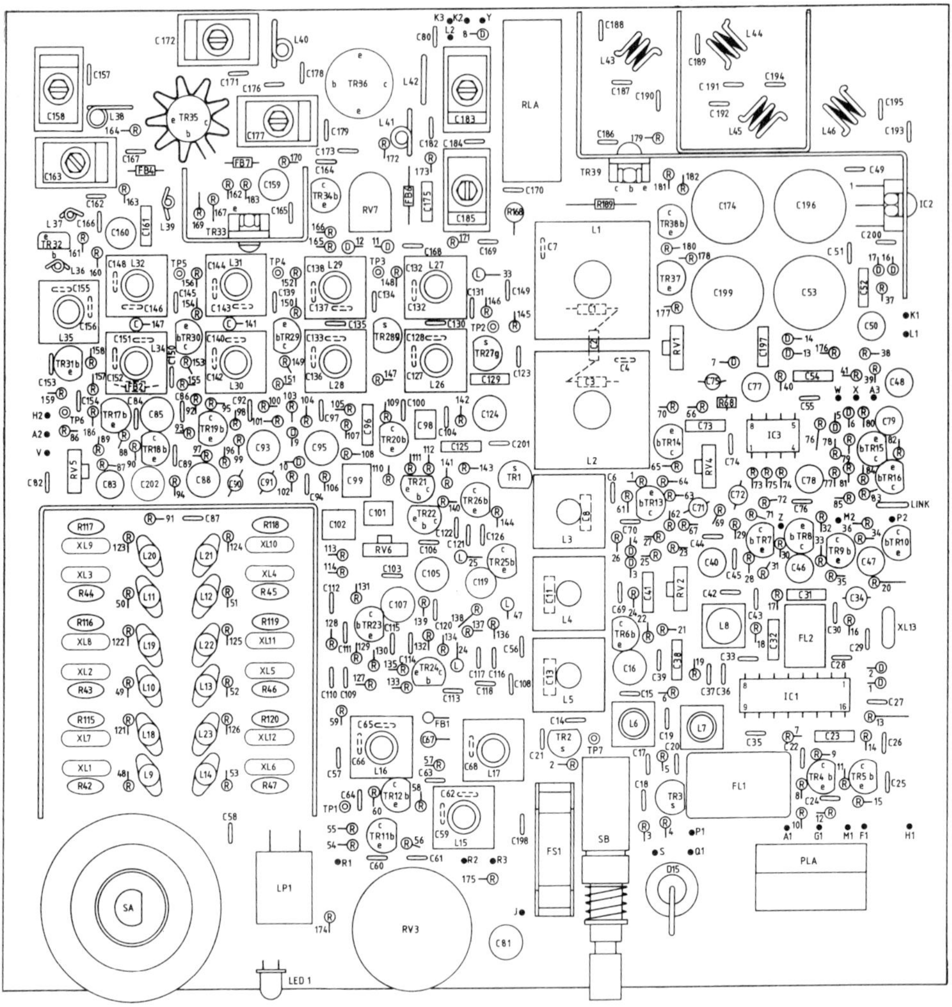

Fig 4.3. Internal components, M294

PTT line to 0V. First adjust RV7, the transmitter power control adjustment, to its fully clockwise position to give maximum power. With your multimeter's negative lead to the set's chassis, set the meter to the 10V DC range and connect the positive meter lead to TP2. With the PTT keyed, adjust C119 for a peak (you'll probably find this is a very small peak), then tune L26 for minimum reading. Transfer the multimeter positive lead to TP3, and adjust L27 for maximum and then L28 for minimum. Transfer to TP4 and adjust L29 for maximum, then L30 for minimum. Transfer to TP5 and adjust L31 for maximum, then L32 for minimum, then L34 for maximum.

You might now see some RF power output, otherwise connect a diode probe to the inner metal adjuster screw of C163 (turn RV7 clockwise if needed to give a reading), and retune L26–L32, L34 and L35, in that order, for maximum reading of RF power or detected

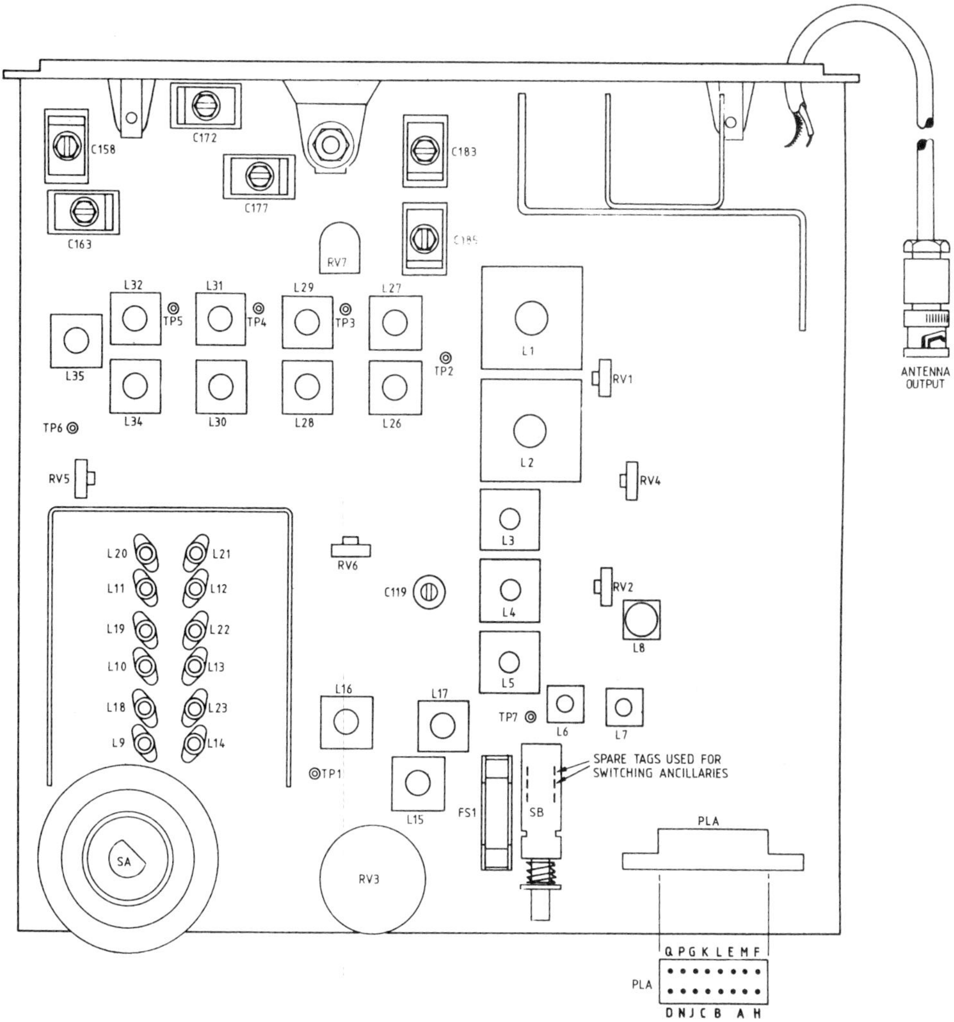

Fig 4.4. M294 alignment diagram

RF; alternatively try tuning for maximum DC current drawn from the supply.

Onto the transmitter PA stages (Fig 4.7). First adjust C185 to minimum capacitance, ie to the position with its plates fully apart, and then adjust C158 and C163 for maximum power output, or for maximum DC supply current if there's no RF initially, followed by a retune for maximum RF power. Two trimming tools, one in each hand, help here.

Adjust C172 together with C177, then C183 together with C185, in pairs for maximum power output. Retune these capacitors, again in pairs, for absolute maximum power output – you should be able to obtain just over 25W. You can, if you wish, now readjust RV7 to give a lower output power. Set your crystal trimmer(s) now for accurate frequency. RV6 is the peak deviation preset control, and the mic gain control is RV5.

M296

You'll find two slightly different versions of the M296, one having a 6W transmitter, the other having an added 25W amplifier PCB bolted to the inner of the set's rear panel heatsink. If you see a PCB with a large transistor fitted, a CD4442, then you're in luck as it's a high-power set. If you find nothing there, it's a 6W set, although make sure the small hairpin loop link is in place on the rear of the set's main PCB if the add-on PA has been removed.

Crystals

The set comes in either T1 or U0 band versions, although for 70cm my experience is that positive-side injection for the receive crystals works well for either band set, whereas negative-side injection will not perform as well on the T1 band set. It thus helps to 'standardise' on crystals in, say, a given club or group. The U band set, however, uses negative-side injection as standard, and you'll probably find this tunes satisfactorily onto 70cm with negative-side injection – just don't 'mix' positive-side and negative-side crystals in a single set as one 'side' then won't work! The crystals are HC-25/U types – the commercial specifications for these are T92RX for both the TX and RX crystals.

The crystal frequencies you need are:

$$\text{TX xtal freq} = \frac{\text{TX freq}}{32}$$

$$\text{RX xtal freq} = \frac{\text{RX freq} + 21.4\text{MHz}}{8} \qquad \text{(T1 band set)}$$

$$\text{RX xtal freq} = \frac{\text{RX freq} - 21.4\text{MHz}}{8} \qquad \text{(U0 band set – see text)}$$

Alignment

A component layout and alignment diagram are shown in Figs 4.5 and 4.6. If your set has a selective calling unit fitted, you'll need to unplug this and check the linking details on the transceiver main PCB. Pin F1 must be linked to pin S – you may find instead that G1 has been linked to S for receive audio switching. For transmit, the lead from pin 3 of the mic socket should go to pin L1 – this may instead have been linked to pin K1 if transmit selective call signalling was used.

To align the receiver, connect a 3–8Ω speaker to the connector with the brown/blue insulated wires (this is the external speaker connector) and connect your 13.8V DC power supply. Switch on and adjust the squelch preset, RV3, fully anticlockwise and make sure you hear squelch noise from your speaker with the volume set to a suitable level – check your links as above if you don't. Connect your multimeter negative lead to the transceiver rear panel chassis and set your meter to the 2.5V DC range. Connect the meter positive lead to TP1 and, with your channel switch in the correct position, adjust L15 and L16 for maximum, peaking both for absolute maximum, then adjust L17 for minimum reading. Switch the meter

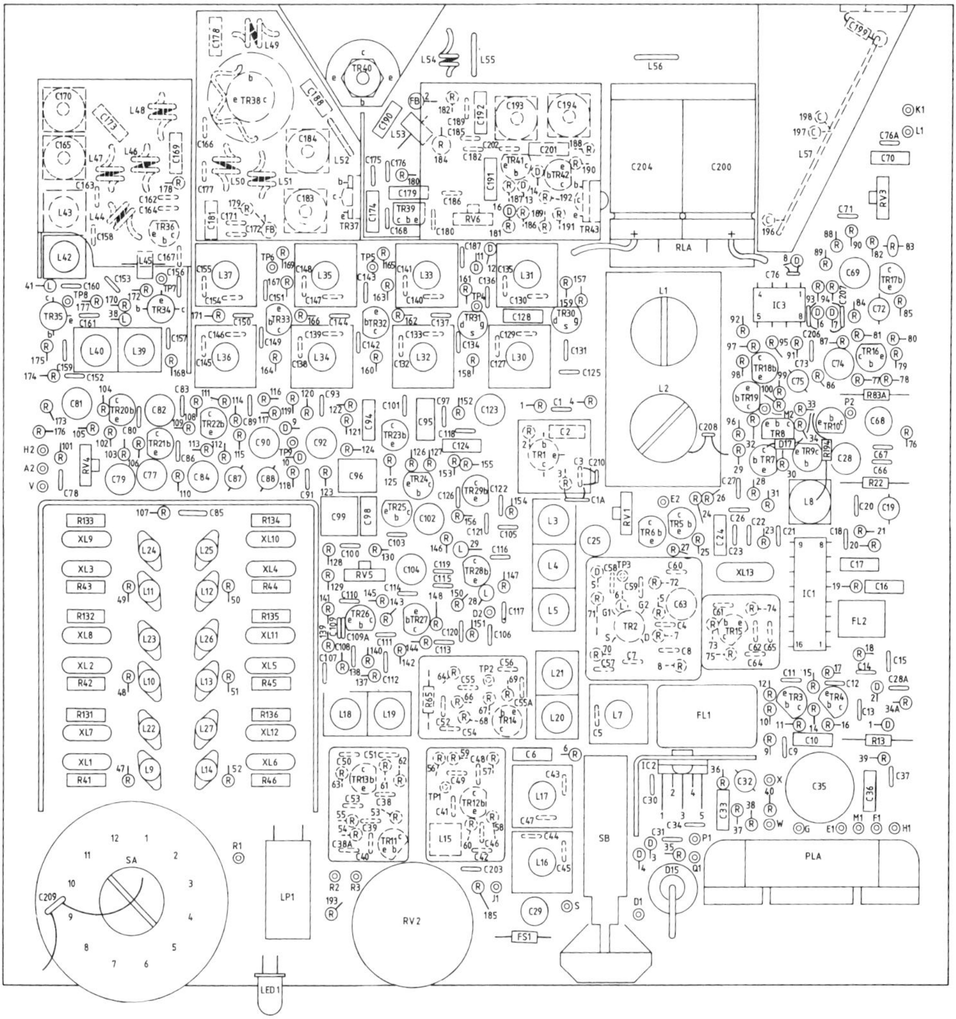

Fig 4.5. M296 internal components

to the 10V DC range and connect the positive lead now to TP2, then adjust L18 and L19 both for minimum voltage reading. Transfer to TP3, switch back to the 2.5V DC range, and adjust L20, L21, L18 and L19 for maximum, then readjust L20 and L21 again for absolute maximum. With a received off-air signal, first adjust the relevant receiver crystal trimmer for best reception, then adjust L1, L2, L3, L4 and L5 for best quieting, reducing the level of the off-air signal as needed. Finally, readjust L1–L5 again for absolute best on a weak signal. Readjust the crystal trimmer(s) as needed, then reset the squelch preset, RV3, as needed.

To align the transmitter, first adjust the transmitter RF power preset, RV6, fully anticlockwise – this can be adjusted through the small hole in the screen in front of the potentiometer. Set your multimeter to the 10V DC range, and connect the meter positive lead to TP4. With the transmitter PTT keyed (pins 3 and 5 connected together on

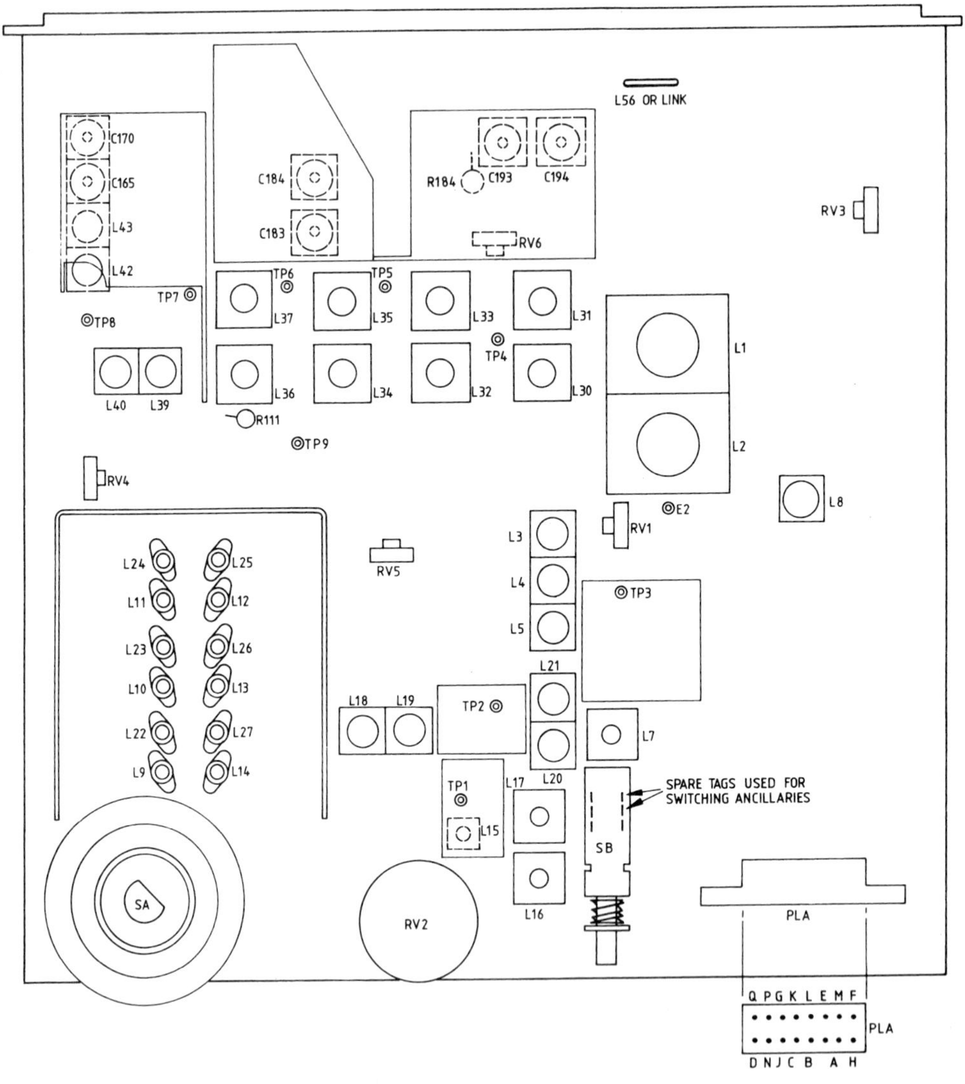

Fig 4.6. M296 alignment diagram

the mic socket), adjust L30 and L31 for maximum multimeter reading. Transfer the meter's positive lead to TP5, switch to the 2.5V DC range, and adjust L32 and L33 for maximum, then L34 for minimum reading. Transfer to TP6 and adjust L35 for maximum, then L36 for minimum. Transfer to TP7 and adjust L37 for maximum, then L39 for minimum. Switch back to the 10V DC range, transferring the meter positive lead to TP8, and adjust L39 and L40 for maximum, then L42 for minimum.

If you're now seeing some RF power output indicated, initially adjust L43 and C165 for maximum power. If not, then connect your multimeter set to a DC current range (around 3A for a 6W set, or 8A for a 25W set) in series with the positive supply to the transceiver and adjust initially for maximum current until RF power is present

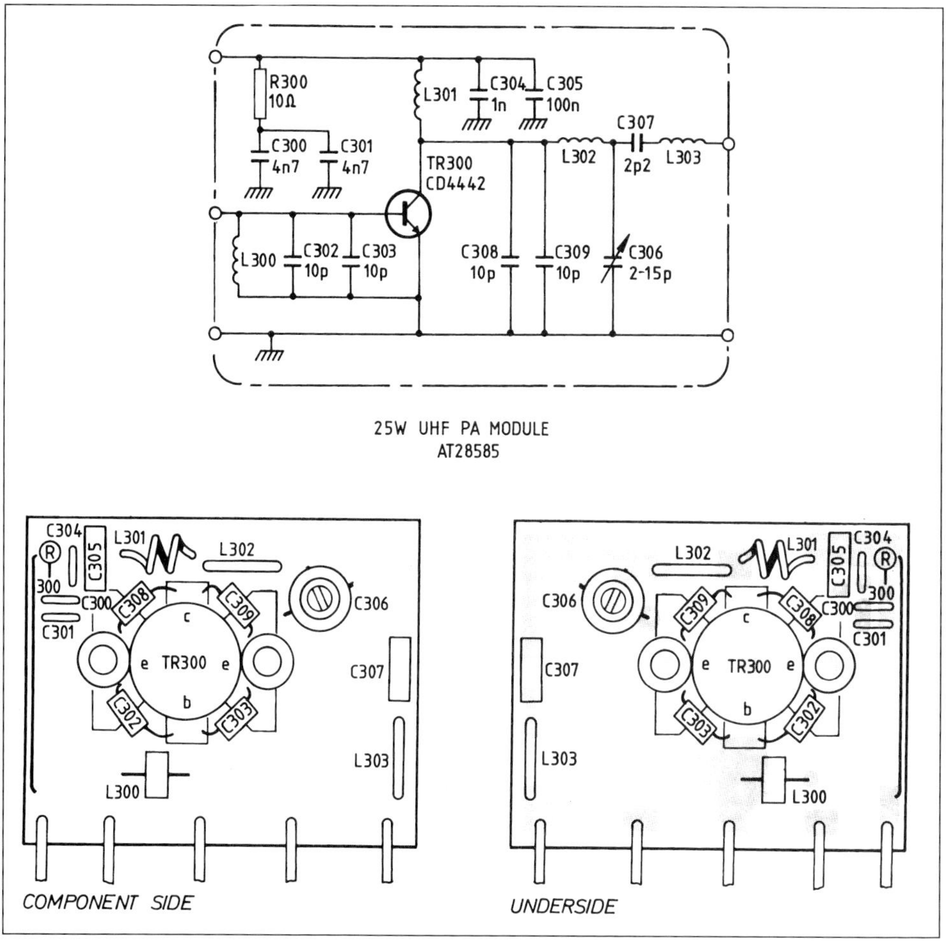

Fig 4.7. The M296 25W power amplifier

at the output, then readjust for maximum RF out. Adjust C170 again for maximum, and then adjust C183 and C184 as a 'pair' for maximum (two trimming tools, one in each hand, are useful here), then C193 and C194 again as a 'pair' and again for maximum. If you have a 25W PA unit fitted, adjust C306 on the add-on PCB for maximum output.

Finally, readjust L39 and L40 for absolute maximum RF output. Preset RV6 can now be readjusted if you wish to reduce the power output, but if so then you should also readjust C193 (and C306 if it's a 25W set) for maximum power again, readjusting RV6 again for the level you need. RV5 is the transmit deviation control, and RV4 is the transmit mic gain which you may wish to adjust after you've correctly set the deviation.

Extra facilities

An external squelch control is sometimes useful – for this simply replace the board-mounted preset with a 10kΩ linear potentiometer

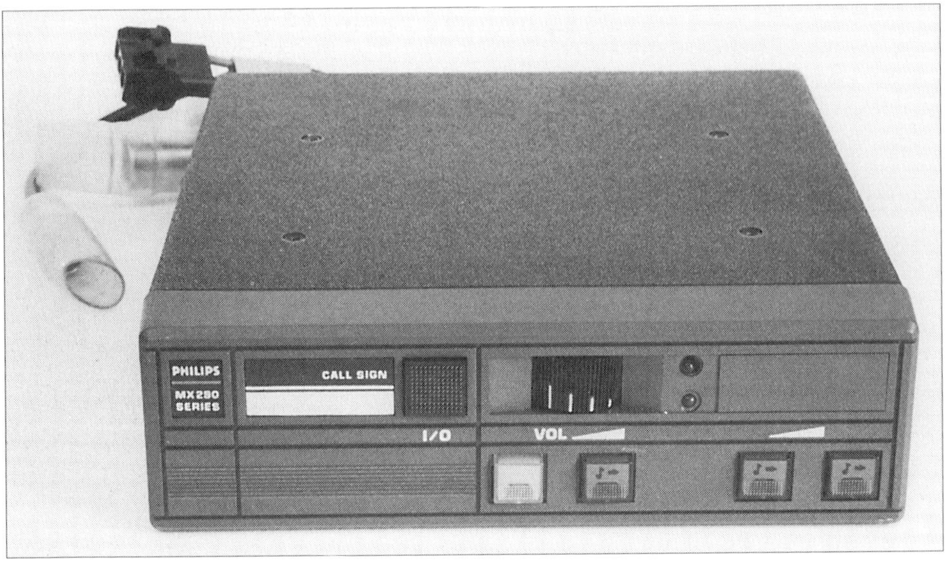

The MX290 series, fitted with a trunking controller in this case

control mounted on the set's front panel. Alternatively, you may wish to add a 'squelch open', ie 'busy', indicator. For this, connect an LED in series with a 1kΩ resistor between the set's positive supply and pin P2, which switches to 0V when the squelch lifts. P2 is often linked to pin M1, which in turn is connected to pin M on the main board.

MX290 SERIES

The MX290 series of sets outwardly look physically similar to the M290 series at first glance. As they can share the same front-panel options, you could easily be excused for mistaking them! A closer look, however, shows that the set is built on a die-cast alloy frame, with top and bottom lids screwed on using two screws on either end of each lid. Also, rather than a 'smooth' rear panel, a small finned die-cast heatsink, which is part of the cast frame, is used, together with a smaller serial number panel. The sets come in four types:

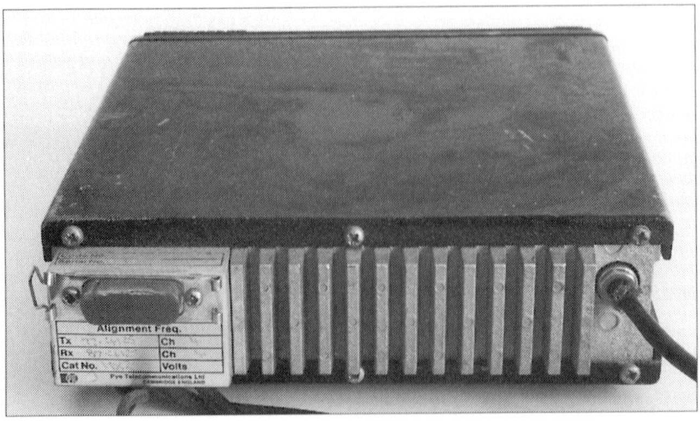

The MX290 series can be identified by a finned rear-panel heatsink

MX293: VHF AM
MX294: VHF FM
MX295: Band III (174–225MHz) FM
MX296: UHF FM

You'll usually find the RF circuitry is fitted with a large metal screen

You'll often (but not always) find a trunking front panel on the MX295, although I've also seen other sets, particularly the MX296, also with trunking plug-ins for MPT1327 and other signalling formats.

The MX293, being AM, isn't detailed here, neither is the MX295 as this requires a substantial amount of RF circuitry changes to 'get it going' onto the amateur bands. The MX294 and MX296 are, however, often ideal for use on 4m, 2m, or 70cm. Although you'll need to expend a little effort in adding suitable frequency control, the end result is a high-performance, multichannel set. I've used an E band (68–88MHz) and an A band (148–174MHz) MX294 continuously for several years at my local hilltop-sited packet radio node for 4m and 2m respectively – indeed, the 70cm port of this node uses an M296.

Identification codes

The rear panel information label will give you the serial, code and catalogue numbers, together with the transmitter and receiver alignment frequencies. The typically found alphanumeric codes are in the order given in Table 4.5.

The MX294 and MX296 come in a variety of forms, the main difference being the front-panel channel control arrangement. You'll usually find this is a edgewise mechanical 16-way channel switch, which appears virtually identical to the M294/M296 type apart from the greater number of switch positions. This switch is occasionally mechanically limited to the programmed number of channels – lift off the outer knob from the switch and remove the small metal ring from the switch itself. This ring will have a

Table 4.5. MX290 series identification codes

Equipment type:	MX294, MX296 etc
Market code:	01 (standard production)
Mobile type:	1 (standard), 2 (with fitted rear facility socket), 3 (for cassette mounting)
Installation items:	A, 1–4 (speaker, mounting brackets etc)
Number of channels:	1–9, X (10), A–F (11–16), Q (up to 256 with special front panel)
Brand label:	0–2 (front panel label)
Internal options:	0 (none), 1 (carrier level detector, eg for trunking sets)
Channel spacing:	S (12.5kHz), V (25kHz), R (20kHz)
TX/RX freq band:	A0, E0 etc.
Channel capacity:	F (up to 16), G (all others)
Freq programming:	T, 1–6 (various programmed options)
Transmit power:	1 (25W), 2 (15W), 3 (10W), or 4 (6W)
Primary options:	1A ('New' front panel), 1B (TEDX), 1C (TED3), 14 (TE1), 15 (TED1), 16 (TED6), 41 (40-chan), 45 (40-chan, TED1), 46 (40-chan, TED6), 81 (80-chan), 85 (80-chan, TED1), 86 (80-chan, TED6), S1 (CX290 trunking)
Secondary options:	00–30 (various mics), 90 (mic with internal TX timer).

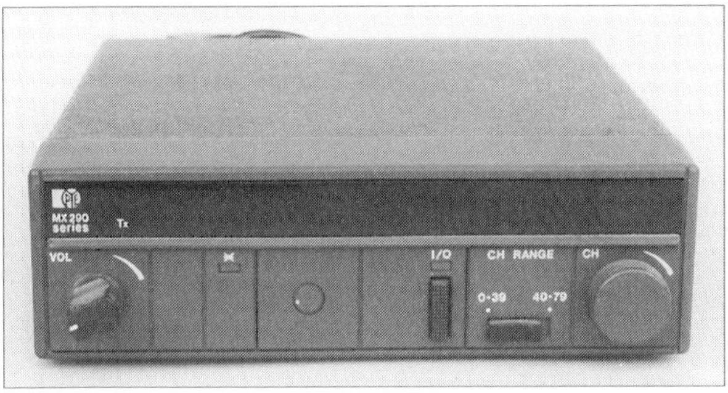

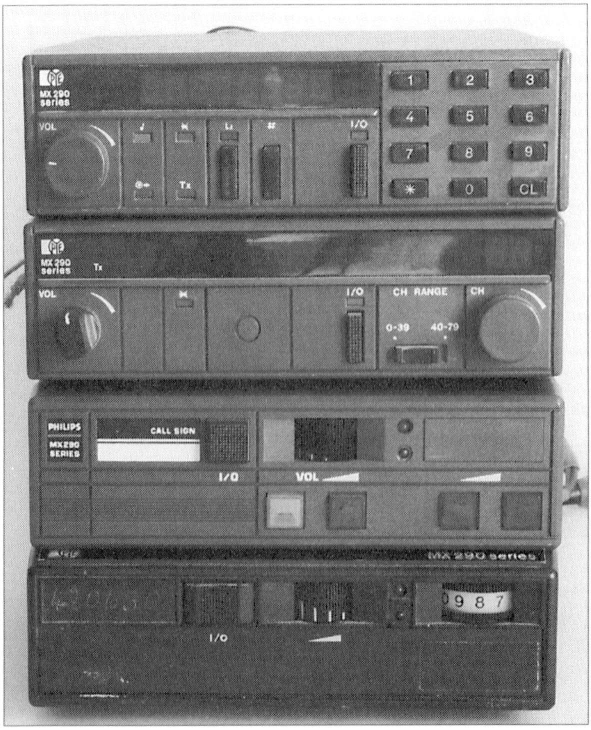

Top: **The MX290 series is usually fitted with a 16-channel switch**

Middle: **If you find an MX294 or MX296 with a 40/80-channel front panel like this, you're in luck**

Bottom: **All these sets are from the MX290 series**

detented 'stop' in it which fits into the appropriate channel position on the rotary switch to act as a mechanical stop. Alternatively, you might find an electronic channel control with a dual seven-segment LED readout giving either 40 channels or 80 channels. In the latter case, an edgewise plug is fitted to the front left of the set's main board to interface with the front panel's channel control. The latter form of front panel of course is ideal for amateur radio use, although you can if you wish add your own BCD switches to give channel control.

Don't be mislead if you see an LCD readout on the front panel along with the 16-way switch – this is a TEDX microprocessor controlled selective calling unit, which has nothing to do with the RF channel control of the set.

You may sometimes find a trunking front panel is used, with a LED readout and keypad but no click-step channel knob. In this case, you'll need to replace this with an added channel switch of your own.

Synthesiser

This uses an NJ8813 synthesiser divider IC and a HEF4750 reference divider IC, the latter in the case of the MX294 plugging into a socket on the main

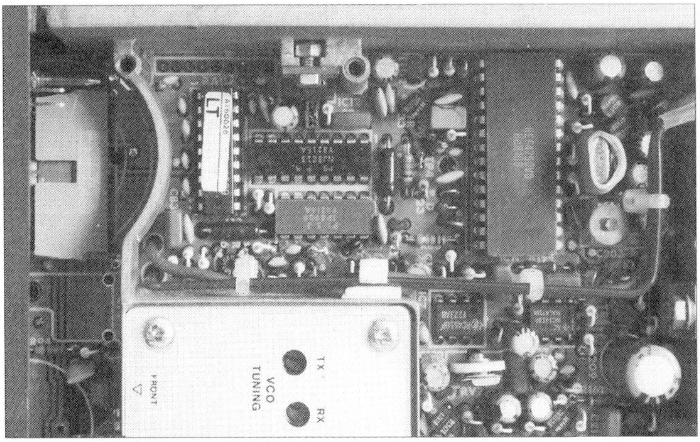

The MX294 synthesiser section – the TTL PROM has a white label attached

board. Note that this isn't an EPROM, even if it looks like one. The frequency control information is stored in a fusible-link TTL PROM. Now, most amateurs don't have programming facilities for these, although EPROM programming facilities for the commonly available 27 series EPROMs are usually readily available. As common 5V logic levels are used for both, with suitable pin-swapping a suitably programmed EPROM can be used as an effective replacement. I've helped supply over 200 such programmed EPROMs to amateurs in the UK for this very purpose.

You'll find that, for 16 channels, a 16-pin 82S129 PROM is used. For 40/80 or more channels, an 18-pin 82S185 PROM is used. The PROM plugs into an IC socket on the MX294 PCB, and this has facilities for either 16-pin or 18-pin IC sockets. Even if a 16-pin socket is used, the 'holes' are there in the PCB for 18 pins – pins 9 and 10 aren't used. To prevent confusion, the pin numbers I've given here always refer to those for an 18-pin socket – for a 16-pin socket simply subtract 2 from pin numbers 11–18 inclusive.

Channel switch

The 16-way channel switch used is a reverse-logic type, which pulls the output lines to 0V rather than connects positive voltage as needed to the PROM address lines. A thin-film resistor array of eight 4.7kΩ resistors is used to 'pull up' to 5V the address lines to the PROM. You'll see a 7805 regulator next to the latter – this is used to supply the stabilised 5V line. You may also see a plug-in link LK1 next to the regulator. This is the 5V line link and should be left connected. You may also see link LK2 next to the PROM. This is used to pull the A7 binary address line (PROM pin 17) down to 0V. This is because the 82S129 has a capacity to store 32 channels, and this facility is used to provide an alignment channel for the set, which is the frequency marked on its serial number plate. By using the LK2 facility, either with a suitably programmed PROM or a replacement EPROM and the A7 line connected appropriately, with the 16-channel switch you can get access to 32 channels, ie all 2m FM 'S' and 'R' channels plus reverse repeater channels. To do this, use the 16-channel switch and add a toggle switch on the front panel, wired to the two pins on LK2 or to short PROM address line A7 (pin 17) to 0V if LK2 isn't present.

You must make the appropriate pin 'crossovers' when using a substitution EPROM. For this you can simply use several wires

Table 4.6. EPROM Substitution for 82S129 PROM

EPROM function	EPROM pin number (18-pin) conn 2716	2732	2764	27128	27256	MX294 PROM socket
A0	8	8	10	10	10	Pin 5
A1	7	7	9	9	9	Pin 6
A2	6	6	8	8	8	Pin 7
A3	5	5	7	7	7	Pin 4
A4	4	4	6	6	6	Pin 3
A5	3	3	5	5	5	Pin 2
A6	2	2	4	4	4	Pin 1
A7	1	1	3	3	3	Pin 17
A8	23	23	25	25	25	0V
A9	22	22	24	24	24	0V
A10	19	19	21	21	21	0V
A11	–	21	23	23	23	0V
A12	–	–	2	2	2	0V
A13	–	–	–	26	26	0V
A14	–	–	–	–	27	0V
O0	9	9	11	11	11	Pin 14
O1	10	10	12	12	12	Pin 13
O2	11	11	13	13	13	Pin 12
O3	13	13	15	15	15	Pin 11
O4	14	14	16	16	16	o/c
O5	15	15	17	17	17	o/c
O6	16	16	18	18	18	o/c
O7	17	17	19	19	19	o/c
Gnd	12	12	14	14	14	0V
Vpp	21	20	1	1	1	Pin 18 (+5V)
OE	20	20	22	22	22	0V
CE	18	18	20	20	20	0V
Vcc	24	24	28	28	28	Pin 18 (+5V)
PGM	–	–	27	27	–	Pin 18 (+5V)

appropriately soldered between the main PCB (with the PROM socket removed) and an EPROM socket mounted on a piece of Veroboard or similar.

Programming codes

The MX290 series synthesiser requires four sequential binary 'words', of 4 bits each, for each TX or RX frequency (Fig 4.8). On the TTL PROM, it sequentially addresses in binary the A0 (pin 5) and A1 (pin 6) lines to obtain these, and the A2 line (pin 7) is used to switch between RX (binary 0) and TX (binary 1). The address lines, A3 (pin 1), A4 (pin 2), A5 (pin 3) and A6 (pin 4) are the 16-channel binary address from the channel switch, and A7 is the 'LK2' address for 'moving up' 16 channels. The first four hexadecimal 'words' programmed in your PROM/EPROM contain the channel 1 receive division code, the next four contain the channel 1 transmit code, the next four channel 2 receive code, the next four channel 2 transmit code etc. For transmit, this is the division code for the transmit VCO frequency, on receive it's the code for the local oscillator injection frequency, which for both 2m and 4m is 10.7MHz above the required receiver frequency, and for 70cm is 21.4MHz away from the receive frequency.

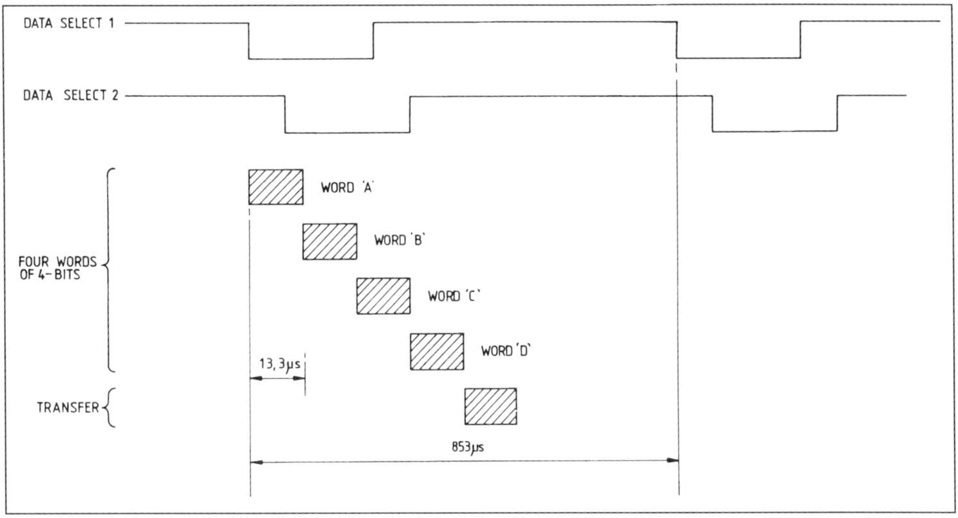

Fig 4.8. MX290 series PROM addressing

If your set is a (rare) 'AW' band (148–174MHz wide-band) or EW band (68–88MHz wide-band) set, identified by a 21.4MHz crystal filter (marked '21xxxx' on the top), then use an injection frequency of 21.4MHz removed from the receive frequency.

The MX296 uses a synthesiser reference frequency of 12.5kHz, and the MX294 uses either a 5kHz or 6.25kHz synthesiser reference. To check on the latter, look at the colour of the thin PCB between the large HEF4750 IC and its socket. If it's blue or red, the synthesiser reference frequency (ie the minimum channel step) is 6.25kHz, as found on virtually all sets in the UK. If it's green (rare in the UK), it's 5kHz. This is important when you work out the codes – a 5kHz reference means you won't be able to program 12.5kHz channel steps, only multiples of 5kHz. The reference frequency is present as a square wave on pin 25 of the HEF4750 if you're in doubt. All codes given in the tables in this section for the MX294 are for the commonly found 10.7MHz receiver IF and reference frequency of 6.25kHz – those for the MX296 are for a 12.5kHz reference and positive-side receiver injection.

Code calculation

To calculate the division code for any required frequency (remember, this is the VCO injection frequency in receive mode), first divide your TX or RX injection frequency by the reference frequency, making sure you keep to the same frequency exponential, ie hertz, kilohertz or megahertz. For example, divide the final VCO frequency in megahertz by 0.00625 (6.25kHz – substitute 0.005 if yours is a 5kHz reference set, or 0.0125 if it's an MX296). Then, subtract 3840 from this number – this is a fixed synthesiser divider offset. Convert the number you now have into a four-digit hexadecimal word, *DCBA*, with *D* as the MSD (most significant bit) and *A* as the LSB (least significant bit). Now change this hexadecimal combination

Table 4.7. Suggested 2m channels

Chan	LK1 in	LK1 out
16	R0	Rev R0
1	R1	Rev R1
2	R2	Rev R2
3	R3	Rev R3
4	R4	Rev R4
5	R5	Rev R5
6	R6	Rev R6
7	R7	Rev R7
8	S8	S16
9	S9	S17
10	S10	S18
11	S11	S19
12	S12	S20
13	S13	S21
14	S14	S22
15	S15	S23

Table 4.8. 2m PROM codes

Frequency (MHz)	RX BCAD	TX BCAD	Frequency (MHz)	RX BCAD	TX BCAD
144.500	0205	5B04	145.275	72C5	CBC4
144.525	0245	5B44	145.300	8205	DB04
144.550	0285	5B84	145.325	8245	DB44
144.575	02C5	5BC4	145.350	8285	DB84
144.600	1205	6B04	145.375	82C5	DBC4
144.625	1245	6B44	145.400	9205	EB04
144.650	1285	6B84	145.425	9245	EB44
144.675	12C5	6BC4	145.450	9285	EB84
144.700	2205	7B04	145.475	92C5	EBC4
144.725	2245	7B44	145.500	A205	FB04
144.750	2285	7B84	145.525	A245	FB44
144.775	22C5	7BC4	145.550	A285	FB84
144.800	3205	8B04	145.575	A2C5	FBC4
144.825	3245	8B44	145.600	B205	0C04
144.850	3285	8B84	145.625	B245	0C44
144.875	32C5	8BC4	145.650	B285	0C84
144.900	4205	9B04	145.675	B2C5	0CC4
144.925	4245	9B44	145.700	C205	1C04
144.950	4285	9B84	145.725	C245	1C44
144.975	42C5	9BC4	145.750	C285	1C84
145.000	5205	AB04	145.775	C2C5	1CC4
145.025	5245	AB44	145.800	D205	2C04
145.050	5285	AB84	145.825	D245	2C44
145.075	52C5	ABC4	145.850	D285	2C84
145.100	6205	BB04	145.875	D2C5	2CC4
145.125	6245	BB44	145.900	E205	3C04
145.150	6285	BB84	145.925	E245	3C44
145.175	62C5	BBC4	145.950	E285	3C84
145.200	7205	CB04	145.975	E2C5	3CC4
145.225	7245	CB44	146.000	F205	4C04
145.250	7285	CB84			

Table 4.9. 4m PROM codes

Frequency (MHz)	RX BCAD	TX BCAD	Frequency (MHz)	RX BCAD	TX BCAD
70.2500	9382	EC81	70.3875	A3E2	FCE1
70.2625	93A2	ECA1	70.4000	B302	0D01
70.2750	93C2	ECC1	70.4125	B322	0D21
70.2875	93E2	ECE1	70.4250	B342	0D41
70.3000	A302	FC01	70.4375	B362	0D61
70.3125	A322	FC21	70.4500	B382	0D81
70.3250	A342	FC41	70.4625	B3A2	0DA1
70.3375	A362	FC61	70.4750	B3C2	0DC1
70.3500	A382	FC81	70.4875	B3E2	0DE1
70.3625	A3A2	FCA1	70.5000	C302	1D01
70.3750	A3C2	FCC1			

from *DCBA* to *BCAD*, because this is the order in which the synthesiser reads the information, *B* first, then *C*, then *A*, then *D*, and this is the order you need to program each frequency into your EPROM or PROM.

I've given typical codes in Tables 4.8, 4.9 and 4.10 for popular amateur FM channels.

Substitution diode matrix

Table 4.10. Typical 70cm EPROM codes

Frequency (MHz)	RX BCAD	TX BCAD	Frequency (MHz)	RX BCAD	TX BCAD
433.000	5807	0F07	433.300	6887	1F87
433.025	5827	0F27	433.325	68A7	1FA7
433.050	5847	0F47	433.350	68C7	1FC7
433.075	5867	0F67	433.375	68E7	1FE7
433.100	5887	0F87	433.400	7807	2F07
433.125	58A7	0FA7	433.425	7827	2F27
433.150	58C7	0FC7	433.450	7847	2F47
433.175	58E7	0FE7	433.475	7867	2F67
433.200	6807	1F07	433.500	7887	2F87
433.225	6827	1F27	433.525	78A7	2FA7
433.250	6847	1F47	433.550	78C7	2FC7
433.275	6867	1F67	433.575	78E7	2FE7

For single-channel use, maybe for packet, you can substitute a low-cost CMOS IC together with a few diodes and resistors for the PROM. I developed the circuit shown here for my 4m MX294 to be used on a hilltop packet node site. See Fig 4.9 and Table 4.11. To program this, fit the diodes needed to give you the correct binary 'words' for each address, in the same *BCAD* order. A diode present in any position provides a logic '1' while the absence of a diode in any position provides a logic '0'. You may wish to produce a PCB, although for the sake of simplicity a stripboard layout is preferred for 'one-off' boards.

Links

If your set was fitted with a selective calling module, than at the front right of the set you'll see a set of links. For 'normal' operation (ie without any front-panel selective calling limitations of TX and / or

Fig 4.9. MX290 series diode matrix PROM replacement

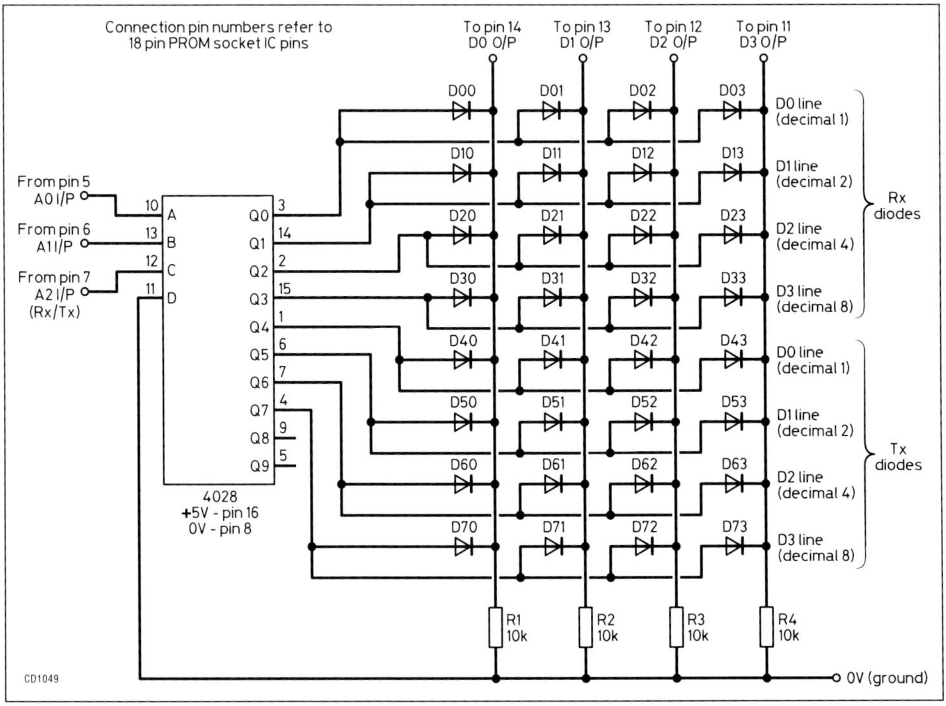

Table 4.11. Binary/hexadecimal codes

Hex	Binary MSB D3x	D2x	D1x	LSB D0x
0	0	0	0	0
1	0	0	0	1
2	0	0	1	0
3	0	0	1	1
4	0	1	0	0
5	0	1	0	1
6	0	1	1	0
7	0	1	1	1
8	1	0	0	0
9	1	0	0	1
A	1	0	1	0
B	1	0	1	1
C	1	1	0	0
D	1	1	0	1
E	1	1	1	0
F	1	1	1	1

RX capability) you need to link F to S and K1 to L, and remove any other links. If your front panel does have some signalling electronics present, just remove the electronics of this, or at least the plug which mates with the radio itself next to these links, before refitting it after conversion.

Preliminaries

The MX290 series uses the same microphone, speaker, and facility connections as the M290 series to provide interchangeability between plug-in modules. Thus, simply refer to the information I've given earlier in this chapter for these connections.

Opening the set up by removing the covers will usually reveal a large metal screen secured to the chassis with a multitude of screws. This is for screening purposes between the RF section and any added selective calling modules, and for amateur purposes without a Selcall unit fitted it can safely be left off if you need the room for an added EPROM board. Don't at this stage remove the lid above the square VCO unit. For tuning purposes I'd advise leaving the lid on which is next to the track side of the main PCB (this is either the top or the bottom lid, depending upon which front-panel control arrangement is used) to ensure the set doesn't short out on any stray metal on your bench. Before doing this, however, quickly make sure the four VCO unit screws on the track side of the main PCB are tight – you'll find if these are loose you'll get superimposed 'scratchy' noises on both transmit and receive due to vibration if you use the rig on the move.

Connect a 3–8Ω speaker to the rear blue / brown speaker lead, and for transmit alignment a microphone to the five-pin 270° DIN mic connector. Now connect your 13.8V DC supply. If you have a channel switch fitted then, with the controls towards you, check there's a red 'lock' LED glowing at the left of the set – this may occur on only a few channels as you rotate the channel knob. This shows the synthesiser is working OK. If it doesn't, then check whether the small black plug-in PROM is missing – it will usually have a white label on it identifying the stored information.

MX294

Two slightly different versions of the MX294 receiver circuitry have been made – one is marked 'AT28790' on the main PCB and is fitted with a bipolar BFQ51 receiver front-end transistor, while the later model is marked 'AT28873' and is fitted with a BF981 which gives slightly better sensitivity. These transistors aren't interchangeable (don't try it!) but the receiver tuning details are identical between the models.

Alignment

Details of the synthesiser layout and circuitry are given in Figs 4.10–4.14. Fit your programmed PROM or EPROM, and initially adjust the multi-turn RX VCO trimmer until the red 'lock' LED lights – then with the radio switched to the centre channel of your programmed frequency range, tune for a voltage of around 6.5V on TP3. You can also check with an oscilloscope or frequency counter that a pulse waveform is present on pin 1 of the HEF4750 reference divider IC – this is the divided VCO signal (a square-wave 6.25 / 5.0kHz reference derived from the crystal source is present on pin 25 for a comparison). As you adjust the VCO trimmer, the frequency of the waveform on pin 1 should vary in sympathy with the VCO frequency. Rotate RV1, the RX squelch control, until you hear noise from the speaker – if the VCO is out of lock you'll find the receive audio is muted. On receiving an off-air signal, adjust all six front-end coils L1–L7 for best signal, reducing the level of the signal as needed. Reset the squelch as needed.

For the transmitter alignment, key the PTT and adjust the TX VCO trimmer until the 'lock' LED lights, then with your set on the centre channel of your programmed frequency range, readjust for 6.5V on TP3. Set the transmit power control RV4 fully clockwise and adjust the three transmitter PA trimmer capacitors C126, C129 and C138 all for maximum transmit power (you'll usually find you can achieve 35–45W output). Readjust RV4 to the power output you wish, typically 25W for normal operation to prevent overheating of the PA

Inside the MX294 – this set has had a BF981 preamplifier added by the author

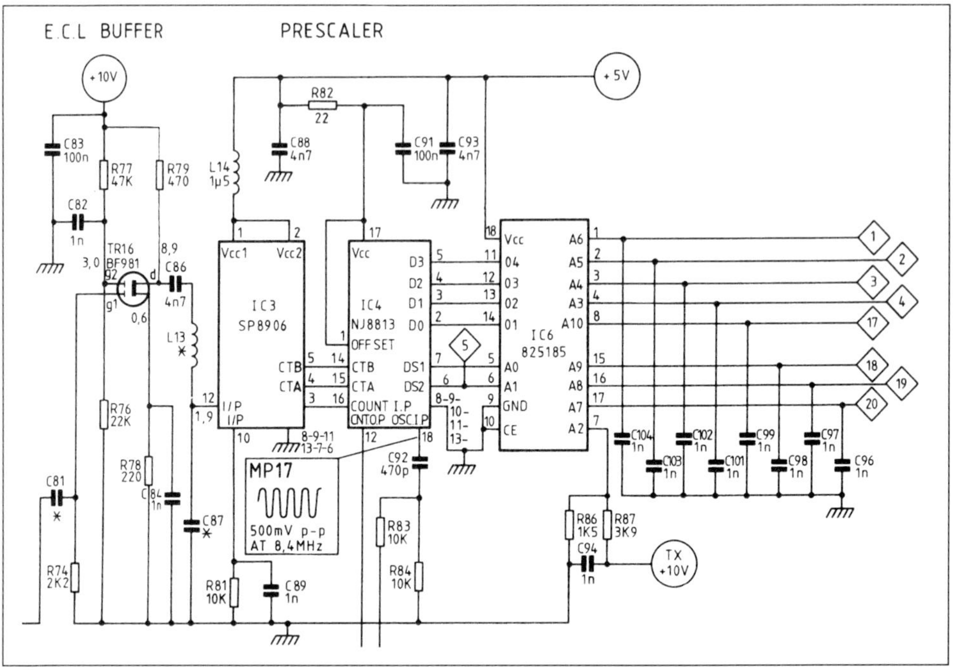

Fig 4.10. MX294 remote channel control and synthesiser circuitry

heatsink. RV6 sets the transmitter deviation but you'll first need to adjust RV7, which is the modulation balance control. Using either a high-impedance AC millivoltmeter or preferably an oscilloscope connected

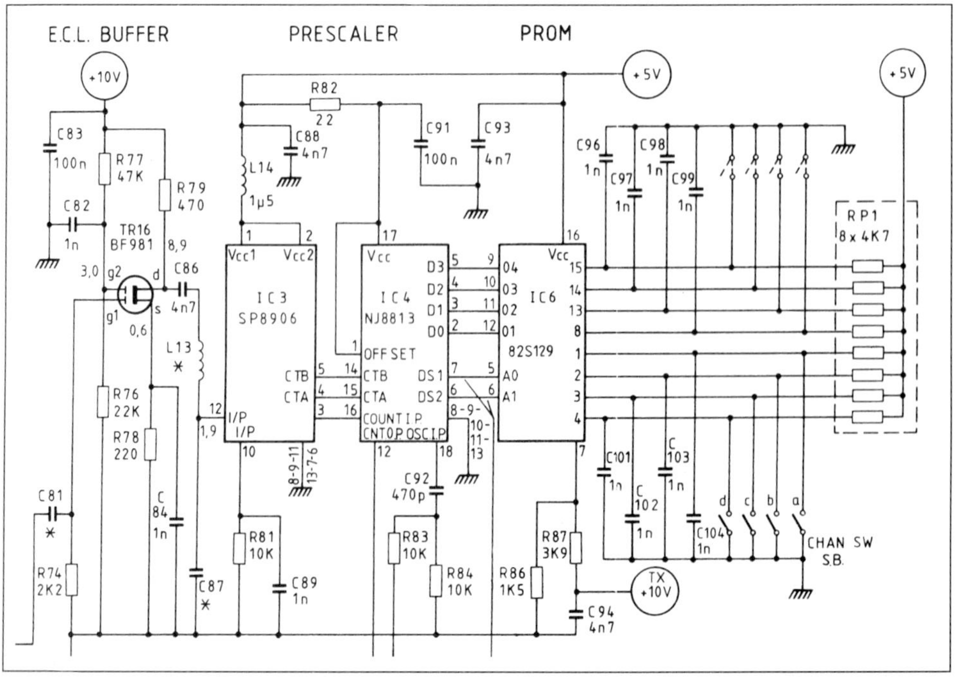

Fig 4.11. MX294 16-channel PROM and synthesiser circuitry

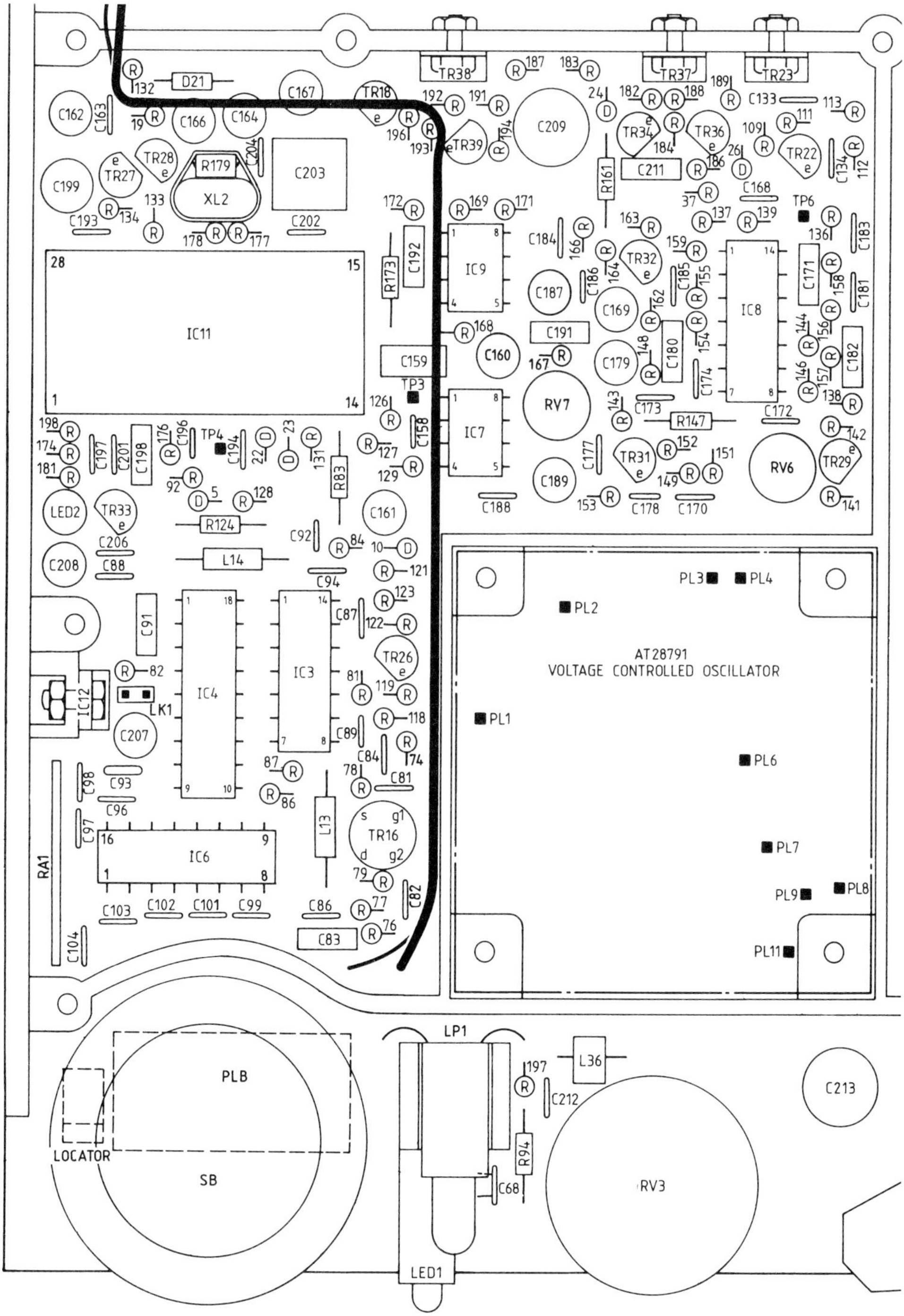

to TP7, adjust RV7 for minimum reading (ie to 'null' the 'stepped' AC waveform to zero at this test point), at the same time as you're providing a modulation input at the microphone. You will normally

Fig 4.12. Synthesiser component layout, MX294

Fig 4.13. MX294 alignment diagram

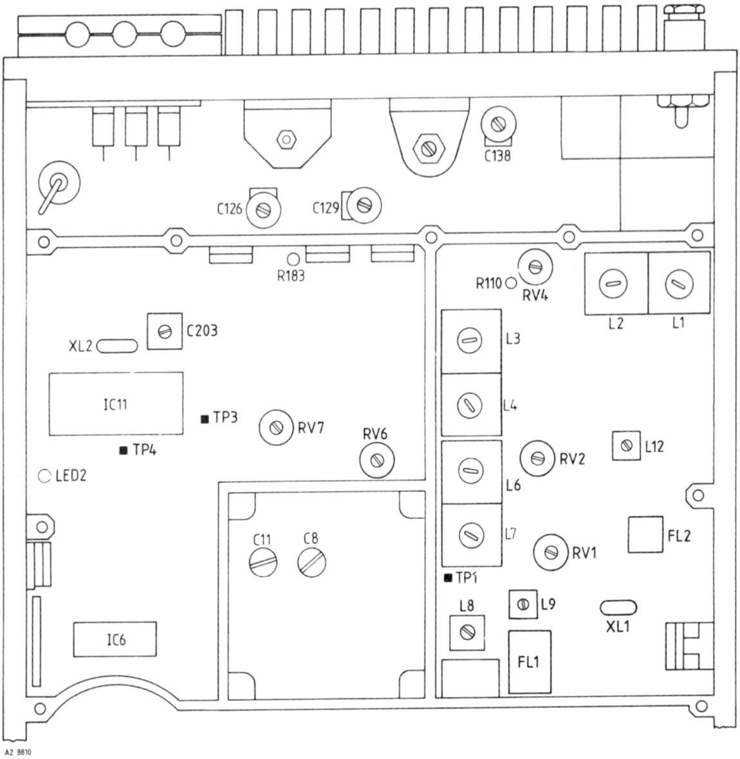

Fig 4.14. MX294 circuit links

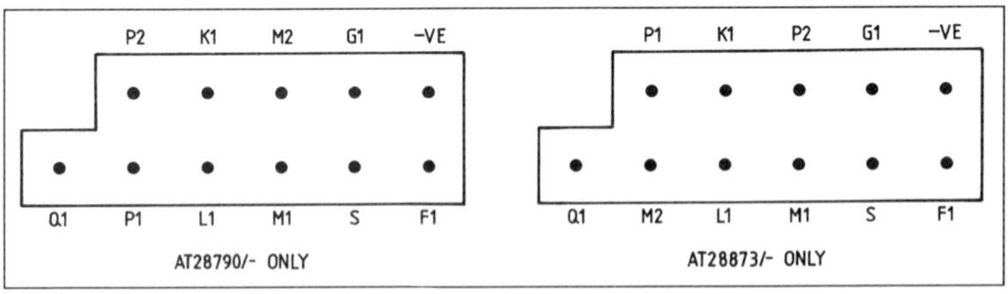

not need to make any further adjustments but C203 is the reference frequency crystal trimmer, which sets the frequency of both transmit and receive on all channels.

MX296

The MX296 is outwardly physically similar to the MX294, and provides around 11W on transmit. After removing the lid and any selective calling module, make links to join pins S to F (RX audio), and pins K1 to L (TX PTT) on the small link header array at the front right hand side of the set's main board. Remove any other links.

Alignment

Details of the MX296 layouts are given in Figs 4.15–4.18. After plugging in your suitably programmed PROM, or wiring in a replacement EPROM having thoroughly checked the connections, connect

Inside the MX296

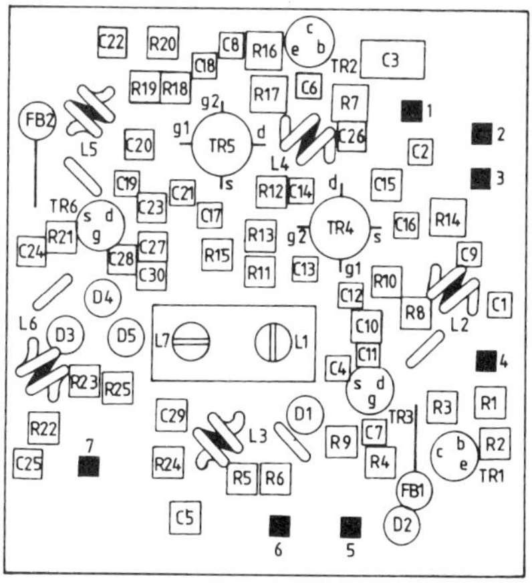

Left: **The MX296 VCO unit**

Above: **Fig 4.15. The MX296 VCO component layout**

your DC power supply and switch the set on. Carefully adjust L1 on the VCO board until the red 'lock' LED illuminates. This L1 adjuster may have some flexible rubbery sealant on it – just remove this if needed. If you find the LED doesn't light, then check your EPROM connections. You can also check with an oscilloscope or frequency counter that a pulse waveform is present on pin 1 of the HEF4750 reference divider IC – this is the divided VCO signal (a square-wave 12.5kHz reference

Fig 4.16. The MX296 VCO circuit

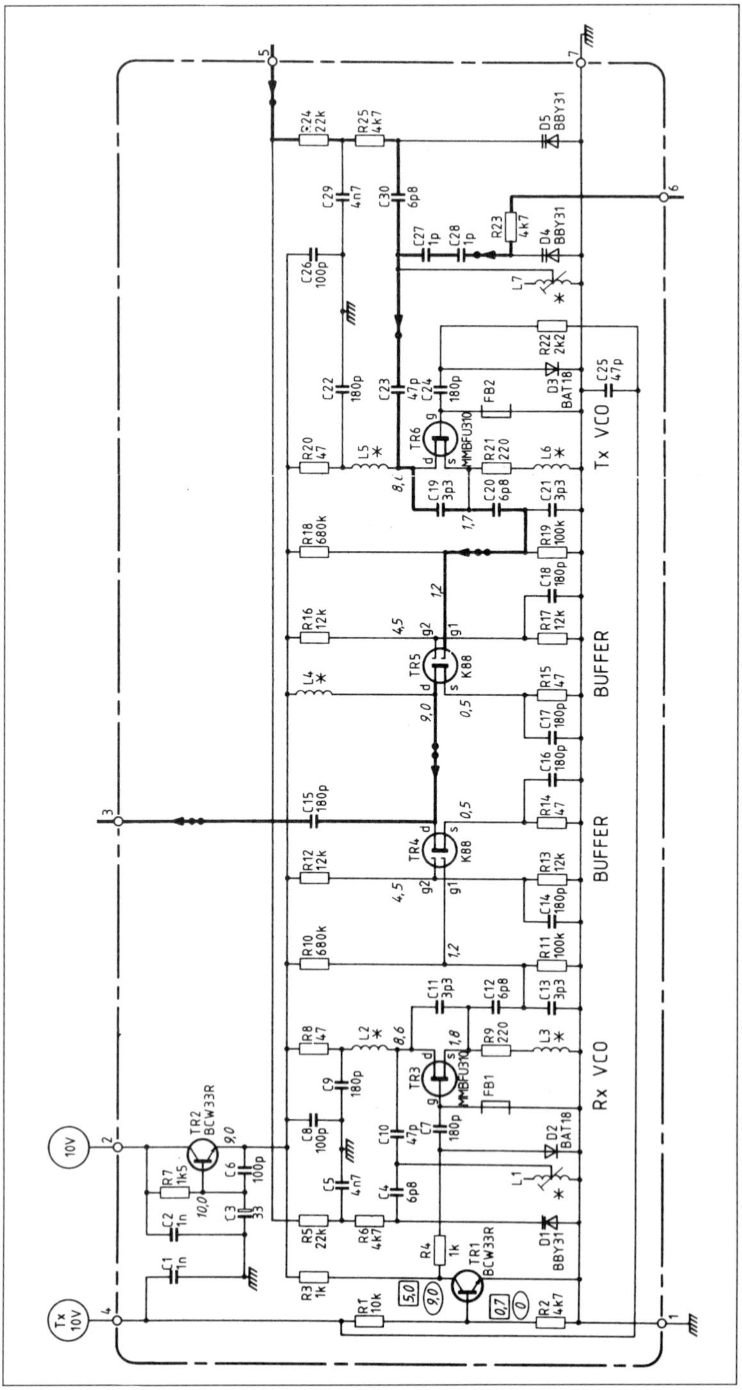

derived from the crystal source is present on pin 25 for a comparison). As you adjust the VCO trimmer, the frequency of the waveform on pin 1 should vary in sympathy with the VCO frequency.

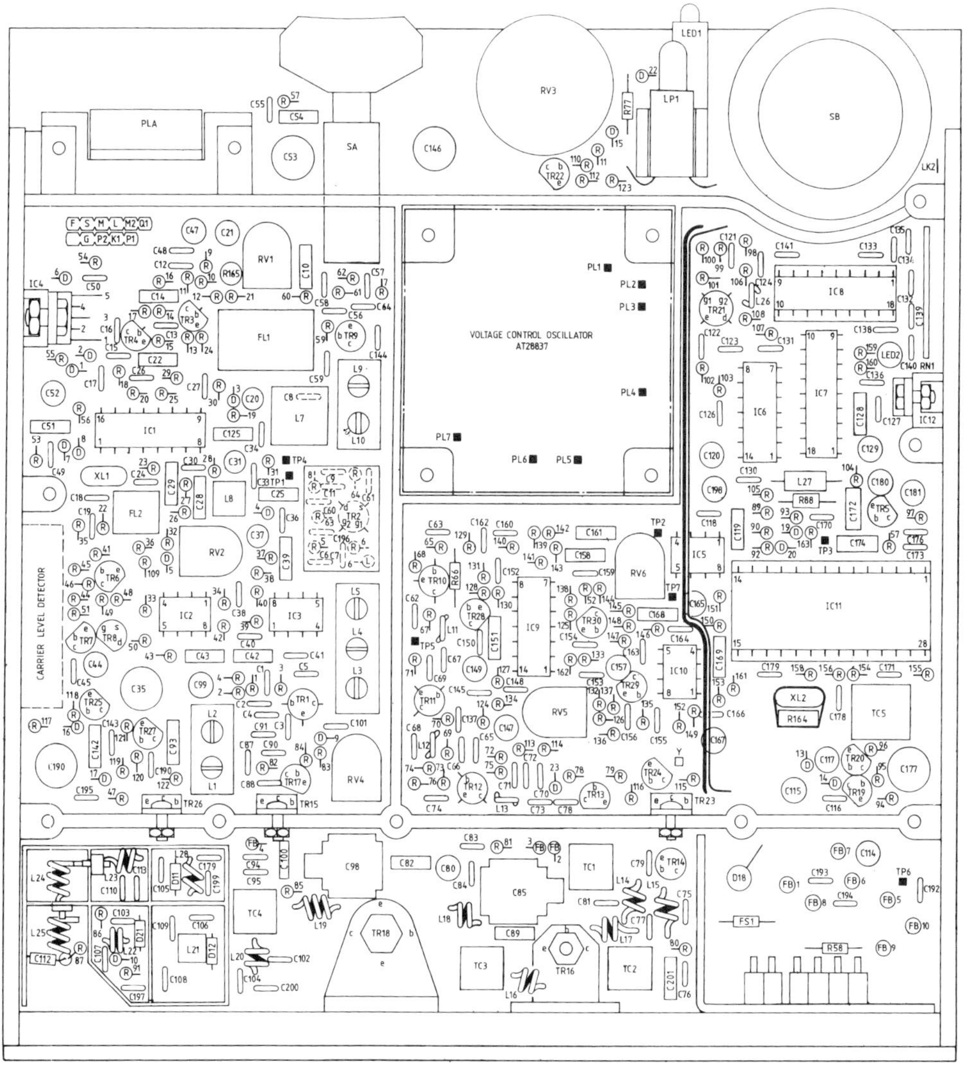

Fig 4.17. MX296 component layout

Assuming you obtain lock, adjust L1 until you get a reading of around 6.5V on test point TP2 – this voltage will vary in sympathy with your tuning when the synthesiser is in lock.

If you find that your VCO will not 'pull' enough for use on 70cm on receive, then you can slightly modify the hairpin coils, L2 and L3, on the receive section of the VCO. First remove the VCO board by removing the four screws securing the lid, followed by the four screws on the track side of the main PCB, and unplug the VCO board by carefully pulling the board-mounted pillars to lift the VCO board out. Unsolder L2 and L3, replacing these with slightly larger hairpin loops so that when the VCO is inserted the tops are just below the nearby metal can. Don't attempt to modify the turns on the coils inside the metal cans – you'll just end up with a mess of melted coil former!

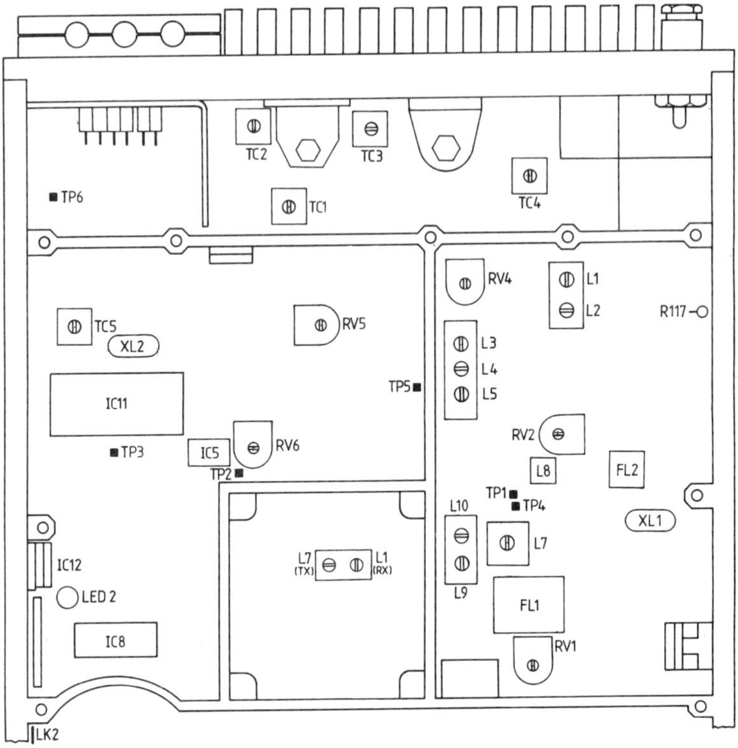

Fig 4.18. MX296 alignment diagram

Initially adjust the squelch preset RV1 so that you can hear receiver noise from the speaker with the volume control suitably adjusted. Whilst receiving an off-air signal, adjust L9 and L10, then L1, L2, L3, L4 and L5 for best reception, reducing the level of signal as needed, and finally retuning these for best sensitivity on a weak signal – then reset the squelch preset as needed.

Now key the transmitter and adjust L7 on the VCO board again until the 'lock' LED lights, then again adjust this for around 6.5V on TP2. RV4 is the RF power preset control, which you should initially set to give maximum output power. Now adjust the transmitter driver and power amplifier trimmers TC1, TC2, TC3 and TC4 for maximum RF output power, repeating the sequence until absolute maximum output is obtained. If you don't get any RF initially, adjust these first for maximum current drawn by the rig from your power supply, then carry on adjusting for maximum RF power.

TC5, which sometimes forms part of a metal TCXO (temperature compensated xtal oscillator) block, is the reference frequency adjustment. If the unit came out of service, this should be accurately set, but may be adjusted if needed – it sets the frequency of all receive and transmit channels.

RV5 is the peak deviation control and, using an AC millivoltmeter or preferably an oscilloscope, adjust RV6 for minimum AC 'stepped' waveform voltage on TP3 while you're applying audio to the set's microphone.

Packet use for the M290 and MX290 series

Low-level receiver audio is present on pin 4 of the microphone connector – note that the front-panel volume control varies the level of this. You may wish to relink this to the top of the volume control for 1200 baud packet use.

Most packet terminal node controllers use a 'ground to transmit' line for PTT, so to interface with the set you'll need to add a suitable interface, like the one-transistor circuit of Fig 4.19. You'll find +10V on pin 5, and you'll need to switch +10V to pin 3 for transmit.

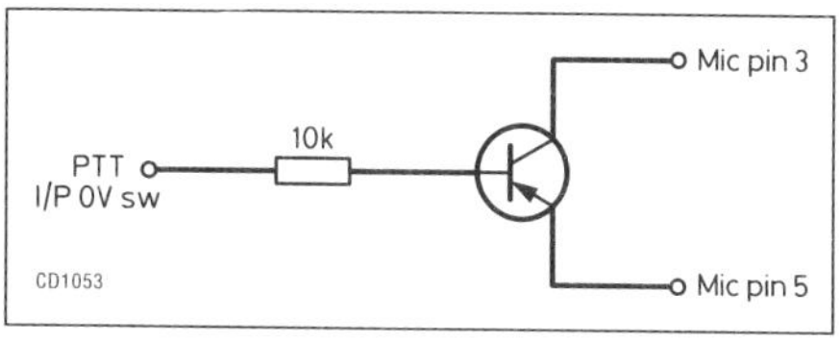

Fig 4.19. M/MX290 series TNC PTT interface

For 9600 baud packet, on receive you can take the receive discriminator audio out from pin 9 of the MC3357 IC in the receiver section on each set, using a series isolating capacitor. On the M294/6, the transmitter uses phase modulation rather than direct frequency modulation, but you can try injecting transmit audio to pin D of the facility connector. On the MX294 remove C187 (2.2μF, next to IC9) and inject your transmit audio to the pad previously connected to the positive lead of C187 via an isolating capacitor of at least 10μF (possibly using the capacitor you removed), with the positive lead to the MX294 connection. On the MX296, remove C165 (10μF, next to IC10, a 1458) and inject TX audio to the pad previously connected to the positive lead of C165, again with an isolating capacitor with the positive lead going to the MX296 connection.

MOTOROLA MC80 ON 70cm

Although Motorola mobiles have in the past been a rarity, there have been a large number of Motorola MC80 transceivers for UHF seen on the surplus market. My thanks go to Colin, G3PSM, for his help in providing me with valuable assistance including a copy of the technical service manual; to Steve, G1FIP, for modification information; to Steve, G3VMW, for his comprehensive information on packet on the MC80; and the notes by G4OAA on 9600 baud packet modifications and connections.

The MC80 is a two-channel set, with simple controls using two knobs for channel and volume adjustment on the left-hand side of the front panel, together with three push switches on the upper right of the front for signalling. The set may be fitted with 'Select 1' ('PL', or CTCSS to the rest of us), or 'Select 5' (five-tone sequential signalling), each of which use an internally fitted board which you'll probably remove for amateur use. The type number of the set is clearly visible below these. The UHF set comes in two band versions, 403–430MHz and 440–470MHz, either of which are suitable for retuning to 70cm. The sets commonly found are 25kHz channel spacing, and use a single IF of 10.7MHz with two crystal filters (Y31 and Y32 on the RX board). The transmitter uses PIN diode changeover (good for packet radio operation) and two transmit power versions are available, nominally 6W and 10W RF output – you'll typically get

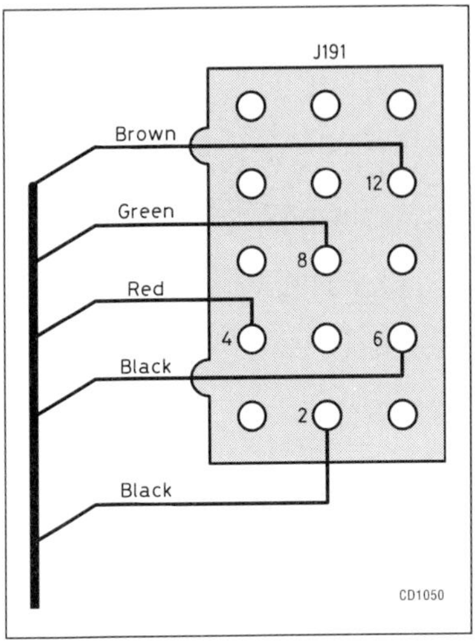

Fig 4.20. MC80 rear-panel connector

around 14–18W maximum output on the higher-power version.

To open the set, remove the screws that hold the set in the trunnion mount, and then pull off the volume control and channel selector knobs. Place a flat screwdriver blade into the slot near the bottom part of the set chassis at the rear panel, and push the screwdriver against the housing until the chassis locking tabs clear the slots in the housing of the transceiver, then slide the transceiver chassis out from the back of the outer plastic housing.

Connections

On the rear panel, a 270° five-pin DIN socket is used for microphone and audio output (Fig 4.20). Note that the connections to this are not the same as for Pye/Philips mics which have an identical socket. The pin connections are:

Pin 1 – Connected to pin 32 on motherboard (see later)
Pin 2 – Mic gnd (screen)
Pin 3 – Gnd (black), linked to pin 2
Pin 4 – Mic live (red)
Pin 5 – Transmit PTT (green)

Also on the rear panel you'll see a 15-way connector, which is used for the DC power and receiver speaker connections, plus an additional TX PTT if required. Many of the pins are unused – the ones we're interested in are:

Pin 2 – Gnd (black)
Pin 4 – DC 13.8V input (red)
Pin 6 – Gnd (black)
Pin 8 – Transmit PTT (green)
Pin 12 – Receiver speaker (brown)

Selcall board removal

If your set is fitted with a Selcall unit, which is located at the rear of the transceiver, either GLN6136B (CTCSS), GLN6135A or GLN6151A (ZVEI five-tone), or GLN6152A or GLN6153A (both CCIR five-tone), you'll need to remove this and remake a few links on the set's motherboard in order to resume 'normal' operation. However, in the case of a CTCSS ('PL') board, you may find that by taking a look at the actual CTCSS frequency fitted it could be used for your local repeater access, or even just for selective calling work in a club or net. This frequency is marked on a 'Vibrasponder' which is visible through an oblong hole in the PL PCB.

To remove the board, if needed, first undo the four screws holding the board to the chassis. There's a wire loom connected to the board and, in the case of a PL unit (by far the most commonly found), the functions of the connections on this are given in Table 4.12.

Table 4.12. Connection functions of MC80 PL unit

Function	Wire colour	PCB connection
RX filter out	Yellow-brown	Pin 35
Hang-up switch	Green	Pin 32
Squelch	Blue-white	Front panel squelch defeat switch
RX filter in	Brown	Pin 14
13.2V DC	Red	Pin 17
PTT out	White-yellow	Pin 37
PL tone in	Red (thick)	Pin 12
PTT in	Yellow	Small PCB above volume control
PL tone out	Violet	Pin 3
Ground	Black	Pin 33

Most of these wires are connected to the main PCB by push-on connectors, which can easily be removed. The TX keying line is broken by pins 36 and 37 on JU102, just in front of the channel switch. To enable transmit PTT, the yellow 'PTT in' wire should be cut at the PL board, and connected instead to pin 37 on the main PCB. The receiver audio path is via pins 14 and 35 on JU61, immediately in front of the front-panel push-switches – you'll need to link these together to reroute the receiver audio.

For TX audio, from the DIN socket on the rear panel, you'll find a screened cable with a red outer connects to pin 40, with the braid to ground. You'll need to link pin 40 to pin 41 (pin 41 is right next to pin 40, on JU101 which is just in front of the channel switch).

After removing and relinking the above, check that when you press the squelch defeat button you hear normal squelch noise from the speaker. If you don't, then check the connection between pins 14 and 35. Also check that when the transmitter PTT is pressed, RF power results (the front-panel LED lights even when there's no RF, so be careful – check with a power meter). If the set doesn't go into transmit mode, check the connection between pin 37 and the small PCB above the volume potentiometer.

Crystals

$$\text{RX xtal freq} = \frac{\text{RX freq} - 10.7\text{MHz}}{9}$$

$$\text{TX xtal freq} = \frac{\text{TX freq}}{27}$$

The crystals are HC-25/U types – ensure you quote the MC80 to your supplier when ordering.

Alignment

See Figs 4.21 and 4.22 for alignment points. You should align the set from the component side. Before realigning to 70cm, you'll find that presetting the coils to the approximate correct positions will help you in the subsequent tune-up. First, on the transmitter coils, preset L121 (and L131 in two-frequency models) eight turns from the top of the coil former. Now, set L141, L142, L143, L144 and L147 to the top of their coil formers. Finally, for 70cm set L149 either to the top of the former (for 403–430MHz equipment) or eight turns in (for 440–470MHz equipment).

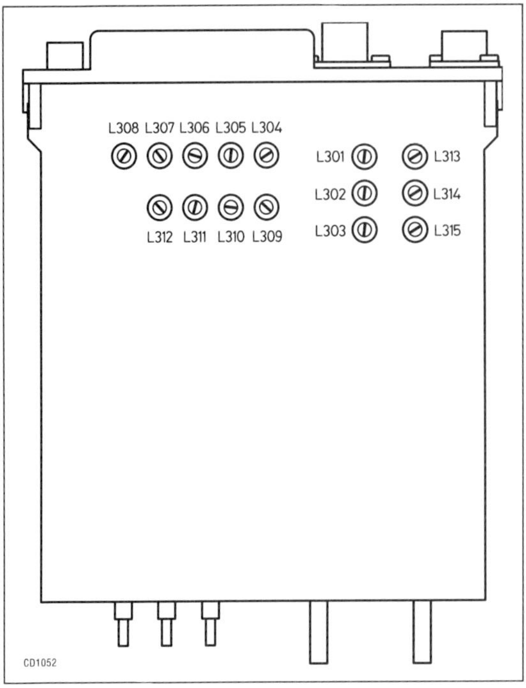

Fig 4.21. MC80 RF deck alignment points (solder side)

On the receiver, set L2 (and L22 on two-frequency models) six turns from the top of the coil former. On the RF front end, set coils L301 to L309 nine turns counterclockwise, starting with their slugs flush with the tension locking nut (around 5mm). Now, for 403-430MHz equipment set L314 10 turns in, with L313 and L315 eight turns in, starting with the slugs flush with the tension locking nuts. For 440-470MHz equipment set L314 six turns in, with L313 and L315 five turns in, starting with the slugs flush with the tension locking nuts.

With your power supply connected and the set switched on, adjust the squelch preset control R342 fully anti-clockwise, and adjust the volume control so that you can hear normal squelch noise (if your set is fitted with a CTCSS unit, see elsewhere in this section for how to disable this). The voltages given here are for a 10kΩ per volt meter sensitivity, and various metering points are given. For receive, connect your multimeter's negative lead to the set's chassis (DC negative), and the meter's positive lead to the metering points given; M1 is J61 pin 1 (2.5V DC range), M2 is J61 pin 2 (10V DC range), and M3 is the pin 10 metering point shown on the receiver IF alignment points diagram (50μA DC current range). For transmit, M3 is pin 8 on J141 with your multimeter negative lead to ground (50μA DC current range), and M5 is positive lead to pin 7 on J141 with the negative lead to pin 5 of J141 (100μA DC current range).

First, if you have a 10.7MHz marker generator, couple this loosely to the base of Q32 and then, with your meter connected to J61 pin 2, adjust the quadrature detector coil L36 for 5V ±0.2V.

Receiver alignment

In some cases, you may find that you'll get a peak meter reading at two points in the tuning range of the coil. You should choose the one where the slug is nearest to the top of the coil former, ie away from the printed circuit board.

First, with your meter on M3, adjust L3 for a peak reading. Now on channel 1, peak L2 for maximum, then switch to channel 2 (if you have a crystal fitted here) and adjust L22 again for peak reading. Now, switch to the lower channel frequency of the two. Still on M3, tune L309 for a peak, then L310 for a dip, followed by L311 for peak and L312 for a dip. If there are two peaks or dips, tune for the highest peak or the greatest dip. If you can't get a peak or dip by adjusting L312, preset the slug in the same position as that of L311.

Now, receiving an off-air signal, adjust L2 (channel 1) and L22 (channel 2) for spot-on reception. If you've a 10.7MHz marker generator, you can tune for 'zero beat' here between the marker generator and an off-air signal. For the multiplier alignment, tune L32, L33 and L34 in that order for maximum M1 reading, reducing the signal generator output level as tuning proceeds to keep the M1 meter indication between 25–35μA.

Now for the receiver front end, although if you don't have a variable level signal source, in order to keep M1 within the above limits, then just tune for maximum quieting, ie best signal.

First adjust L308, L307, L306, L305 and L304 for a peak on M1, then L302, L301 and L303 also for peak reading. If there are two peaks, tune for maximum peak meter reading. Now tune L309, L310, L311 and L312 in that order for peak reading, then L32 and L33 again for peak. Repeat the above as needed for best signal. Now, if you've a two-channel set, switch to the higher of the two channels and readjust L311 and L312 for a peak M1 reading. That's it for the receiver – just reset the squelch preset as needed.

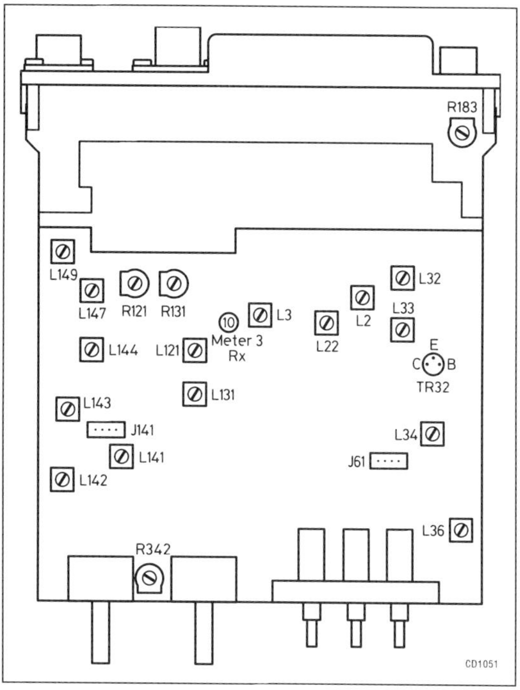

Fig 4.22. MC80 receiver IF and transmitter alignment points (component side)

Transmitter alignment

Initially, adjust the preset R183 'power set' potentiometer fully anticlockwise to give maximum power. If you've two channels fitted, initially select the lowest transmit frequency on the channel switch. Key the transmitter, and adjust L142 and then L143 for a peak M3 reading (limit 15μA), then adjust L143 for a dip on the M3 meter reading. Now, adjust L144 and then L147 for a peak M5 meter reading (limit 15μA minimum, 40μA maximum). Then adjust L143 for a peak on M5.

Now, you should be getting an RF power reading on your wattmeter, so adjust L314, L313, and L315 in that order for maximum RF power. Then readjust L143 followed by L149, both for a peak M5 reading. Repeat the alignment of L147, L144 and L143 (all for peak M5 reading) in that order.

Reset the preset power output potentiometer R183 if you need less than the maximum power (ie down to 6W for 6W models and 10W for 10W models, and finally adjust R121 for the required peak deviation.

Packet use

For 1200 baud packet, you can use the rear-panel five-pin DIN microphone connector to link to your TNC. The only additional connection which needs to be made is the receive audio. Pin 1 connects to pin 32 of the motherboard, and you can if you wish link this to the top of the receiver volume control, which will give an ample level to drive most TNCs, without the receiver volume setting affecting the level.

The set is also useful for operation at 9600 baud, and the PIN diode changeover helps fast transmit/receive switching. A set with a channel spacing of 25kHz is essential for 9600 baud operation. If yours is a 12.5kHz version (±3.75kHz bandwidth), then you'll need to replace the 10.7MHz IF filters with similar types but for ±7.5kHz bandwidth.

9600 baud modifications

On transmit, the screened microphone input lead from the rear panel DIN socket can be disconnected from the main circuit board and replaced with a connection to the top of the deviation potentiometer R121, ie the 'hot' side. The PCB track between R121 and the associated input amplifier circuit for the microphone should then be cut. This track runs on the top of the PCB and goes between the two small green tantalum capacitors near the channel 2 deviation potentiometer. If the set is a two-channel transceiver, the tracks to R121 and R131 from the microphone amplifier need to both be cut to give audio isolation, so also cut the PC track connecting the 'hot' side of R131 (the deviation pot) to the output of the mic amplifier.

On the receive side, you'll need to take the audio output to your 9600 baud modem directly from the discriminator IC, which is a CA3089E. Take this output via a screened cable from pin 1 of the DIN socket on the rear apron of the MC80 (J601) to pin 35 on the main PCB (which should be linked to pin 14). If you add an isolating capacitor in series, make sure this has a value of at least 10μF. C80, a 6.8nF capacitor, forms part of the receiver de-emphasis network – this is close to the four-way test header next to the CA3089 IC. Remove this capacitor, as it's connected across the discriminator output to ground. With 6kHz peak deviation, the p/p audio level across R121 is around 1.6V.

This completes the modification to give you acceptable 9600 baud performance, although you may find a further improvement if you take the output from a higher-level point along the audio chain with further appropriate component modifications to retain the flat frequency response. This modification will increase the audio level to the modem by 20dB, up to the level gained when an audio loop-back is made on the latter. For this, remove the 0.15μF capacitor C83 which is near test point 52, and which is the larger of two blue 'block' capacitors. This capacitor connects from audio preamplifier collector to ground. Next, we need to increase the value of C81 from 0.1μF to a value of 2.2μF. C81 is the blue block capacitor near test point 35. A non-polarised capacitor is needed here, as the DC level on the discriminator output can fluctuate widely around the base voltage of the amplifier transistor. You can fabricate this by connecting two 4.7μF electrolytic capacitors in series, with the two positive terminal connections soldered together. Now, change C82, a small tantalum capacitor near to D32, from 4.7μF to 15μF. Remove the 820pF capacitor C56 from the RX discriminator output – it's connected to pin 6 of the CA3089 discriminator IC. Finally, change the audio output connection from TP35 to the 'hot' pad left by the removal of C83, and use the squelch defeat button on the front panel to disable the receiver squelch.

I'm told there's a tendency for the receiver crystal oscillator to 'chirp' slightly when it's energised following a transmit period. To overcome this and thus provide a faster TX/RX data turnaround, the receive oscillator can be left running when the set is in transmit mode. For this, disconnect or remove D32, which is positioned halfway between L22 and L33, near to the receiver frequency adjustment coil.

On transmit, the audio high-frequency response can be improved by reducing the value of R122, a 47kΩ resistor. This is positioned between the corner of the transmit frequency adjustment coil can and the receiver oscillator multiplier chain. Add a 10kΩ resistor in parallel with this resistor – a convenient place is to solder this on the underside of the PCB.

OTHER MOTOROLA MOBILES

Later models of Motorola equipment are invariably synthesised, and require programming via a PC. Even though some of these sets are classed as 'obsolete' and appear on the surplus market, you'll need the appropriate Motorola software and PC/transceiver interface to reprogram the set onto the amateur bands. Unfortunately, this realistically means that you'll need to pop along to your local Motorola dealer for this, as the software usually costs over £100 with the interface typically also over £100, different software and interfaces being used for different series of rigs. However, you may find a set offered in working condition just out of PMR service at a bargain price, as I have done in the past, and can maybe justify the £25 reprogramming charge or whatever. Of course, if you're friendly with your local dealer . . .

Besides the MC80 crystalled set, detailed above, synthesised rigs in the Motorola Micro series are sometimes found, and I hope the following is useful in identifying what's actually inside the set.

The rear of the set has a code/part number, consisting of a sequence of 14 alphanumeric characters. Typical ones are shown in Table 4.13.

By giving the model number a quick check before purchase, you can check whether it's worth pursuing. For example, I'd avoid the 'trunking' control and Band III (174–225MHz) models, as you can identify from the above information, unless you really do know what

Table 4.13. Motorola Micro codes	
1	Market code identifier, 'M' indicates Europe
2	Further ID, usually 'A'
3	Mount, 'U' indicates a universal mount
4	Transmit power, 0 (up to 1W), 1 (1–6W), 2 (1–10W), 3 (25W)
5	Operation band, 2 (low-band VHF, ie 4m), 3 (high-band VHF, ie 2m), 4 (UHF, ie 70cm), 6 (Band III)
6, 7	Type of five-tone signalling standard, ie EEA, ZVEI etc
8	Supply voltage, 'A' indicates 12V
9	Squelch, 1 (normal FM squelch), 3 (CTCSS), 5 (trunking), 9 (Select-5 sequential five-tone)
10	Channel facilities, J (32-channel), G (trunking)
11, 12	Channel spacing, 00 (25kHz), 13 (20kHz), 22 (12.5kHz)
13, 14	Series and model package

you're getting into! Although this relates to the Micro series, I'm told that a number of Motorola sets follow the same numbering sequence, although I can't personally confirm this.

SMC545L1 AND SMC1045L2 UHF MOBILES

Identification

The SMC545L1 is a crystal-controlled, single-channel UHF transceiver – a seven-channel version is also available as the SMC545L7. The transmitter can give up to 10W output, although it's type approved for 5W use in the UK – hence the '5' code number.

The SMC1045L2 is a compact, two-channel, crystal-controlled rig, and uses the same types and frequencies of crystals as the SMC545L1. The information here deals with the UHF sets, but note that VHF band sets with a similar appearance are also 'around', although to nowhere near the large extent on the amateur ex-PMR market as these two UHF rigs.

The 1045L2 can also be used as a full-duplex rig, ie giving simultaneous receive and transmit operation, as long (of course!) as you use a suitable transmit/receive spacing and an appropriate antenna separation or a duplexer. This is because it uses separate transmit and receive boards on either side of a screened chassis.

Each set is available in two frequency bands, 420–440MHz, which are the 545L1(B) or 1045L2(B) sets, and 450-470MHz, which are the 545L1(D) and 1045L2(D) sets. You'll find this isn't marked on the set itself but for the 545L1 just take a look at the transmitter power amplifier module. This will be a M57704L module for 420–440MHz, and a M57704H module for 450–470MHz.

The B model is the easiest to get going on 70cm – the D model receiver will only align down to no lower than 435MHz (typically 438MHz) without changes to the front-end helical filters. You'll also find the transmitter power output is restricted towards the lower end of 70cm unless you change the TX module to the correct version.

The channel spacing available can be either 12.5kHz or 25kHz, depending whether the set came out of UK PMR service (which will

The SMC545L1

The SMC1045L2

The rear panel identifies the SMC1045L2

invariably be 12.5kHz) or a 'new, surplus' when it could be either type. A change to 25kHz spacing entails a few filter and component changes, which are detailed a little later. The channel spacing can be checked by taking a look at the two small black or grey plastic ceramic filters in the receiver section of either set. A type number ID on these of 'LF-B8' (8kHz bandwidth) indicates 12.5kHz, while 'LF-B15' (15kHz bandwidth) indicates 25kHz spacing.

Alignment of the SMC545L1

Receiver alignment points are given in Fig 4.23. To align the receiver, adjust the crystal trimmer capacitor initially for correct frequency reception, then T103 and T104 for maximum sensitivity, then CV103 again for maximum sensitivity. If you have access to an RF voltmeter or a sensitive diode probe, then you can connect to the base of Q105 and adjust T103 and T104 for maximum reading, then transfer the probe to gate 2 of Q102 and adjust CV103 for maximum. Now with a received on-channel signal, adjust the trimmers on CV101, CV102 and CV103 (eight trimmers in total) all for best received signal. Repeat the adjustments as needed (plus the crystal trimmer for centre frequency) on a weak signal for absolute best. If you have access to a frequency counter, connect to the base of Q105 via a 10nF capacitor and adjust the crystal trimmer for the exact receiver injection frequency, which is the receive frequency less 21.4MHz, all divided by three. T101 is there for frequency compensation only – its adjustment is very critical so I wouldn't advise touching this.

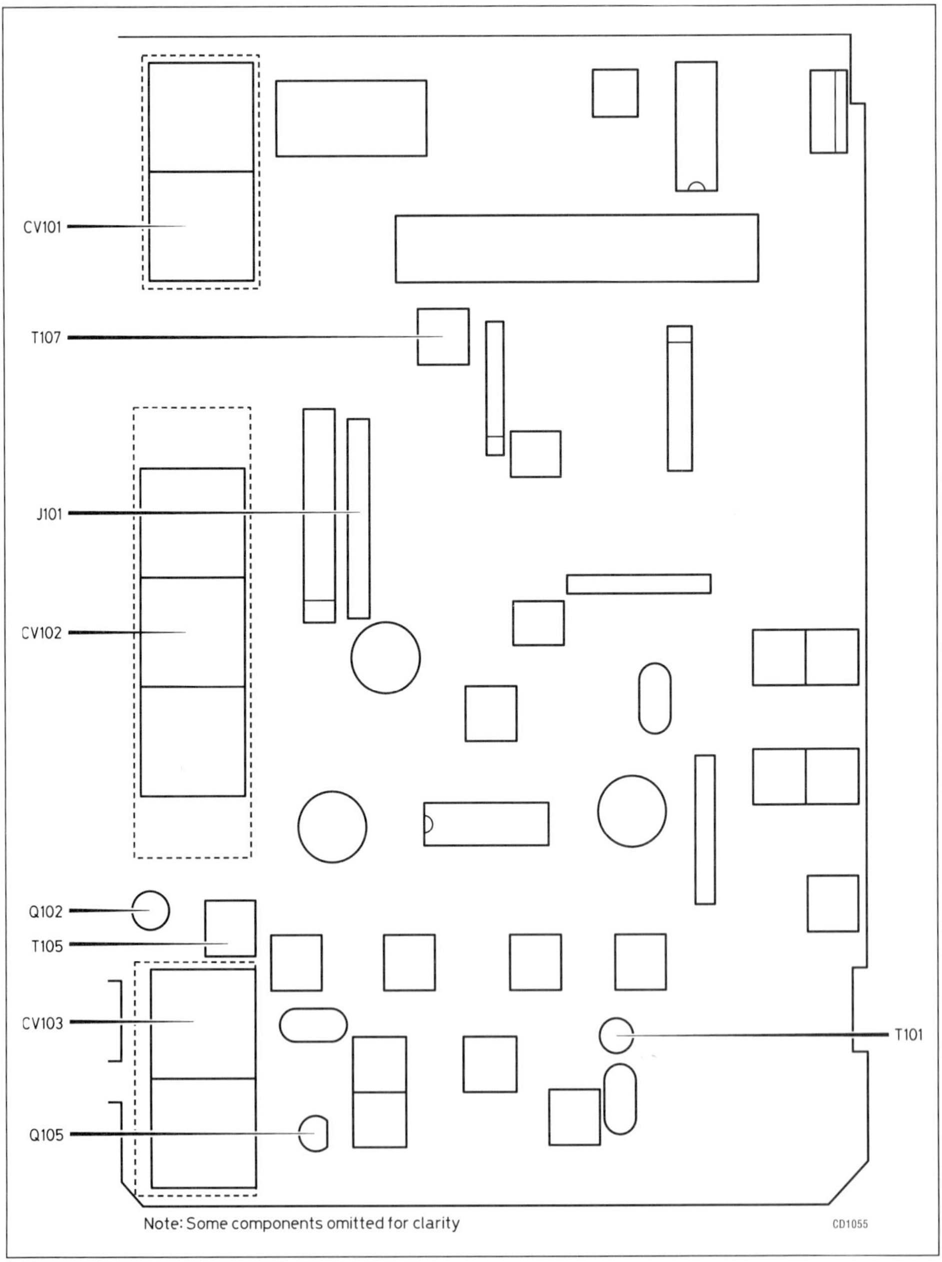

Fig 4.23. SMC545L1 receiver alignment points

Transmitter alignment points are given in Fig 4.24. To align the transmitter, connect a dummy load to the antenna socket with some form of relative power meter indication in line. With the transmitter keyed, adjust T203 for maximum reading on an RF voltmeter or diode probe on the base of Q203. Transfer to the base of Q201, and adjust T202 for maximum, then detune it until 80% of the maximum reading produces a stable output. Don't adjust T201, it's for

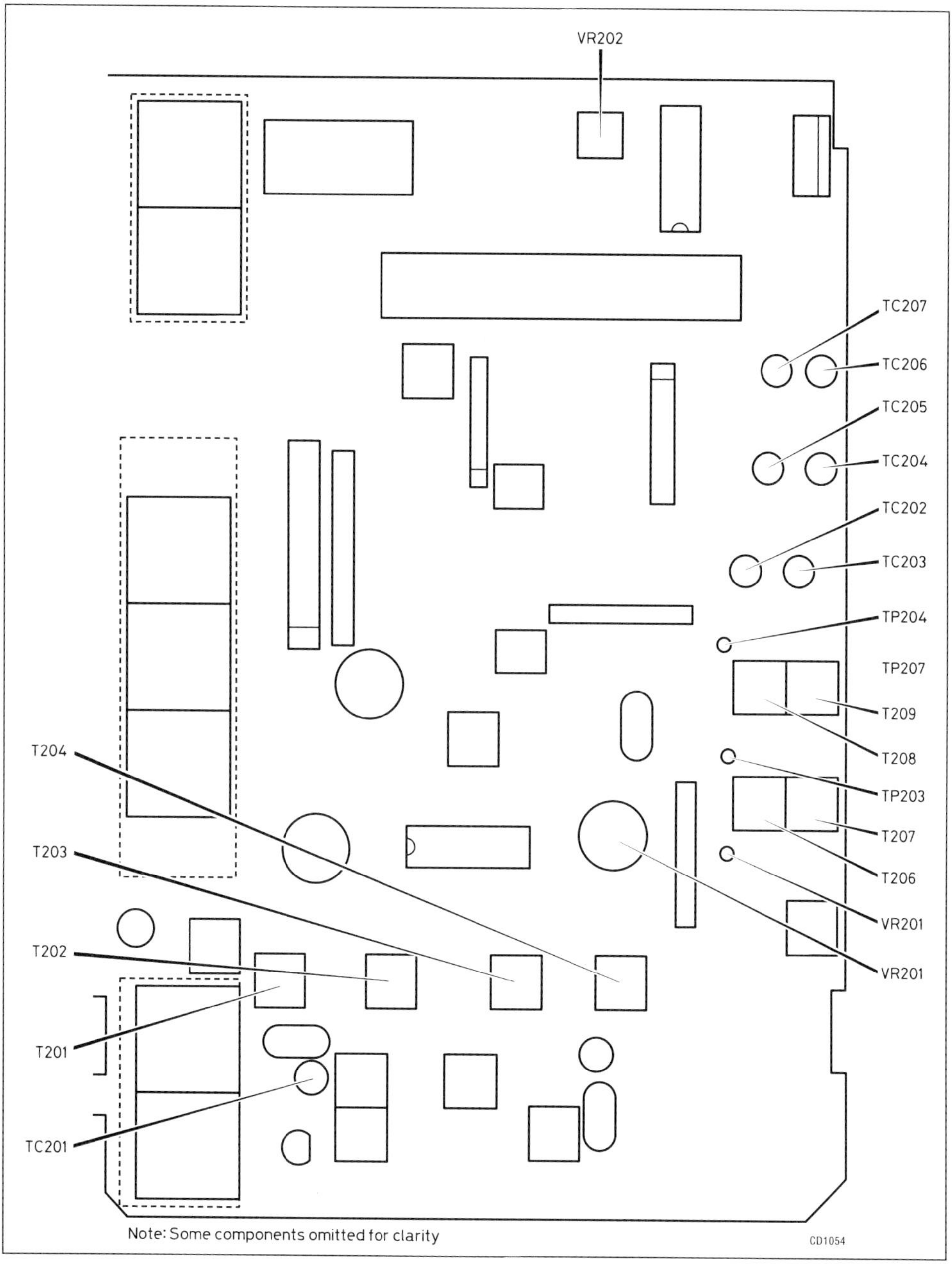

Fig 4.24. SMC545L1 transmitter alignment points

frequency compensation and its alignment is again very critical. Now for the multiplier stages.

Turn VR202 fully clockwise, and connect a DC voltmeter between TP202 and ground. Adjust T205 and T206 for minimum indication on the voltmeter. Now connect the meter to TP203, and adjust T207 and T208 for minimum indication on the meter. Transfer to TP204, and adjust T209 for minimum reading. Transfer to TP205, and adjust

Inside the SMC545L1

TC202 and TC203 for minimum reading. Transfer to TP206, and adjust TC204 and TC205 for minimum reading.

By now, you may be seeing an indication of RF power, so readjust T206 to T209 and TC202 to TC207 for absolute maximum RF power. Adjust the crystal trimmer for the exact required transmit frequency. The peak deviation control is VR201, which you should adjust for a maximum of 5kHz deviation. If you've access to a distortion meter, then you can adjust T203 and T204 for minimum distortion, readjusting the peak deviation as required. VR202 adjusts the RF power output, which should be set to around 10W to guard against overheating.

That's it – you should now have a fully operational set, ready for your first contact.

Alignment of the SMC1045L2

Alignment diagrams for the receiver and transmitter are given in Figs 4.25 and 4.26 respectively. First of all, plug in your receive and transmit crystals, switch on, and adjust the receiver crystal trimmer capacitor so you can at least hear a signal on your chosen channel (ie tune it onto channel). Remember to select the correct channel with the front panel switch! Now adjust TC1006 to TC1006, TC1009, and TC1010, T1001 and T1002 all for best quieting of the received signal, reducing the level of this as needed. Finally, repeat these adjustments on a weak signal to achieve the very best sensitivity possible, realigning the crystal trimmer for 'spot-on' reception as needed. If you've a frequency counter, you can measure and thus set the receiver local oscillator injection frequency precisely (in this case the receive frequency minus 21.4MHz) – tap onto the base of Q1004 via a 1nF capacitor to measure this.

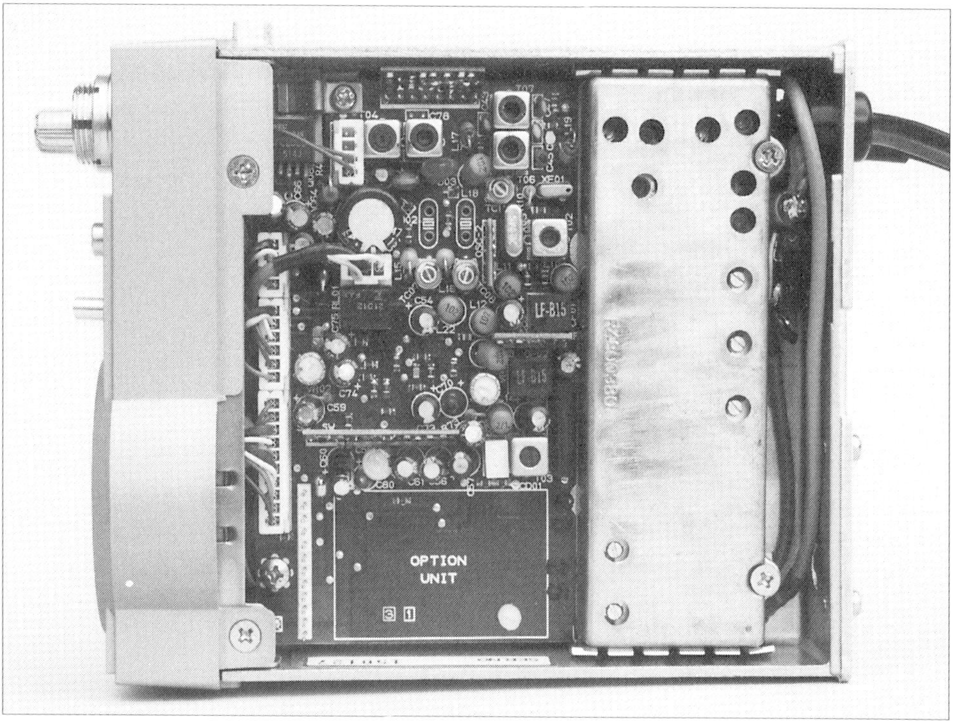

The SMC1045L2 receiver section

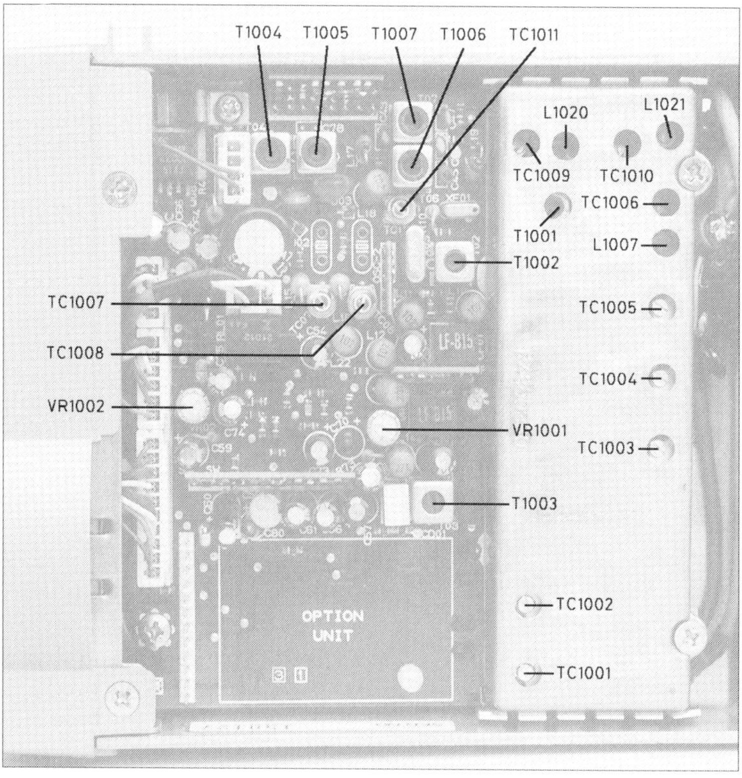

Fig 4.25. SMC1045L2 receiver alignment points

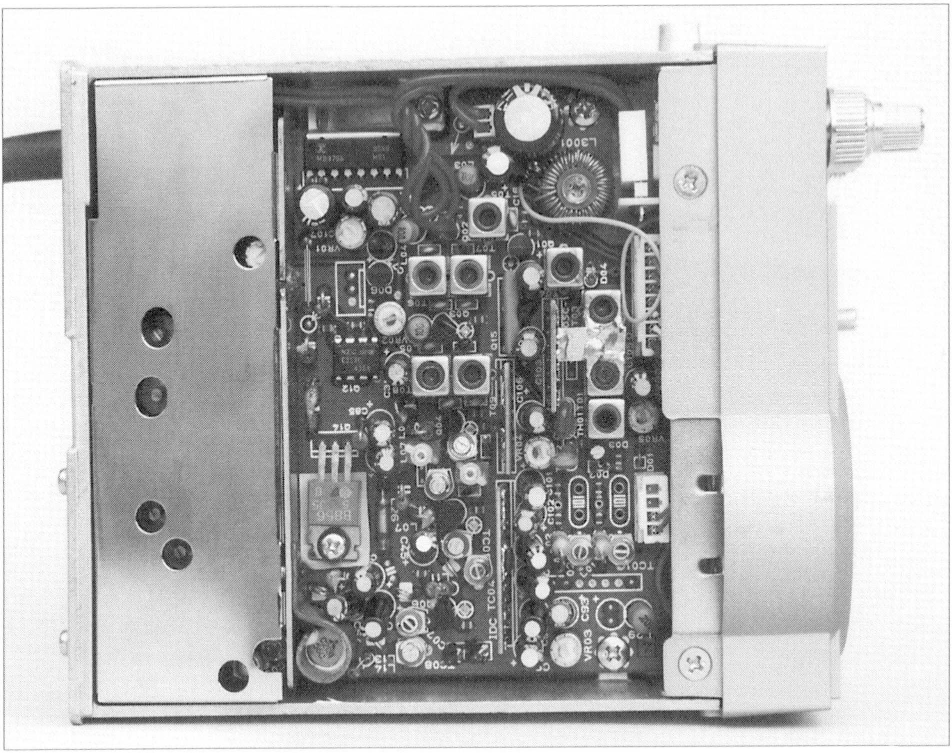

The SMC1045L2 transmitter section

The transmitter alignment is similarly easy. With the transmitter keyed, adjust T2005 to T2009, TC2003 to TC2006, and TC2007 to TC2014, all for maximum RF output power. Then adjust VR2002, the RF power level control, for 10W RF output. Finally, adjust the relevant crystal trimmer capacitor for the correct transmitter frequency. The peak deviation control is VR2004, which you should set as needed (eg 5kHz maximum deviation), and VR2003 is the mic gain adjustment. That's it for the 1045L2 alignment.

Channel spacing modifications

If you wish to change the channel spacing, you'll need to change the two plastic-cased 455kHz ceramic filters and the two small 21.7MHz monolithic dual crystal filters (which look like tiny metal-cased crystals). After replacement, each set should then operate satisfactorily for amateur purposes. However, if you'd also like to 'fine tune' the crystal filter matching, after changing to 25kHz filters, on the 1045L2 change capacitor C14 to 5pF and resistor R10 to 1.8kΩ, and on the 545L1 change C149 to 7pF and R121 to 1kΩ.

Crystal data

Type:	HC-25U or HC-42/U
Crystal frequency:	TX xtal = TX freq ÷ 12
	RX xtal = (RX freq – 21.4MHz) ÷ 9

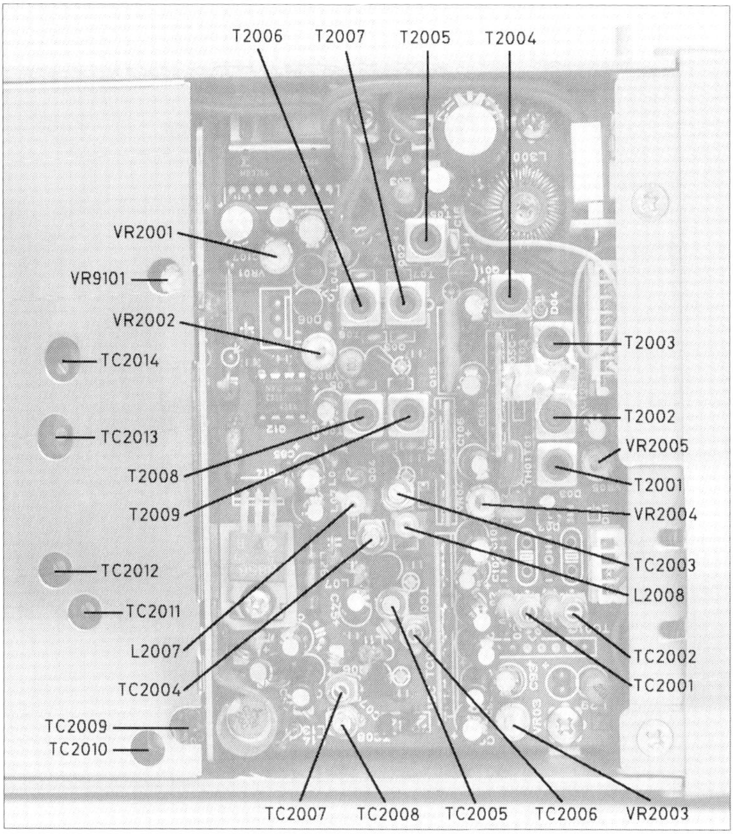

Fig 4.26. SMC1045L2 transmitter alignment points

Load capacitance:	TX, 40pF + 50Hz
	RX, 32pF – 120Hz
Drive level:	TS683/TMS 2mW
Shunt capacitance:	TX, 4.7pF ± 0.5pF
	RX, 4.4pF ± 0.5pF
Equivalent series resistance:	16Ω
Mode:	3rd overtone

Channel spacing filter changes

Ch spacing	Ceramic filter	Crystal filter
12.5kHz	LF-B8	21J2F2
25kHz	LF-B15	21J2B2

DYMAR LYNX TO 4m

In PMR use, the low-band version of the set is usually found to be operational on around 83MHz, and will require some component changes to operate on the 4m amateur band. Following modification, the transmitter typically gives 25W, the receiver's sensitivity being 0.25μV pd.

The crystals are H-18/U and the frequencies required are:

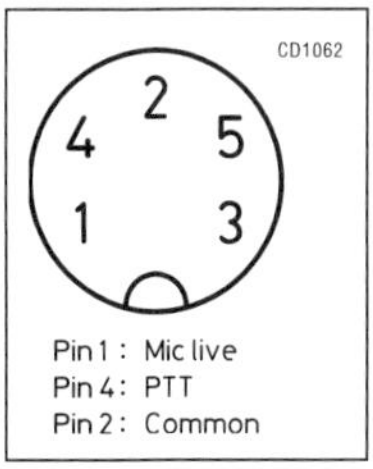

Fig 4.27. Dymar Lynx microphone connections

$$\text{RX xtal freq} = \frac{\text{RX freq} + 10.7\text{MHz}}{6}$$

$$\text{TX xtal freq} = \frac{\text{TX freq}}{12}$$

Receiver modifications and alignment

Locate the receiver PCB in the bottom section of the set, and fit eight capacitors each of 22pF across the following inductors: L302, L301, L308, L307, L310, L311, L313 and L314 as shown in Fig 4.28.

With your new crystal fitted, adjust L304 and L305 for maximum meter reading at test point TP302 (crystal frequency × 3). Transfer to test point TP303, and adjust L313 and L314 now, again for maximum meter reading (crystal frequency × 6). Now whilst receiving an off-air signal, align L301, L302, L307, L308, L310, L311 for best received signal.

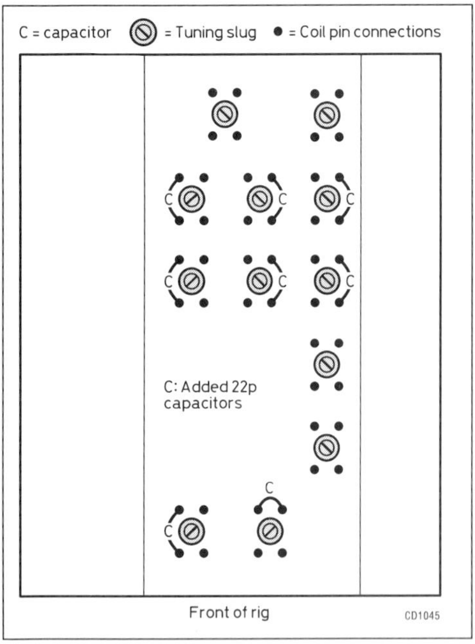

Fig 4.28. Dymar Lynx receiver section, showing the added 22pF capacitors

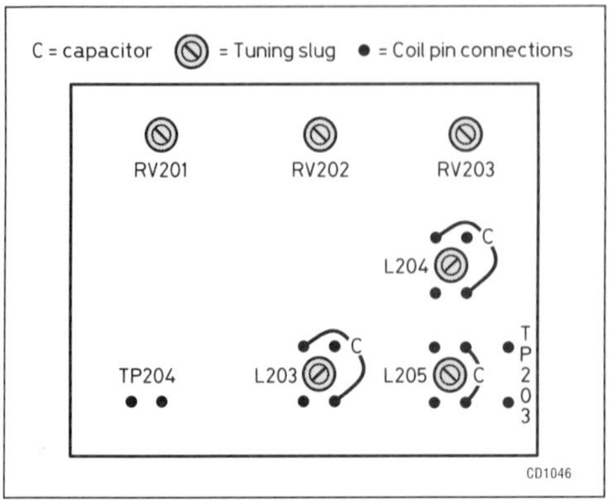

Fig 4.29. Dymar Lynx modulator

Transmitter modifications

First locate the modulator, multiplier, and power amplifier modules. Remove the screening covers from these for component identification.

Modulator

Fit three capacitors of 47pF each across L203, L204 and L205 as shown in Fig 4.29. With your new crystal fitted, retune L203, L204 and L205 for maximum reading at TP208 (typically 0.75V).

Multiplier

Locate L101, L106 and L107 on the underside of the RF board. The RX boards can be hinged up out of the way to aid this. Fit three 22pF capacitors, one across each of L101, L106 and L107 as shown in Fig 4.30. Refit the receiver boards.

Power amplifier

Locate the PA coil located between capacitors C145 and C147. Remove this coil and replace this with a new coil, 12mm long, wound on a 6.3mm mandrel using 18 SWG wire.

Transmitter alignment

With the PTT keyed, adjust L101 and L102 for maximum voltage at TP102 (typically

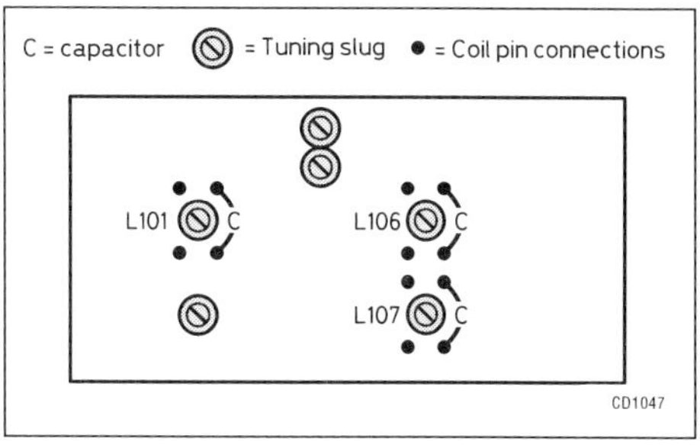

Fig 4.30. Dymar Lynx multiplier

1.25V). Adjust L103 and L104 for max voltage at TP103 (typically 2.5V). Adjust L106 and L107 for maximum voltage at TP104 (typically 0.75V). *Do not* refit the multiplier screening cover at this stage. Compress the turns on L107 for a minimum length coil (being careful not to short the turns). Adjust C126, C127 and L108 for maximum voltage at TP105 (typically 0.5V). Compress L113 in the same way as L107. Adjust C132 and C133 for maximum voltage at the base of transistor VT106 (typically 2.0V). Adjust C139 and C143 for maximum voltage at the base of transistor VT107 (typically 0.75V). Adjust C146 and C147 for maximum RF power output into your dummy load (you should achieve around 25W). Refit the modulator and PA screens, and recheck the output. During the transmitter alignment, check that each stage is operating at the correct multiplication frequency with a wavemeter – the PA especially can be mistakenly tuned up to 140MHz.

My thanks go to Steve, G0HQH, for the above information.

5 Base station equipment

THIS chapter deals with some of the most commonly found base stations on the ex-PMR market. Of course, mobile rigs *can* be also used in a 'base station' environment in your shack, simply by connecting an outdoor antenna and suitable power supply. However, the equipment described here can additionally be used for very different purposes: a voice repeater and/or a simplex or full-duplex packet radio link.

DUPLEX REPEATER USE

The equipment in this chapter is capable of full-duplex operation, and will typically be used for an amateur repeater. You will need sufficient isolation between the receiver and transmitter antenna systems for this, so as not to cause desensitisation to the set's receiver when the transmitter comes into operation. This is commonly achieved by the use of separate antennas plus one or more high-Q cavity filters in both the transmit and receive antenna lines. In the receive line, this is to prevent blocking by the transmitter carrier, and to reduce the effects of reciprocal mixing from the receiver's

Above: **A high-*Q* 70cm cavity filter provides effective filtering**

Right: **A typical circulator for 70cm**

local oscillator. In the transmit line, this is to prevent transmitter noise present on the receive frequency. For single antenna working, a ferrite circulator or a purpose-made cavity duplexer (such as the Procomm 70cm duplexer for 1.6MHz TX/RX split shown here) can be used.

Multiple receivers and transmitters can be connected to a single antenna system by using more elaborate combining techniques, such as hybrid combiners and receiver distribution amplifiers. Remember that the SMC1045 mobile, described elsewhere in this book, can also be adapted to full duplex use, again by adding a suitable filter.

IDENTIFICATION AND EQUIPMENT CODES

I've given an even higher emphasis in this chapter on equipment identification, including the different control and audio versions available because, depending

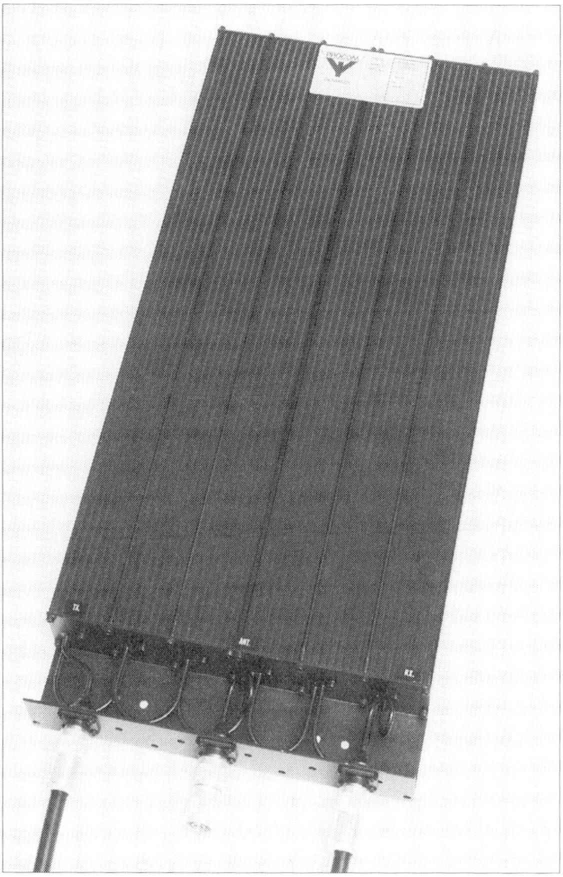

Above: A purpose-designed cavity combiner for 1.6MHz TX/RX split on 70cm for single antenna working

Left: Four-channel hybrid combiner for shared radio site use _(photo courtesy Airtech Frequency Management)_

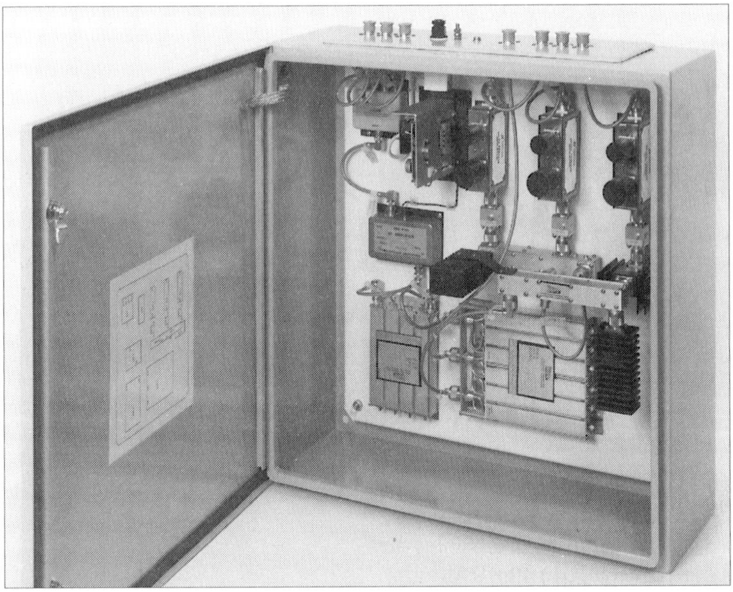

Wall-mounted combiner system for multiple TX/RX operation *(photo courtesy Airtech Frequency Management)*

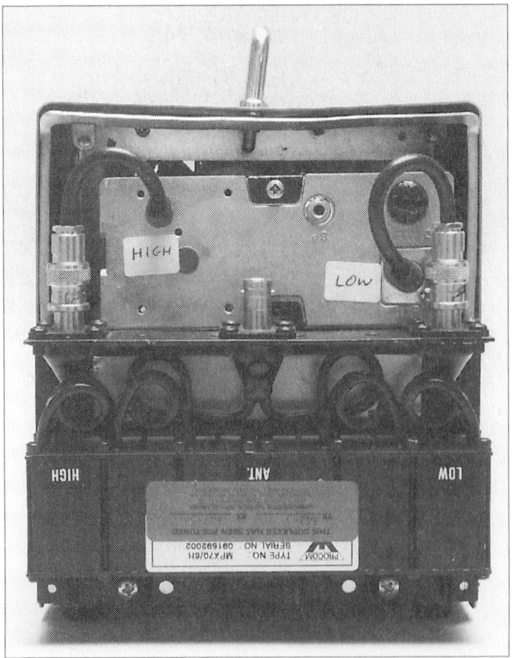

Add a duplexer to the SMC1045L2 and you've a full-duplex set in a small case

upon the equipment's previous PMR use, it may be capable of either simplex, repeater, or 9600 baud packet link operation, and be powered from 12V DC, 24V DC, or AC mains. The equipment may again *look* similar from the outside, but could be capable of operation on either 2m, 70cm, or even 23cm, depending upon what's inside the box! I've tabulated the various equipment codes which you'll need to carefully check on the rear panel label, to see exactly what the equipment is. Be warned, the tables may at first glance look the same, but they're *not* – the sequence is also sometimes just different enough to matter, *so be careful.*

F494 AND F496

The F494 and the F496 are wall-mounting base stations designed for either remote or 'nearby' local operation, usually connected to a desktop controller. Alternatively, the set can be operated as a stand-alone carrier or CTCSS-operated repeater. It's essentially based upon two partly assembled M290 series boards, one with all the relevant receiver components fitted, the other with the transmitter components fitted. An internal mains power supply and a built-in control board are added to provide a 'stand-alone' unit.

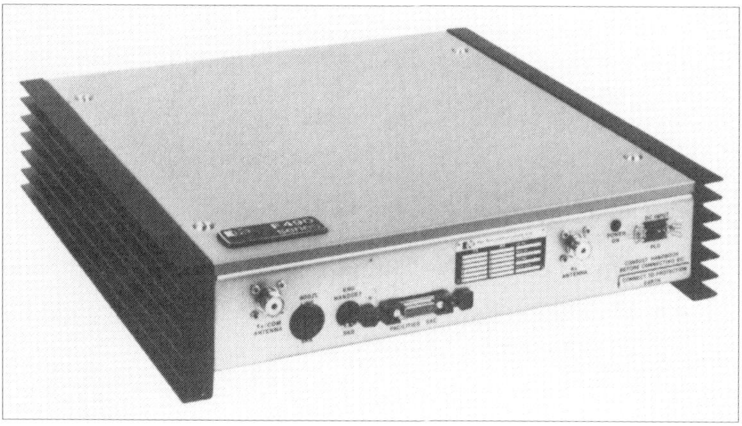

The F490 series is a wall-mounting base station

The F494 unit uses the RF circuitry of two M294 boards, ie for VHF operation, and the F496 for UHF is, you've guessed it, based on M296 circuitry. At the time of writing, the F496 is by far the most commonly found unit on the surplus market, and this will be detailed here. The control and linking arrangements are identical between the two models. So, for the F494 just follow the M294 alignment details which are given elsewhere in this book, bearing in mind the additional information here regarding socket connections etc.

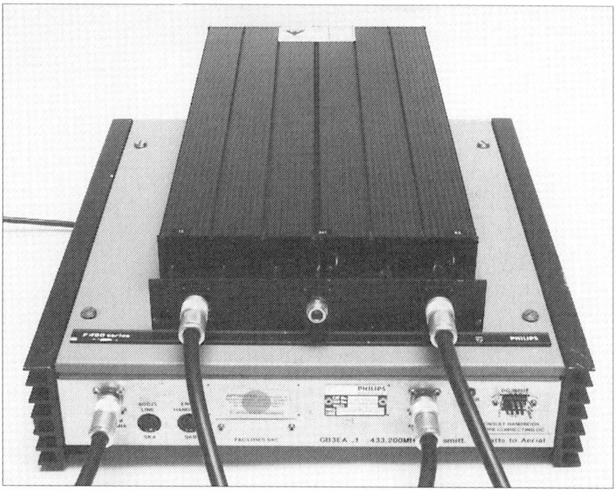

The F496, complete with an external 70cm duplexer for 70cm repeater operation

Identification

Take a look at the equipment identification label. This will be made up of the codes with the meanings shown in Table 5.1.

Connections and ancillaries

Connections are shown in Fig 5.1 and the photo. If you're lucky, you'll also find a T-shaped wall-mounting bracket (Fig 5.2) supplied with the base station set, and maybe also a DC lead with fitted plug. The DC connector uses a seven-pin 'Jones' type in-line socket; suitable types are available from some component and connector suppliers (as well as, at the time of writing, from the equipment manufacturers themselves) but they're rather on the expensive side. You can, however, easily solder your DC cable to the connector pins, but note this connector does *not* use the same connection pins as those for the Westminster and Europa mobile transceivers, which use an identical DC power connector. Rather than the connections

Table 5.1. F494/F496 identification codes

Format: F49x aa b c d e f g hh ii jj kk ll with the following meanings:

F49x:	F494: VHF, F496: UHF	
aa:	Market code:	01: Standard production
b:	RF power output:	1: 25W (standard setting for high-power use) 2: 15W 3: 10W 4: 6W (standard setting for low-power use) 5: 1W
c:	Power supply:	1: AC mains with 24V DC standby, neg gnd 2: AC mains with 12V DC standby, neg gnd 3: 24V DC, neg gnd
d:	Antenna:	1: Two-antenna working (ie as a repeater with external duplexer) 2: Single-antenna working with internal antenna changeover
e:	No of xtalled channels:	0: Less crystals 1–6: No of crystalled channels
f:	Not used	
g:	Channel spacing:	S: 12.5kHz R: 20kHz (rarely found in the UK) V: 25kHz
hh:	TX band:	E0: 68–88MHz B0: 132–156MHz A0: 148–174MHz M1: 105–108 P5: 79–88MHz T1: 405–440MHz U0: 440–470MHz
ii:	RX band:	E0: 68–88MHz B0: 132–156MHz A0: 148–174MHz P8: 96–106MHz T1: 405–440MHz U0: 440–470MHz
jj:	No of channels:	U: Single channel V: Fitted for six channels
kk:	Control:	11–13: Systems and link base station 21–27: Remote control base station with line switching 41–47: Local control base station 51: Free-running repeater 57: CTCSS-controlled repeater
ll:	Ancillaries:	00, 10, 20, 30: No internal CTCSS 01, 11, 21, 31: CTCSS fitted

used in the mobile rig pin-outs, in the case of the F490 series base station, positive volts go to pins 2, 4 and 6 (internally linked), and negative volts go to pins 1, 3, 5 and 7 (again internally linked).

Power supply

The majority of sets I've seen have an internal AC mains supply. There's also an option for a DC 'standby' supply, which could be

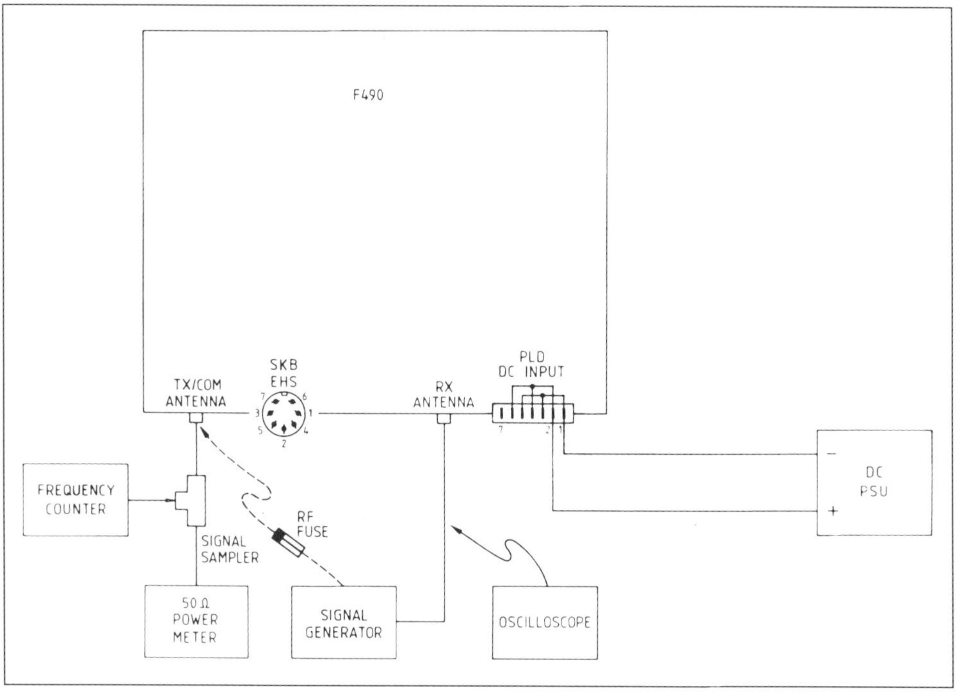

Fig 5.1. F490 series external connections

useful for repeater and packet node applications. The 24V DC standby supply is connected to plug PLD and is internally protected by a fuse (FS1) plus a reverse protection diode. If the mains supply fails, an internal relay (RLA) is de-energised, and the DC input from the socket is fed straight through to the internal 24V to 12V DC regulator. If your set is a 12V DC standby version, it's basically similar to the 24V type but with the exception of RLA being positioned on the input of the low-current regulator.

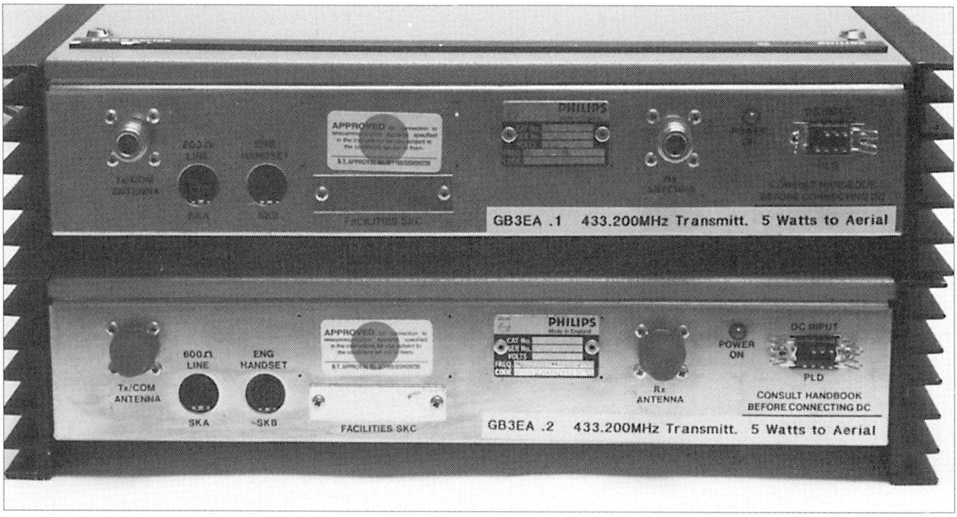

F490 series panel connections

Table 5.2. SKB engineer's handset socket connections

Pin	Function
1	PTT 'break' – disconnected from pin 3 on TX
2	Mic audio
3	PTT common
4	Earpiece audio
5	PTT 'make' – connected to pin 3 for TX
6	Earpiece gnd
7	Mic gnd

Table 5.3. Transmitter PCB connector PLA

Pin	Function
D	TX CTCSS tone input
N	+13.5V
J	TX +10V
C	TX in-band tone encode
B	EHS mute
A	Gnd
H	+10V output

Table 5.4. Receiver PCB connector PLA

Pin	Function
Q	+10V output
P	Gnd
G	RX audio return (used with CTCSS options)
K	Not connected
E	RX audio for tone decoders
M	Tone valid (used with CTCSS options)
F	Receive audio

Table 5.5. Control unit TX connector PLE

Pin	Function
1	Mic audio
2	Mic gnd
3	Not used
4	+10V
5	+ve to TX/RX c/o relay
6	+13.5V
7	TX +10V
8	TX line audio (700mV p/p typical for 3kHz dev)

Table 5.6. Control unit RX connector PLF

Pin	Function
1	0V
2	13.5V
3	Not used
4	RX +10V
5	Tone valid (used with CTCSS options)
6	Squelch detect
7	+10V
8	RX audio output

Before testing the set for amateur use, I'd advise a quick check of the fuses. FS1 is the chassis (mains input) fuse which should be 2A. FS1 and FS2, both on the internal regulator board, should each be 10A types.

Crystals

The required crystals are identical to those needed for the M294 and M296 transceivers, so take a look at the formulae for these (in Chapter 4 – 'Mobile equipment') for the required crystal frequencies. If you already have an M294 or M296 on the amateur bands, you can temporarily use a pair of crystals from these if you wish to give the base station a functional test, before buying additional crystals.

Alignment

Alignment diagrams are given in Figs 5.3–5.9. The RF

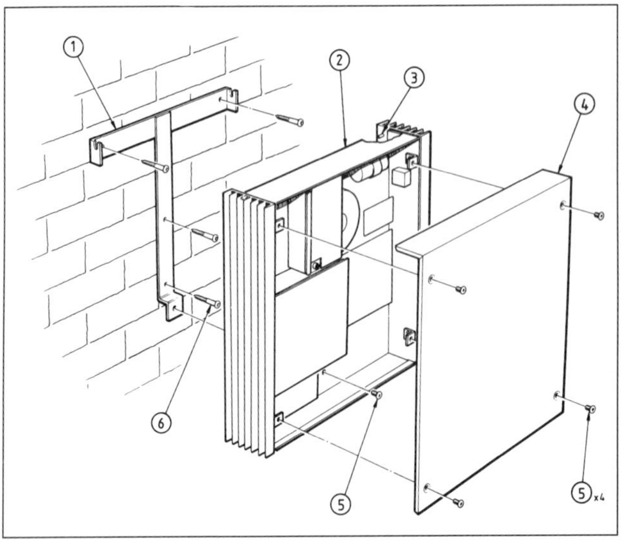

Fig 5.2. Wall-mounting arrangement

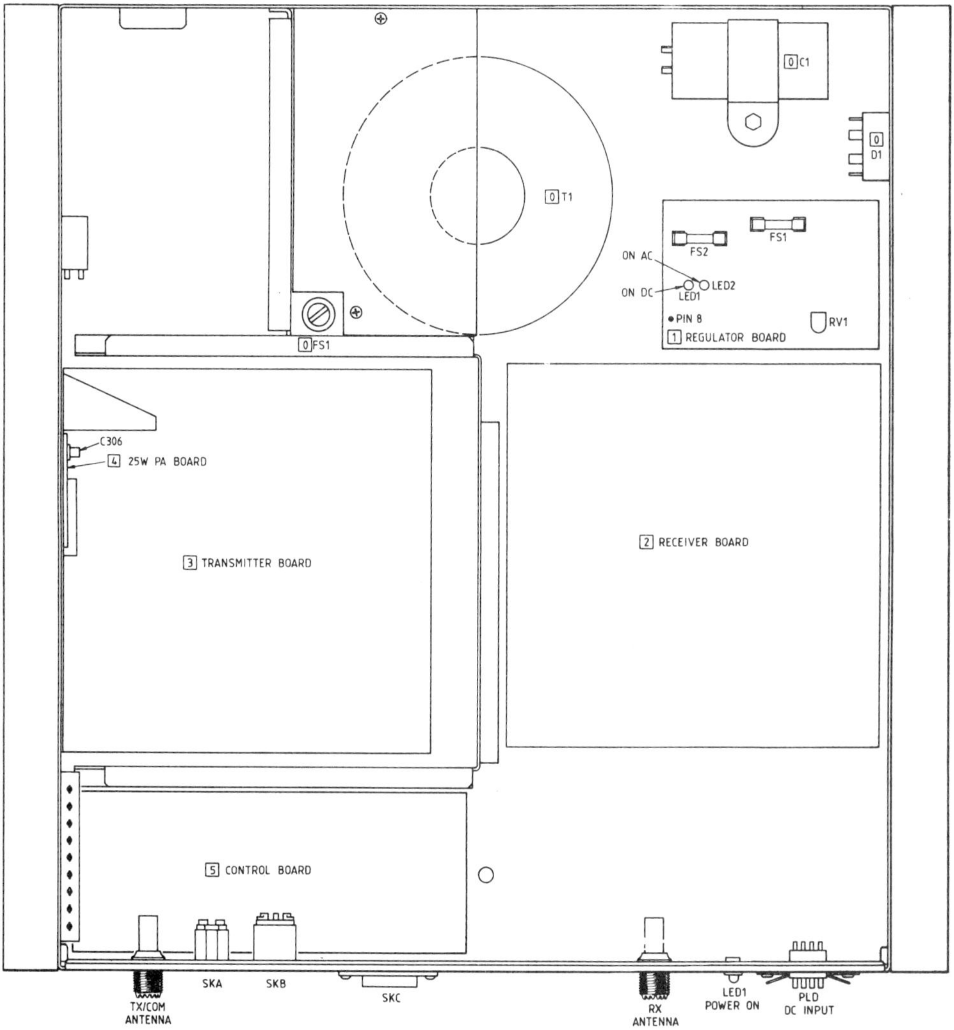

Fig 5.3. F490 series transceiver layout

stage alignment is again similar to the M294 and M296 series. However, as there isn't a speaker, microphone, or PTT switch fitted then you'll need to make appropriate connects to the set for these. You'll find that the socket SKB on the chassis, which is marked 'EHS', is for an engineer's handset – this is a very handy 'tap-off' point for alignment and test purposes. The receiver audio output here is at earpiece level, and the preset resistor RV1 on the control PCB sets the level of the audio to this pin. Remember that, as with the M296, the maximum power output of the F496 may be ether 6W or 25W, depending upon whether the high-power PA stage is fitted to the transmitter.

Unless you want to use the set just as a simplex or duplex base station under 'local control' in this way, it's unlikely you'll use the existing control board that's fitted inside the base station for amateur purposes. To interface the set to your own repeater controller,

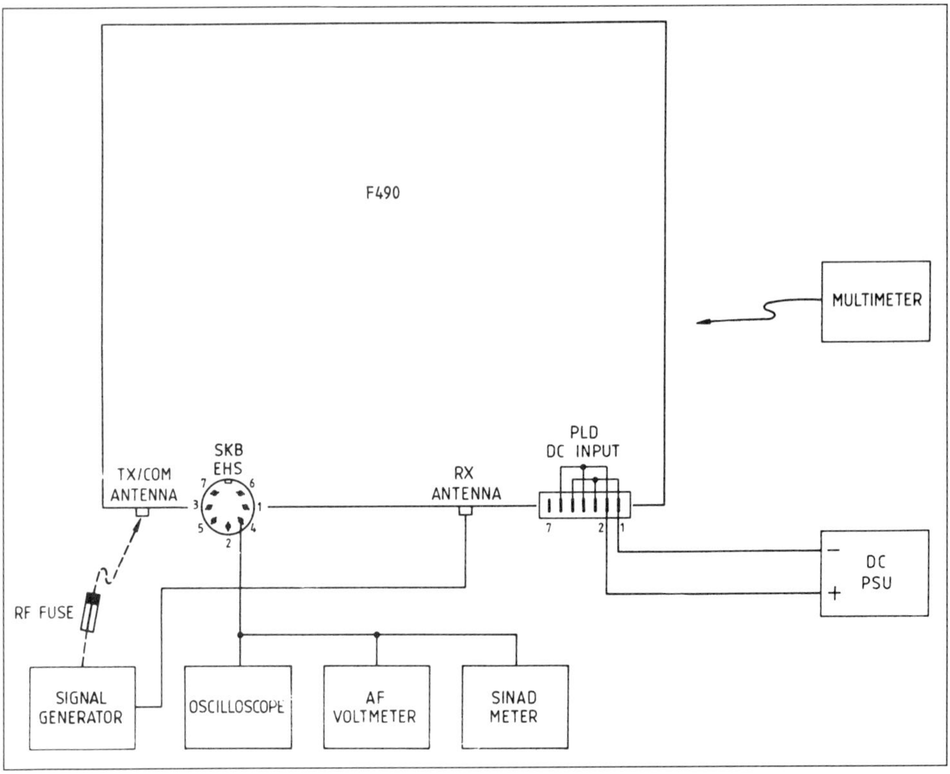

Fig 5.4. F490 series receiver test circuit

packet radio TNC, modem or whatever, the transmitter and receiver boards each have a board-mounted pin array plug, PLA, which carries various audio and control lines. The control board (of whichever type) also has a TX connector (PLE) and RX connector (PLF)

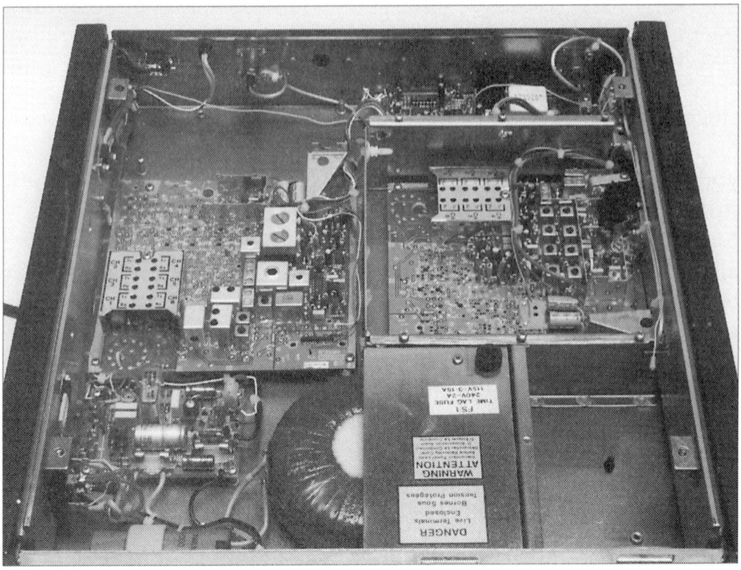

Inside the F496

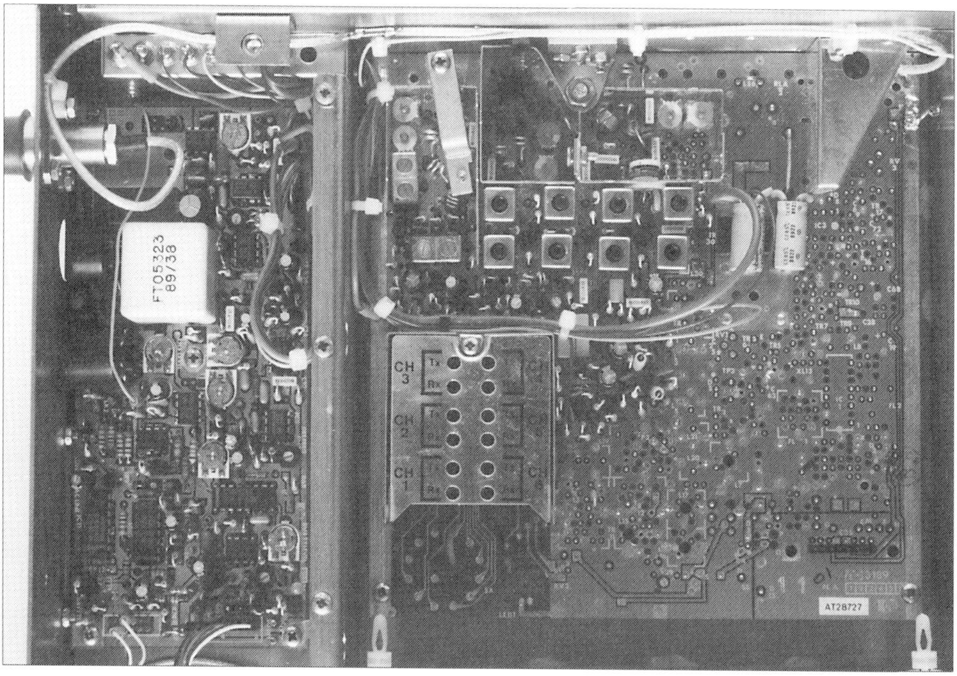

The F496 transmitter and control module

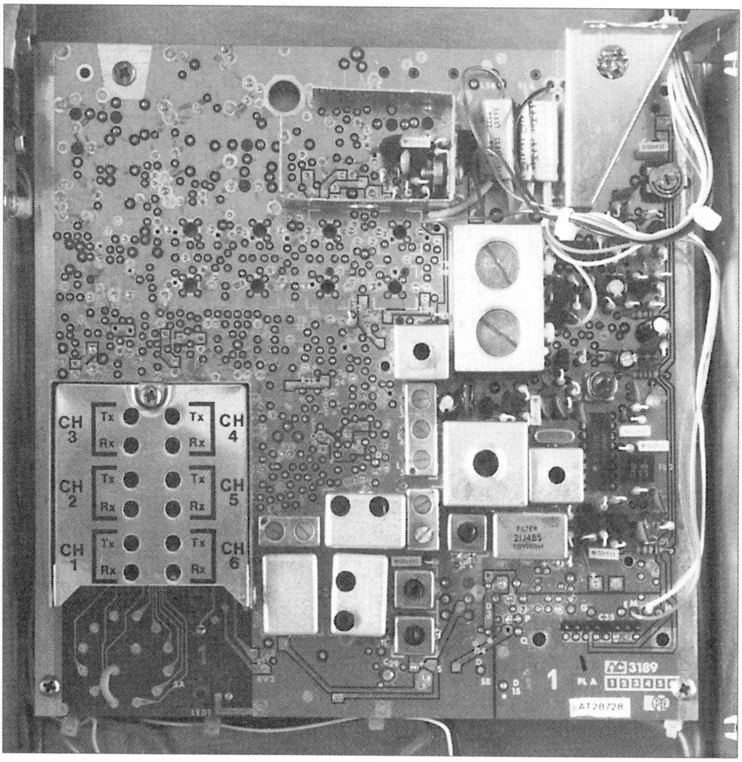

The F496 receiver section

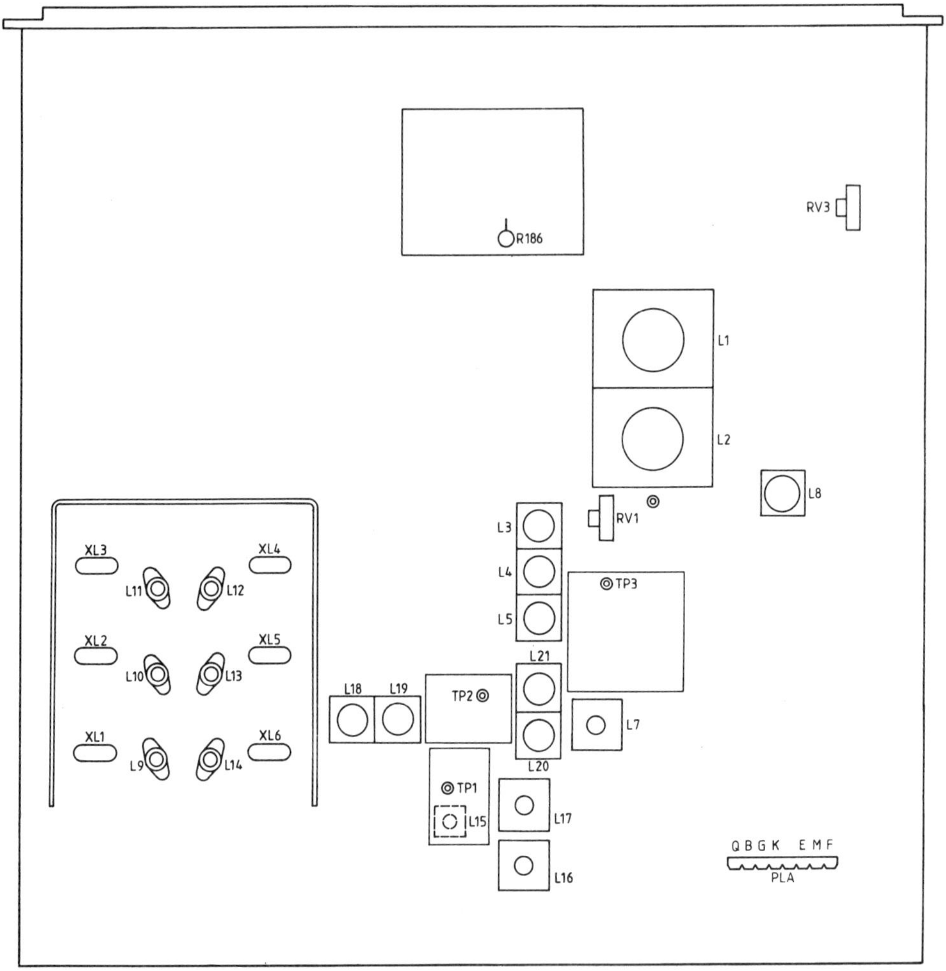

Fig 5.5. F496 receiver alignment diagram

which respectively link to sockets SKE and SKF on the TX and RX circuits.

Although the set is based upon mobile radio boards rather than high-specification base station units specifically designed for communal radio site use, internal screening between the transmitter and receiver improves isolation substantially. Two recent F496 base stations which I've set up are used as the main and standby units for my local 70cm repeater, with great success. The repeater is sited just a few hundred metres away from a main police UHF radio site, and very well it works too with no reported problems in either direction.

R400/T400 AND R4000/T4000 SERIES

These are purpose-designed, high-specification base station units, which are intended for, besides local desktop operation in 'local control' mode, 'communal site' use. In the latter case, several base

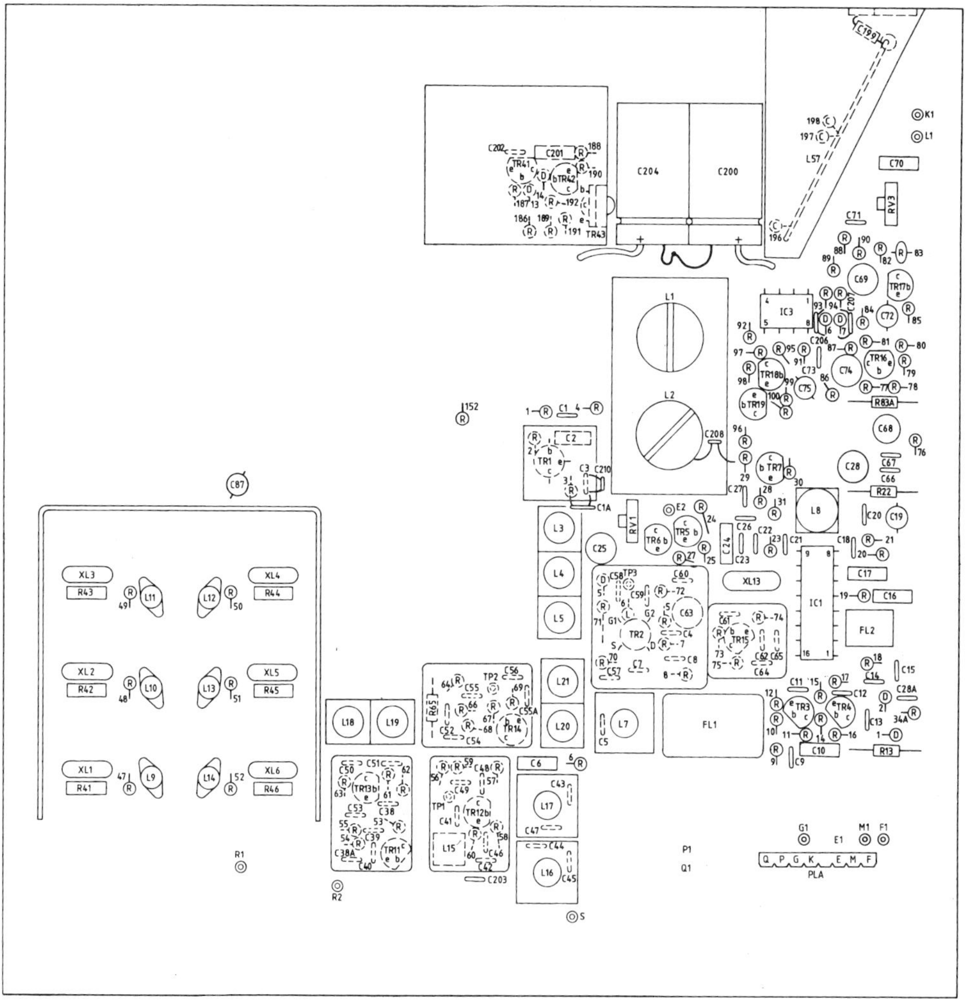

stations all operate on the same site and use the same mast, sometimes even the same antenna system. 600Ω remote control is typically used, with tone-controlled 'transmit' and receive 'busy' status signalling, plus other options. Differing control facilities are available from the front panel, depending upon whether control module 1 or module 2 is fitted – module 2 adds three push-buttons to the centre of the set's front panel. These are 'REM' for remote operation, 'LOC' for local operation, and a 'Talkthrough' mode. The difference isn't usually anything to worry about for most amateur radio purposes, although with control module 2 talkthrough mode can be easily switched on and off by the front-panel button which could be handy for emergency communication group use.

Fig 5.6. F496 receiver component layout

The base station is made up of a separate receiver and transmitter – the transmitter has a T400 series number, the receiver an R400 series number. These are marked on the front panel of the equipment in

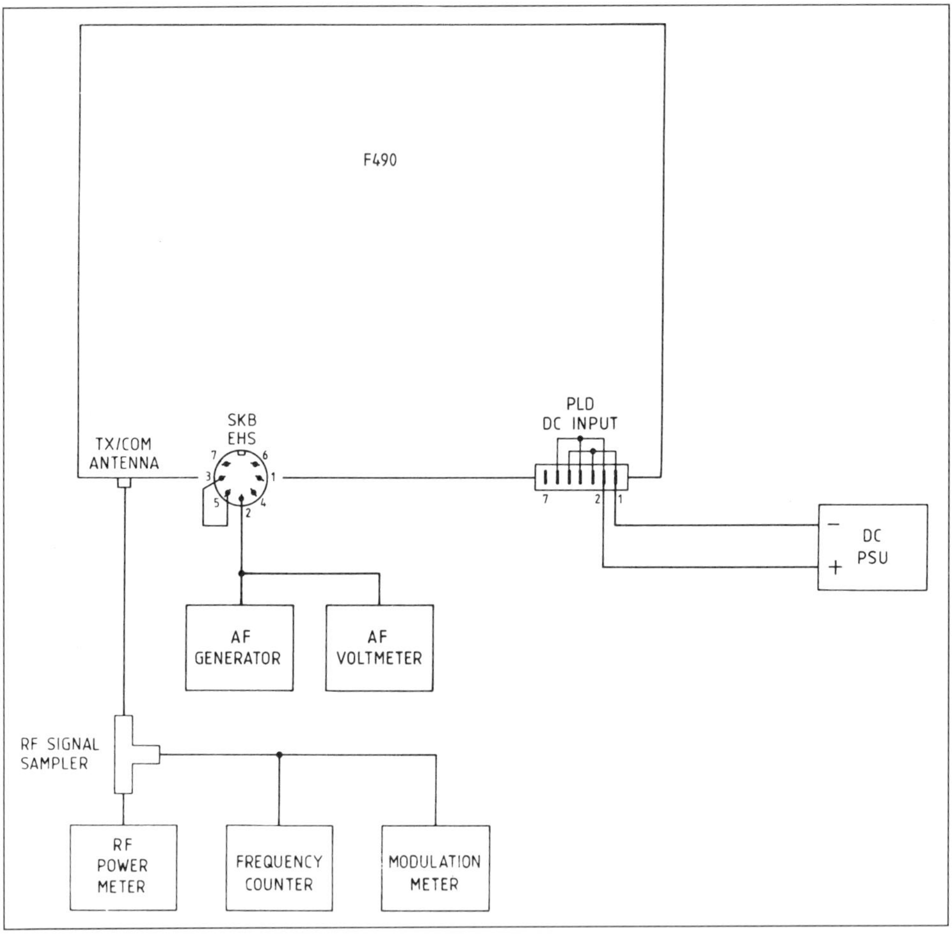

Fig 5.7. F490 series transmitter test circuit

each case. The sets are designed not only for PMR audio use, ie to communicate with mobile and portable radio users, but also for 'link' use with extended audio bandwidth, from DC upwards to 9kHz in some cases. This can be very useful for dedicated high-speed packet link applications. Besides being available for 4m, 2m and 70cm, one model in the range, which has found its way onto the ex-PMR market, is a version for 1400MHz links which may be modified for use on 23cm. The link versions of the transmitters have a very flat and distortion-free response, and the squelch rise time of the link receivers is less than 2ms, making them very useful for fast data applications.

The R4001 and T401/T4001 are VHF AM sets. I don't intend to give retuning details on these sets here – just be aware that they're *not* FM rigs, even though they may look the same from the outside.

If you're buying the R400/T400 and R4000/T4000 series as a pair, then check to see if the rear panel connecting lead, between the facilities connector SKA on the transmitter and the facilities connector PLB on the receiver, is still there. Otherwise, you'll need to make

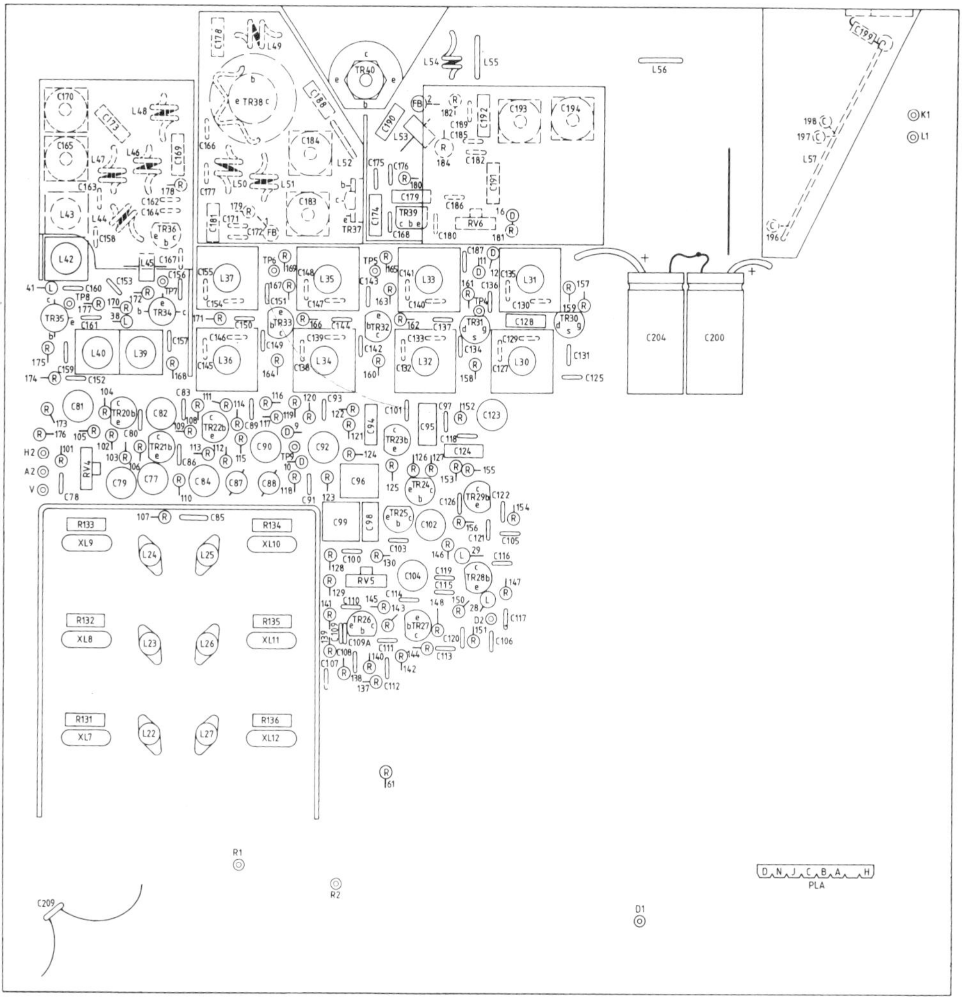

Fig 5.8. F496 transmitter component layout

up your own links for TX/RX control, voltage supply from the TX to the RX if required, and so on. For simplex use you'll also need a short coaxial cable link between the receive antenna output socket on the transmitter and the antenna socket on the receiver. The facility connections are similar between the sets and are given in Tables 5.7 to 5.9.

The engineer's handset connection on the front of the transmitter units uses the same connection arrangement as given earlier in this chapter in the F494/F496 description.

R4002/R4004

The R4002 is a VHF FM receiver, designed for single-frequency or two-frequency simplex, or two-frequency duplex/talkthrough operation, usually in conjunction with the T4002 transmitter, to provide a locally or remotely controlled base station. The R4004 is again a VHF receiver, operating over 132–174MHz, but instead is designed

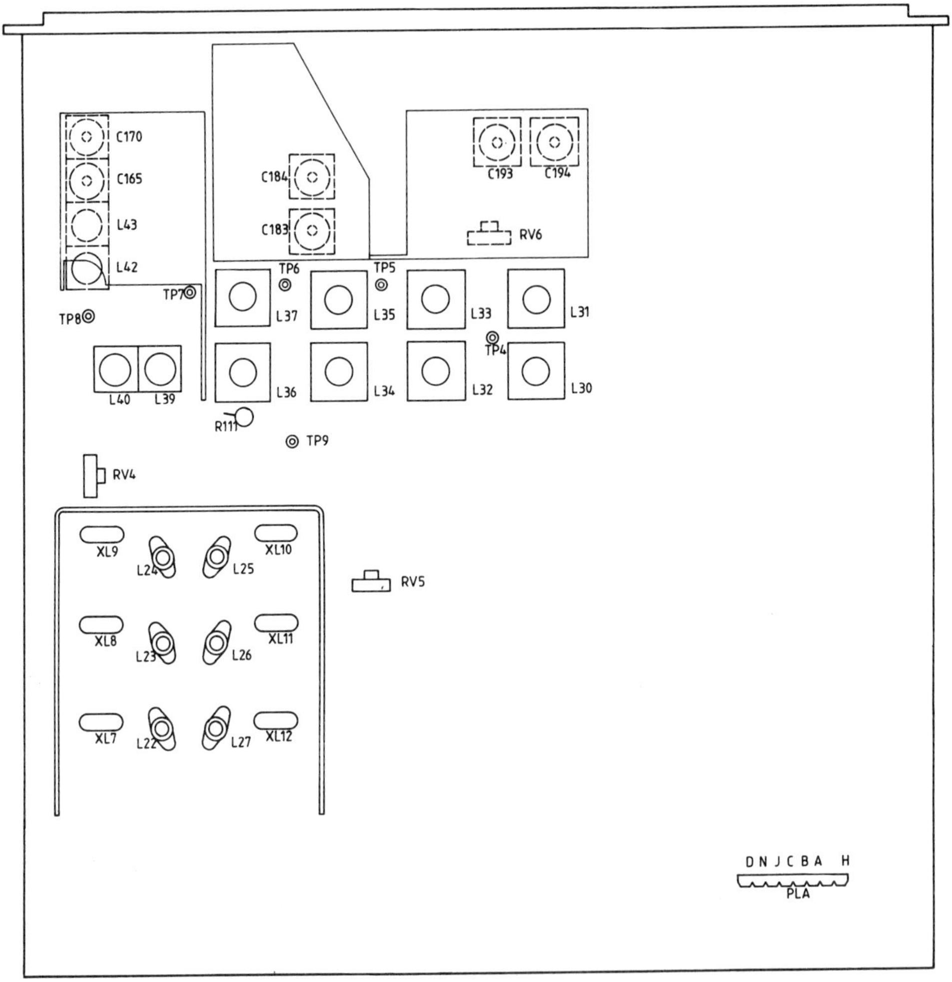

Fig 5.9. F496 transmitter alignment diagram

for continuous point-to-point duplex working in conjunction with the T4004 link transmitter. Both types are designed for minimal group delay to provide good data performance.

The R400 series receiver

The receiver can be found with various control options and facilities, which are dependent on the type and programming of the

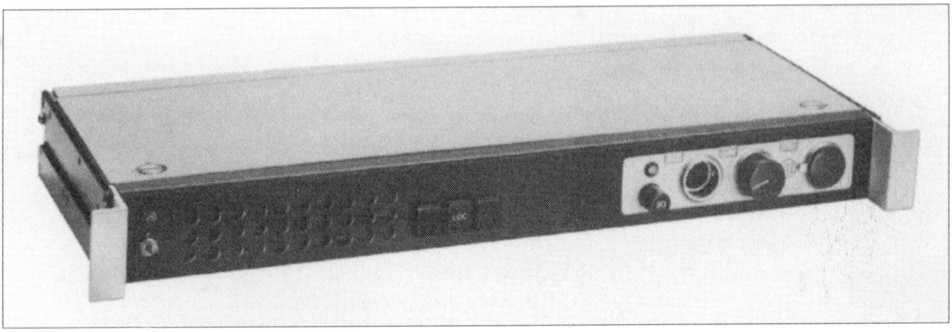

Table 5.7. TX facility connector (SKA on rear panel)

Pin	Function
1	Chassis
2	Common return
3	+24V DC
4	0V (–ve)
5	EHS common
6	TX switching i/p
7	EHS earpiece hi
8	Mic lo
9	Mic hi
10	600Ω lo
11	600Ω hi
12	EHS make
13	EHS break
14	Regulator switching i/p (T412/414/434) or internally linked (T4002)
15	Antenna c/o relay hi (13.5V)
16	TX key logic o/p
17	Antenna c/o relay lo
18	Not connected
19	Carrier fail
20	Not connected
21	Facility relay pole (T412/14/34), or protection logic o/p (T4002)
22	Facility relay make (T412/414/434), or not connected (T4002)
23	Facility relay break (T412/414/434), or internally linked (T4002)

Table 5.8. RX facility connector, Type 1 control module (PLB, on rear panel)

Pin	Function
1	Chassis
2	–ve o/p
3	+ve unreg from TX
4	–ve unreg from TX
5	Not used
6	RX sw i/p
7	Earpiece o/p hi
8	Not used
9	Not used
10	600Ω line lo
11	600Ω line hi
12	Mon amp o/p hi
13	Mon speaker i/p hi
14	Mon amp o/p lo
15	Squelch enable i/p
16	Squelch logic o/p
17	Squelch release o/p
18	Squelch relay make 1
19	Squelch relay break 1
20	Squelch relay pole 2
21	Squelch relay pole 1
22	Squelch relay make 2
23	Squelch relay break 2

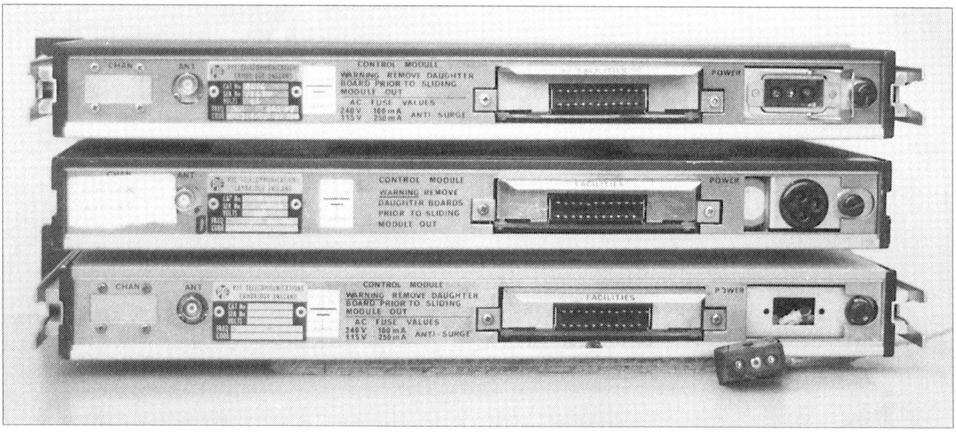

Above: **Rear panel connections are used to interface the R400/T400 series to the outside world**

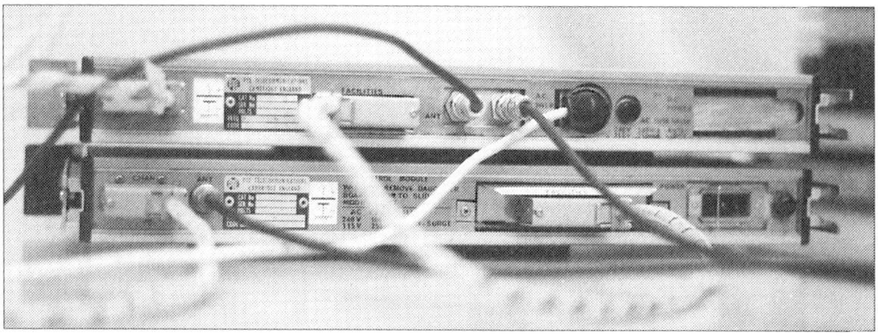

Left: **You're fortunate if you can obtain the required rear panel linking cables and connectors**

Table 5.9. RX facility connector, Type 2 control module (PLB, on rear panel)

Pin	Function
1	Chassis
2	Common return
3	+ve unreg i/p from TX
4	–ve unreg i/p from TX
5	EHS pressel pole
6	TX switching o/p
7	EHS earpiece hi
8	Mic low o/p
9	Mic high o/p
10	External speaker
11	600Ω line high o/p

internal control module fitted. Various power supply options are also found, from either 24V DC, with either positive or negative earth (so be careful!), or an AC mains supply. You'll usually find the receiver is designed for DC operation, taking its power from the companion transmitter.

Identification

A look at the equipment identification label will show the equipment code having the format and meanings given in Table 5.10.

Crystals

The crystals required are:

A0 band (147–174MHz): Xtal freq = (RX freq – 10.7MHz) ÷ 3
B0 band (132–156MHz): Xtal freq = (RX freq – 10.7MHz) ÷ 3
E0 band (68–88MHz): Xtal freq = (RX freq + 10.7MHz) ÷ 2
G5 band (45–54MHz): Xtal freq = (RX freq + 10.7MHz) ÷ 2

The commercial specification of the crystals (even if you state you just want the 'amateur' version of these) is T84W (5ppm), E71DQ (10ppm, R4002 only) or, if you've a crystal oven fitted to the receiver, P56DQ (5ppm, R4002 only) and P99DQ (2ppm, R4004 only).

Receiver alignment

Layouts and alignment details are given in Figs 5.10–5.16. If your receiver is fitted with a CTCSS unit (check the equipment code if you're not sure), then you won't hear anything unless you disconnect the optional tone lock board. Then, to relink the receive audio, link plug PLC pins 1 to 2 and pins 5 to 6.

R4002 only: For a Type 1 control module, link pins 12 and 13 of PLB (on the rear panel facilities connector). On the 600Ω audio board,

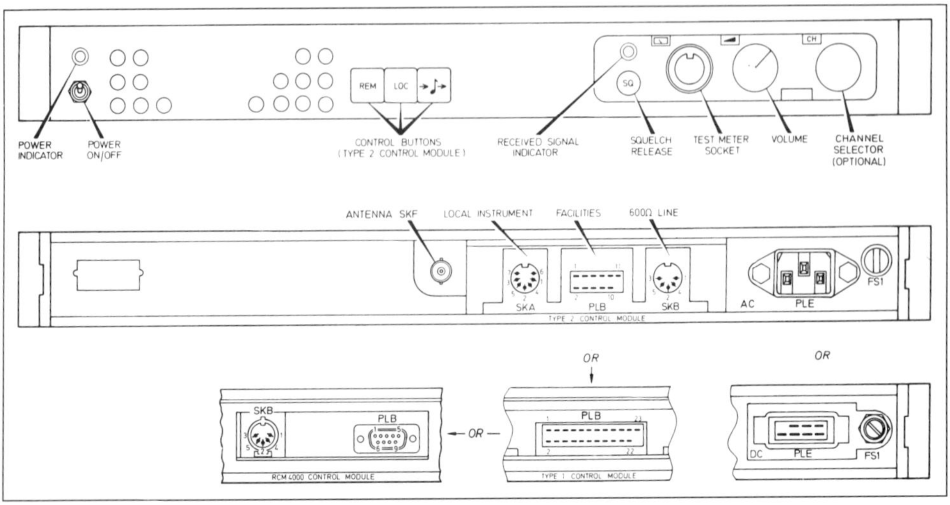

Fig 5.10. R400 series front and rearpanels

Table 5.10. Identification codes for R4002/R4004

Format:	**R400x aa bb cc d e ff g h i jj kk** with the following meanings:
R400x:	R4002: standard receiver, R4004: link receiver
aa:	01: Standard production (UK specifications) 02: French specification
bb:	(R4002: Not used) L3: 300Hz–3kHz audio bandwidth L6: 300Hz–6kHz audio bandwidth L9: 300Hz–9kHz audio bandwidth
cc:	1A: (R4004) Type 1 control module 1B: (R4004) Type 1 control with 600Ω audio amp 1C: (R4004) Type 1 control modified for voting encoder 2A: TX/RX, two-wire loop switching 2B: TX/RX plus controlled talkthrough, two-wire and earth 2C: TX/RX plus receiver-call, two-wire and earth 2D: As 2C but two-wire only 2E: TX/RX plus controlled talkthrough and receiver call, two-wire and earth 2F: TX/RX plus line-fail, two-wire 2G: TX/RX plus power fail, talkthrough, two-wire and earth 2H: TX/RX plus power fail, talkthrough and receiver call, two-wire and earth 2J: TX/RX plus tone lock 2K: TX/RX plus controlled talkthrough and tone lock 2L: TX/RX plus power fail talkthrough and tone lock 2M: TX/RX, local simplex or duplex 2N: as 2M, with UED6 encode/decode as required 2P: as 2M, with UED6 encode/decode 2Q: Local simplex with CTCSS talkthrough 2R: Local duplex with CTCSS talkthrough 5x: TX/RX, two-wire 6x: TX/RX, four-wire
d:	0: Less crystals 1: Crystal for 1 channel fitted (R4004) 1–6: Crystals for channels 1–6 fitted (R4002)
e:	S: 12.5kHz channel spacing R: 20kHz channel spacing (R4002 only) V: 25kHz channel spacing
ff:	A0: 148–174MHz B0: 132–156MHz D0: 88–108MHz E0: 68–88MHz (R4002 only) G5: 45–54MHz
g:	1: Single-channel capability 6: Six-channel capability (R4002 only) Y: Crystal oven fitted, single channel
h:	1: AC input, neg earth 7: 24V DC, neg earth 8: DC from associated TX, neg earth 9: 24V DC, pos earth A: DC from associated TX, pos earth
i:	0: No channel switch (single channel) 1: Locally switched channels 2: Channel switched from associated transmitter R: Remote channel change
jj:	00–67: Defines various mountings/supplied mating connectors
kk:	00: No secondary options 01: Tone lock decoder

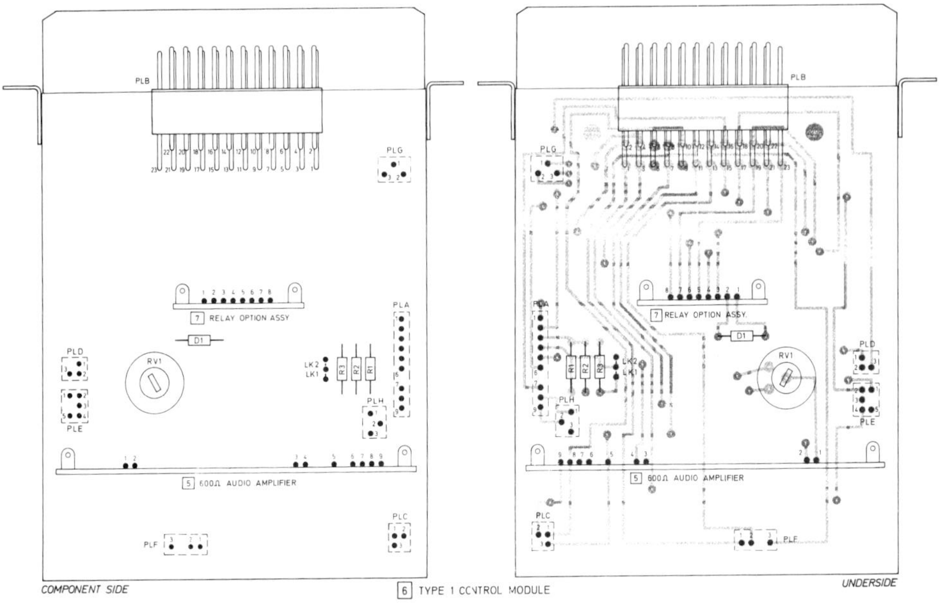

Fig 5.11. Type 1 control module layout

check that LK1 is linked A to B. For a Type 2 control module, link pins 1 and 4 of socket SKA (on the rear panel local instrument connector), and press the front panel 'Local' button.

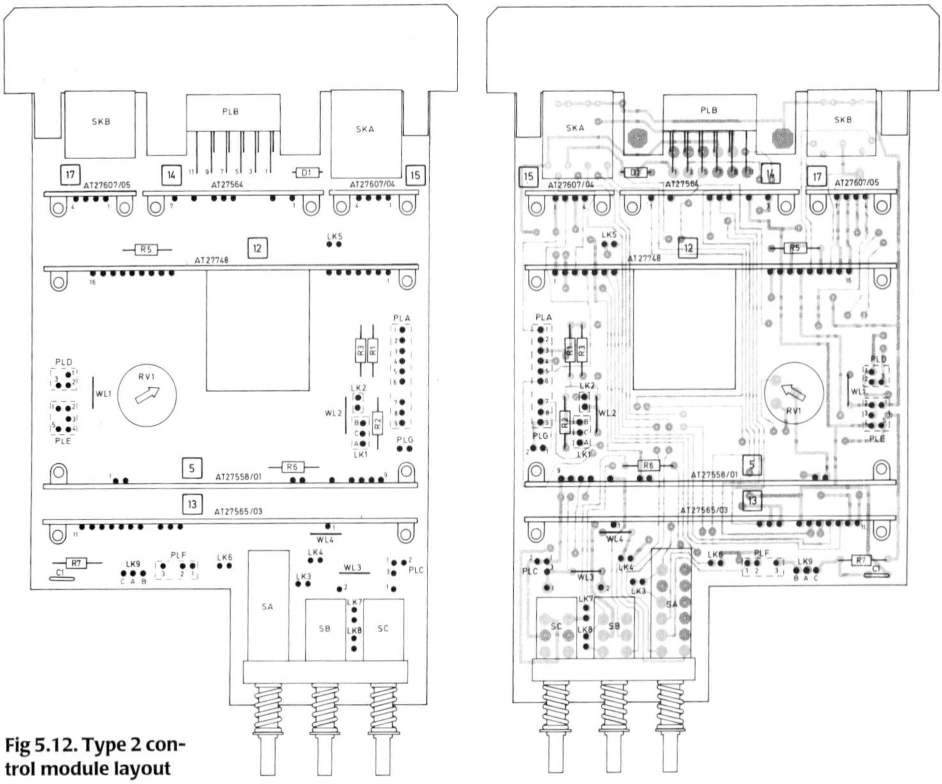

Fig 5.12. Type 2 control module layout

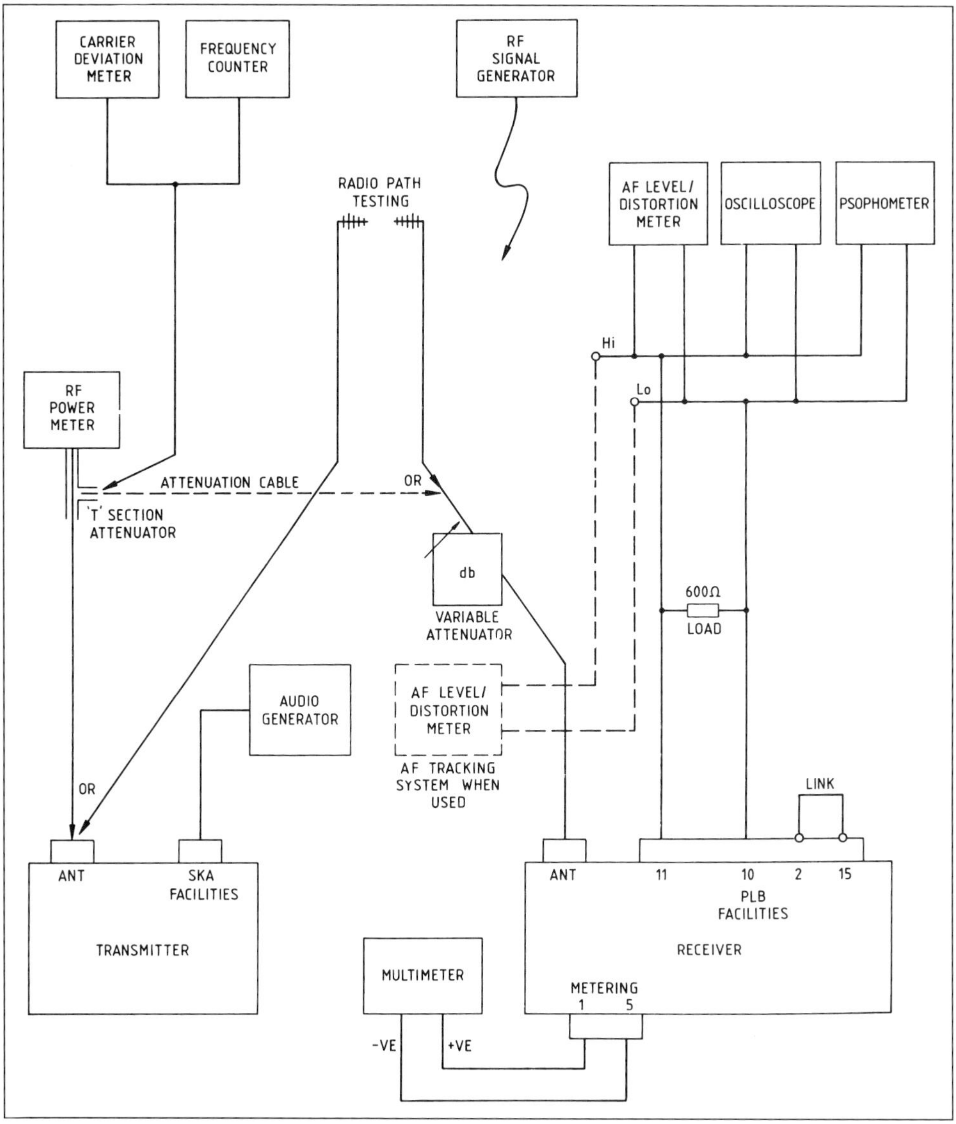

Fig 5.13. Connection of test equipment – R400/T400 series

R4004 only: Link PLA pins 2 to 3, PLB pins 1 to 2, LK1 in, LK3 out, and LK2 *in* for L3 and L6 audio responses or *out* for L9 audio response. On the 600Ω audio board, check LK1 A to B is made, and on the Type 1 control module, check that LK1 is fitted.

The squelch control is RV2 (J) on the receiver board, which you can adjust clockwise to raise the squelch, or just keep the 'Monitor' button on the front panel pushed to defeat the squelch temporarily.

Now for the RF alignment. Coils L1 to L6 should be tuned for peaks when their cores are nearest the base ends of their formers, and coils L8 to L10 and L12 to L15 should be tuned for peaks when their cores are nearest the top end of their formers. Set your multimeter to the 2.5V DC range, and connect the negative lead to TP7 on the

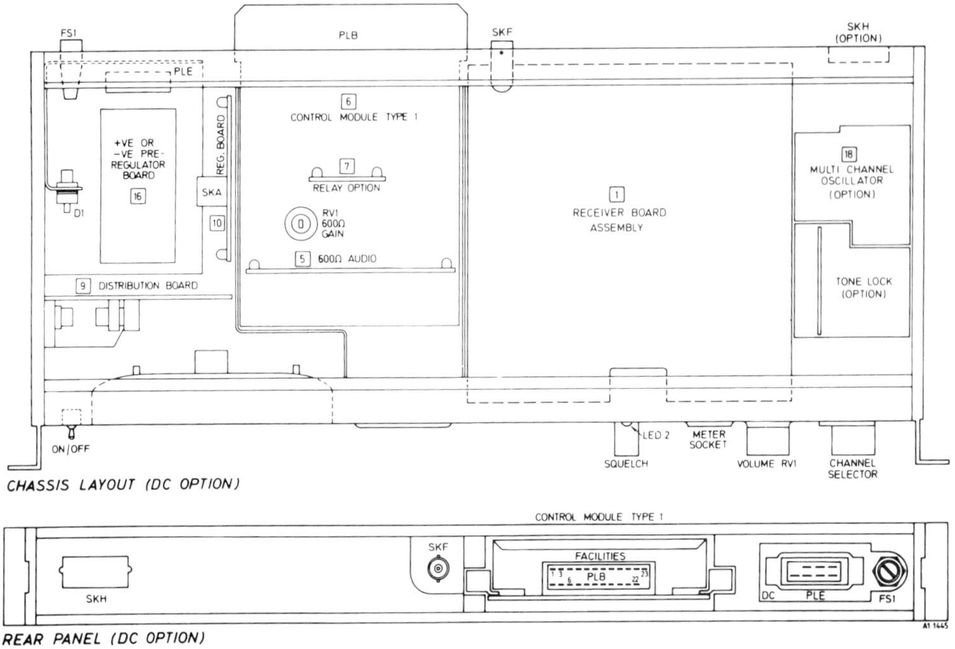

Fig 5.14. R4002 layout with Type 1 control module

receiver board assembly, and the positive lead to TP3. Now tune L12, or the appropriate coil on the multi-channel oscillator board, for a maximum reading on your meter. L12 (D) is the crystal trimmer, so don't worry if it doesn't visibly peak – we'll adjust it for correct frequency later. You can check that the crystal is oscillating by temporarily unplugging it and checking the voltage falls by at least 0.2V.

Now with your multimeter set to the 10V DC range and the positive lead connected to TP4, tune the exciter coil L13 (E) for a maximum, and L14 (F) for minimum reading. Transfer your multimeter positive lead to TP5, and tune L8 (G) for maximum, then L13 and L14 again for maximum.

Now, whilst receiving an off-air signal (readjust the crystal trimmer L12 as needed), tune L1 (K), L2 (L), L3 (M), L4 (N), L5 (P), L6 (Q), L9 (R) and L10 (S) on the receiver board for best signal. Following this, finally retune L13(E), L14 (F) and L8 (G) for maximum reading on your multimeter.

You shouldn't need to adjust the audio level potentiometers if the set came out of working service, but RV1 (H) on the receiver board is the audio control potentiometer, and RV1 (U) on the control module is the 600Ω gain control.

T4002

The T4002 is the matching transmitter to the R4002. It can run 30W continuously, the large front-panel heatsink keeping the transmitter PA cool. In the past I've run the T4002 for a number of years as a busy 2m hilltop amateur repeater. There's an engineer's handset socket on

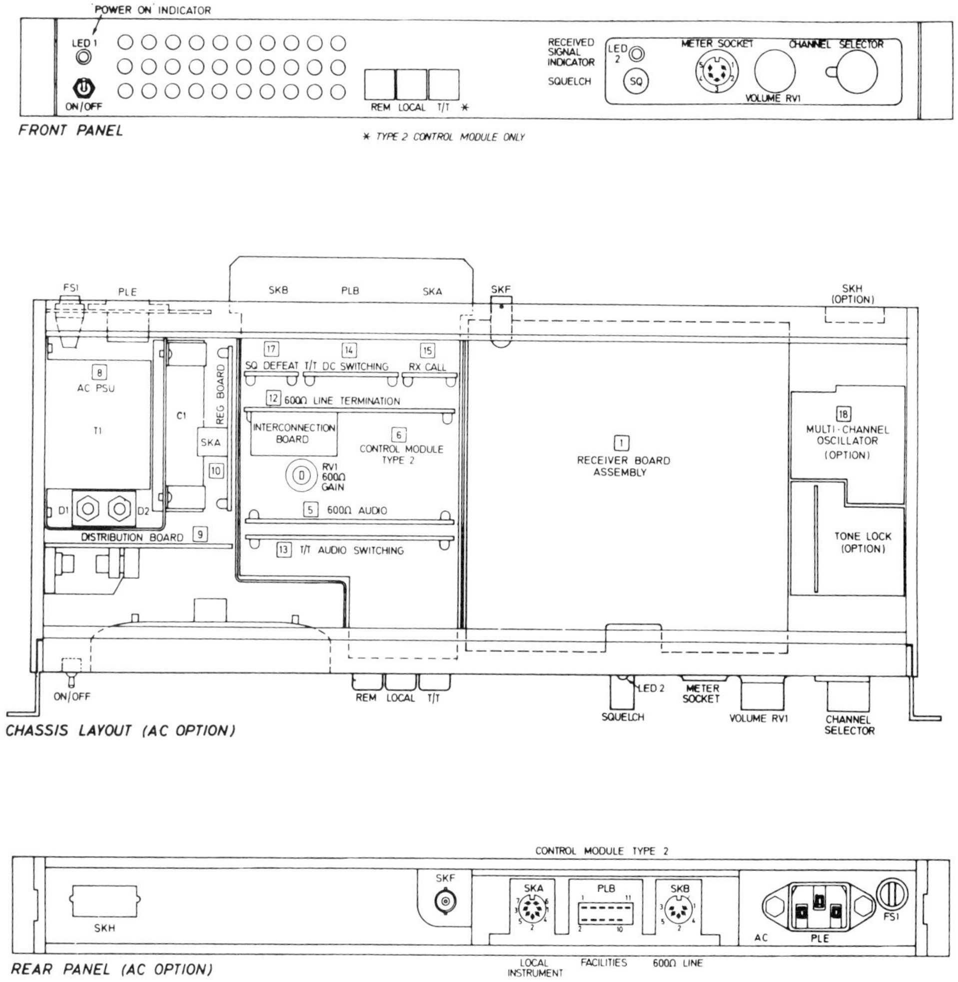

Fig 5.15. R4002 layout with Type 2 control module

the front panel, which is useful for desktop operation as well as checks and alignment (or of course, 'local control' of the repeater while you're on site), and a variety of rear-panel connections are available.

Identification

The equipment code format and meanings are given in Table 5.11.

Crystal information

The transmitter crystal formula for all band variants, ie A (148–174MHz), B (132–156MHz), D (88–108MHz) and E (68–88MHz) is the same, and is the final transmit frequency divided by 12.

Transmitter alignment

Layouts and alignment details are given in Figs 5.13 and 5.17–5.23. First, remove the screen lid from the RF driver module, and then

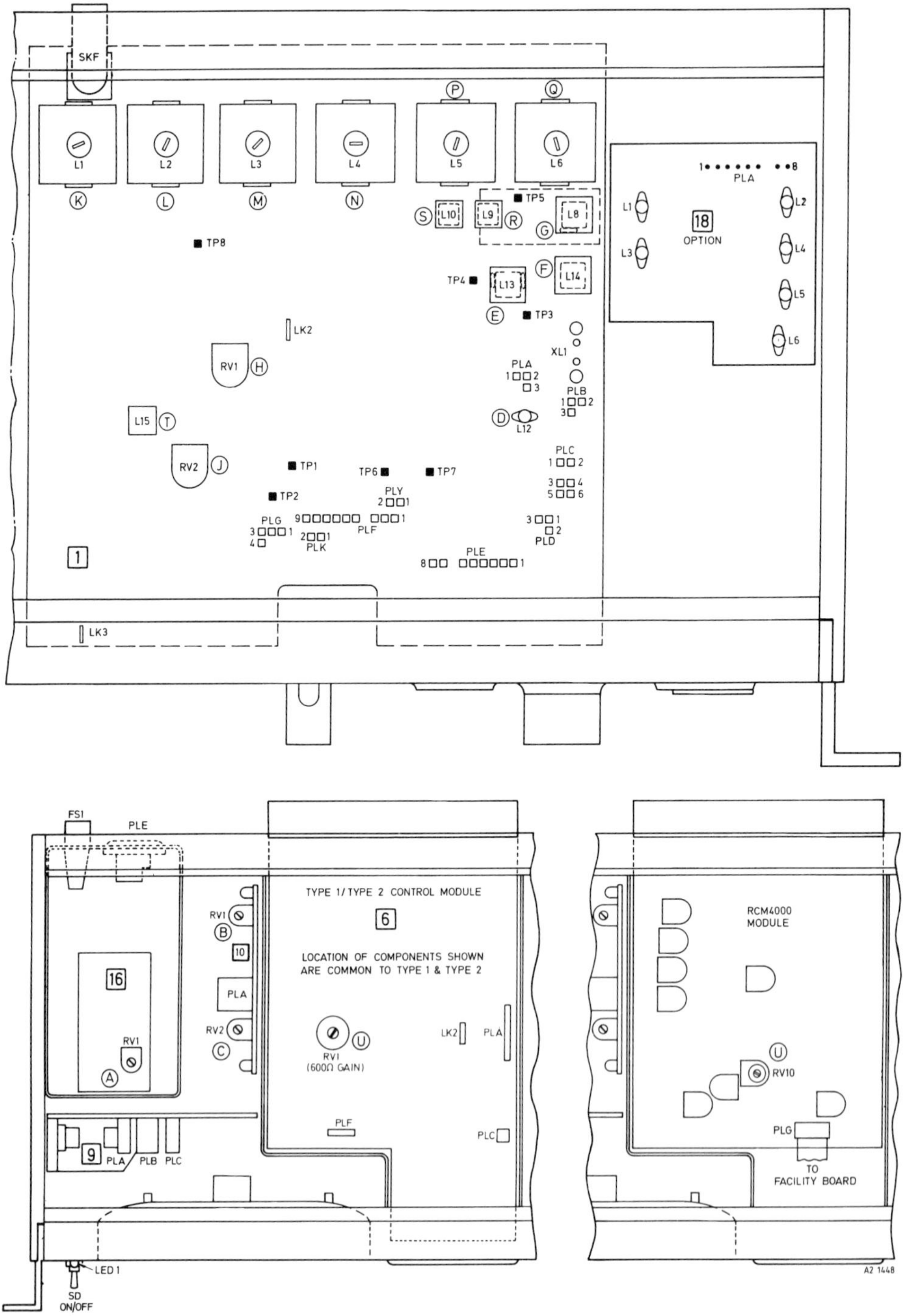

Fig 5.16. R4002 alignment diagram

disconnect link LK1 from pin 14 of this module. Disconnect the 24V supply lead from C6 (on the driver module screen), and make sure the free end of this doesn't short to the set's chassis. Again on this

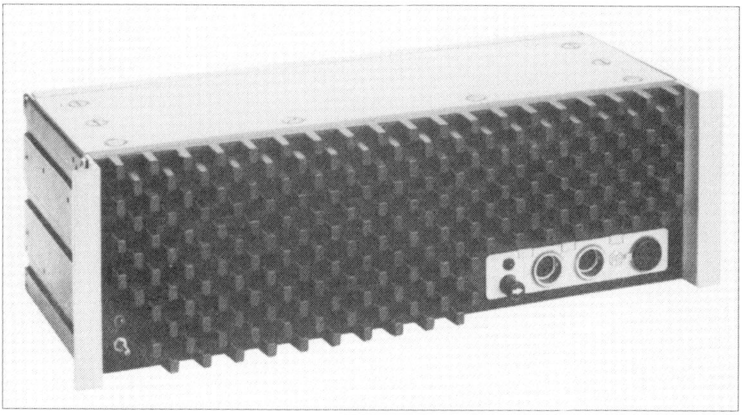

The T4002 transmitter

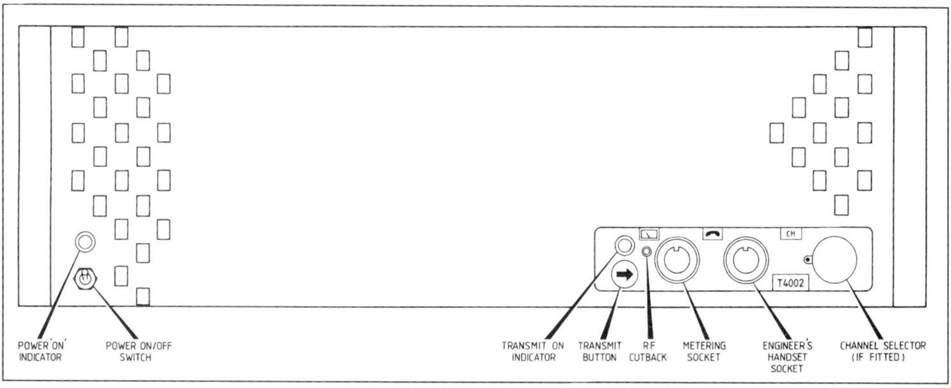

Fig 5.17. T4002 front-panel controls

module, unplug the coaxial plug PLA, and connect this to a low-power wattmeter, one which you'll be able to read up to 300mW RF output on. Now preset the following:

RV3 on the transmitter module, board 1 – fully clockwise (RF power)
RV1 on the RF driver module, board 5 – fully counter clockwise (power adjust)

Set up the test equipment as shown in the diagram, connect your power supply to the transmitter, and switch on. Switch your multimeter to the 10V DC position, and connect the multimeter positive lead to TP4 or TP5 on board 1, and connect the negative lead to the test points as detailed.

On module 10, connect to TP1 and tune L1 for maximum, L2 for maximum, and then L3 for minimum (typically 4.0V). Transfer to TP2, and tune L4 for maximum, L3 for maximum, then L5 for minimum (typically 2.75V). Transfer to TP3, and tune L6 for maximum, L5 for maximum, then L7 for minimum reading (typically 2.5V). Transfer to TP4 and tune L8 for maximum, L7 for maximum, then L9 for minimum (typically 1V). You may by now be seeing some RF power indicated, so tune L10 and then L9 for maximum RF power – you'll typically see between 170mW to 300mW. You'll now need to

Table 5.11. Identification codes for T4002

Format:	**T4002 aa b c d e ff g h i jj kk** with the following meanings:
aa:	01: Standard production (UK specifications)
bb:	C: Local/remote control, simplex, duplex, or talkthrough. Microphone and unbalanced 600Ω inputs, antenna c/o relay, engineer's handset facility, AC or DC supply D: As above but balanced 600Ω
cc:	0: Without crystal oven 1: Crystal oven fitted, single channel
d:	0: Less crystals 1–6: Crystals for channels 1–6 fitted
e:	S: 12.5kHz channel spacing R: 20kHz channel spacing V: 25kHz channel spacing
ff:	A0: 148–174MHz B0: 132–156MHz D0: 88–108MHz E0: 68–88MHz
g:	1: Single-channel capability 6: Six-channel capability (R4002 only)
h:	1: AC input, neg earth 7: 24V DC, neg earth 9: 24V DC, pos earth
i:	0: No channel switch (single channel) 1: Locally switched, six channels
jj:	00–60: Defines various mountings/supplied mating connectors
kk:	01: Tone lock decoder 05: Line termination unit (for pagers) 30: Audio drive monitor 99: Standard equipment

adjust RV3 on the transmitter module to give 150mW output to the next stage. Now unkey the transmitter, switch off the power supply, and reconnect PLA to SKA. For the next stage of the alignment, temporarily connect a short length of coaxial cable between the low-power wattmeter and the RF driver module pin 14 (inner) and

Fig 5.18. T4002/R4002 rear-panel interconnections

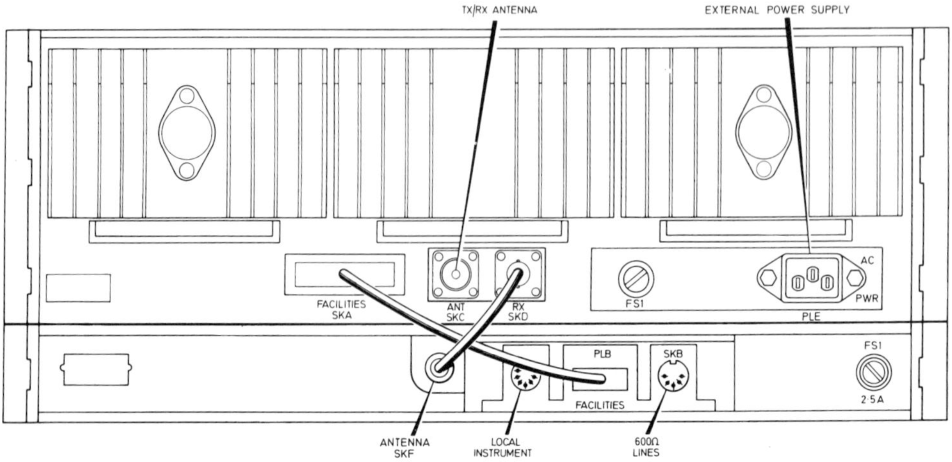

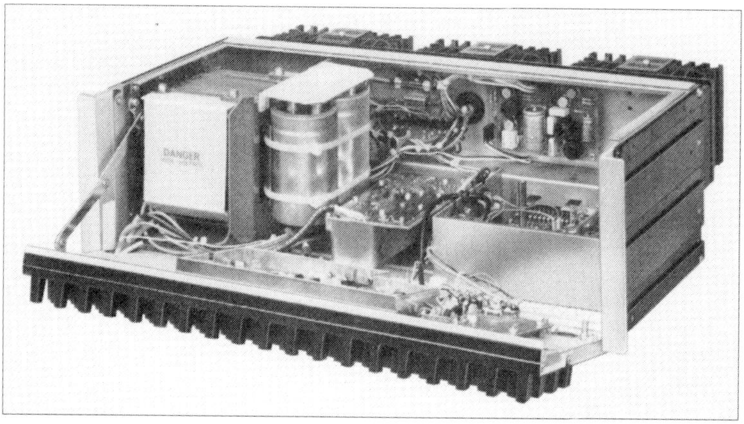

The T4002, ready for alignment

COMPONENT SIDE

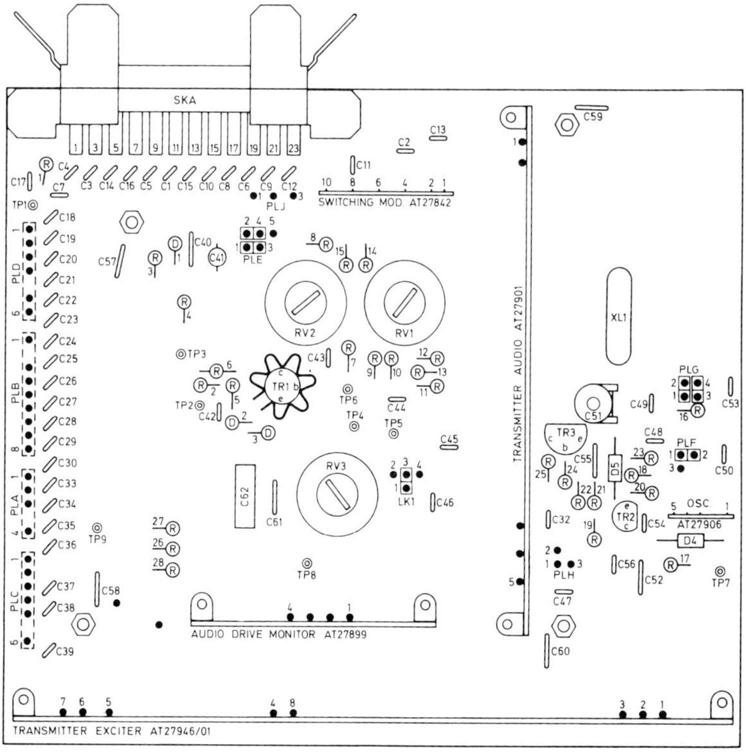

Fig 5.19. T4002 transmitter module

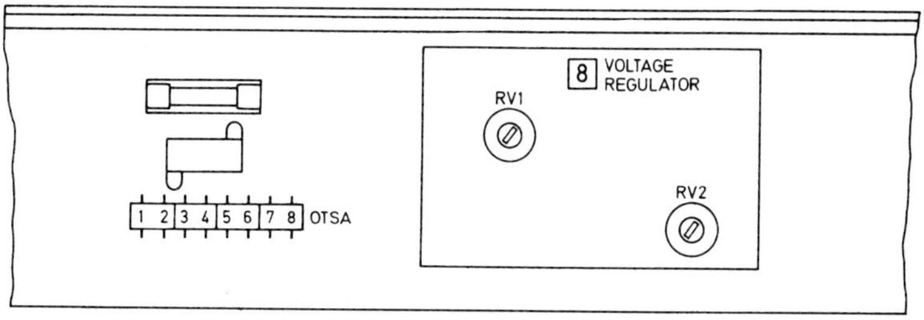

Fig 5.20(a). T4002 alignment diagram

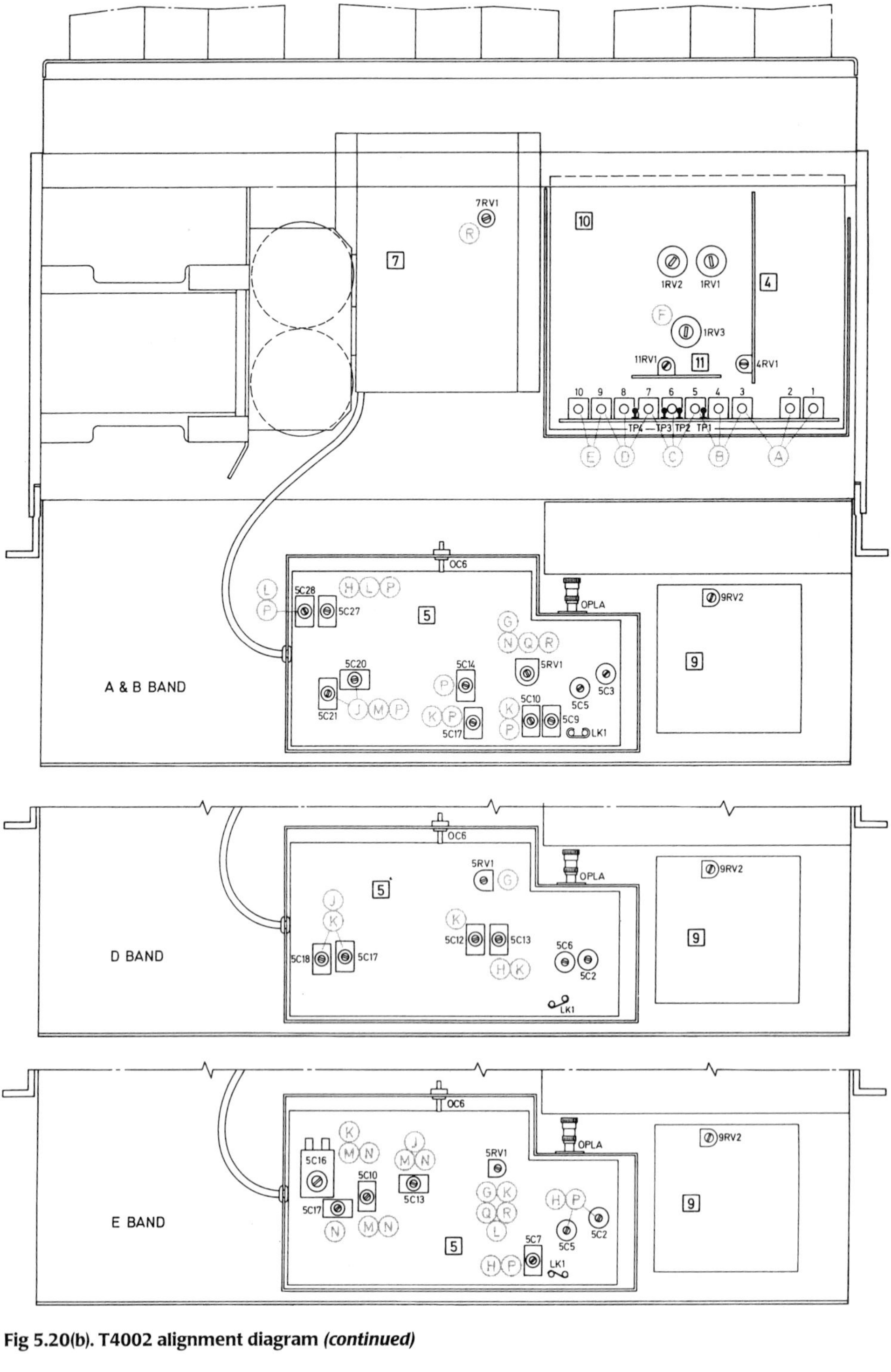

Fig 5.20(b). T4002 alignment diagram *(continued)*

Fig 5.21. Location of T4002 test points

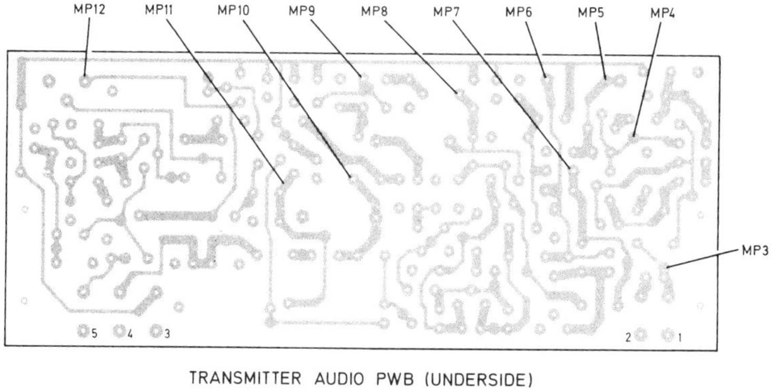

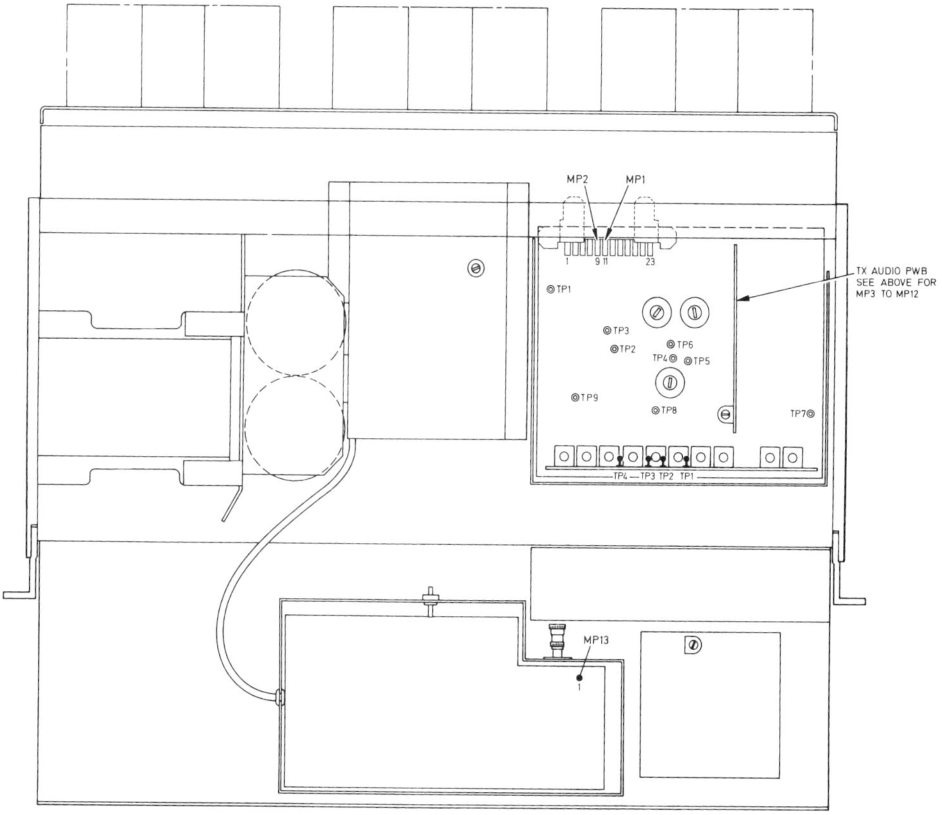

pin 10 (braid). With the power on and the transmitter keyed again, tune C3 and C5 on board 5 for maximum indication on the power meter – you should get at least 90mW here. Unkey the transmitter and switch off the power supply, and unsolder the coaxial lead. Reconnect link LK1 between pins 13 and 14, and connect your multimeter, set to DC *current* range of 5A, between C6 (on the driver screen) and the 24V DC lead previously disconnected. Connect your RF power meter / dummy load to the antenna connector on the rear panel of the set.

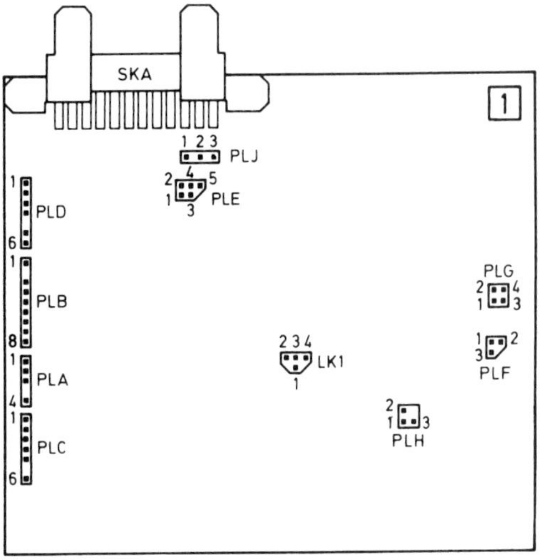

Fig 5.22. Location of T4002 links, TX assembly

2m transmitter (A and B band sets)

First set the trimmer capacitors as follows:

C21, C20, C17, C14, C10 and C9: maximum compression minus half a turn.
C27: maximum compression minus a quarter turn.
C28: maximum compression.

Refit the RF driver module screen lid, switch your power supply on and key the transmitter. You should now see some RF power being indicated, so initially adjust RV1 on board 5 for around 3–5W power output – if needed adjust RV3 on board 1 to get this. Now tune C27 for maximum power, then C21 and C20 in that order, then alternately, again for maximum power. Then tune C17 followed by C10 for maximum power, then C28 and C27 alternately, and C21 and C20 again alternately, all for maximum power. Now adjust RV1 either for 25–30W power output, or to three-quarters of its travel, whichever comes first, then readjust C27, C28, C21, C20, C17, C10 and C14 in that order until a power output of more than 30W can be obtained by varying RV1. Finally set this to 30W, making sure your ammeter reads less than 3.5A, then release the PTT, switch off, and reconnect the 24V DC lead in place of your ammeter.

4m transmitter (E band sets)

First set the trimmer capacitors as follows:

C7: maximum compression
C10: maximum compression minus half a turn.
C13: maximum compression minus a full turn.

Fig 5.23. T4002 test equipment interconnections

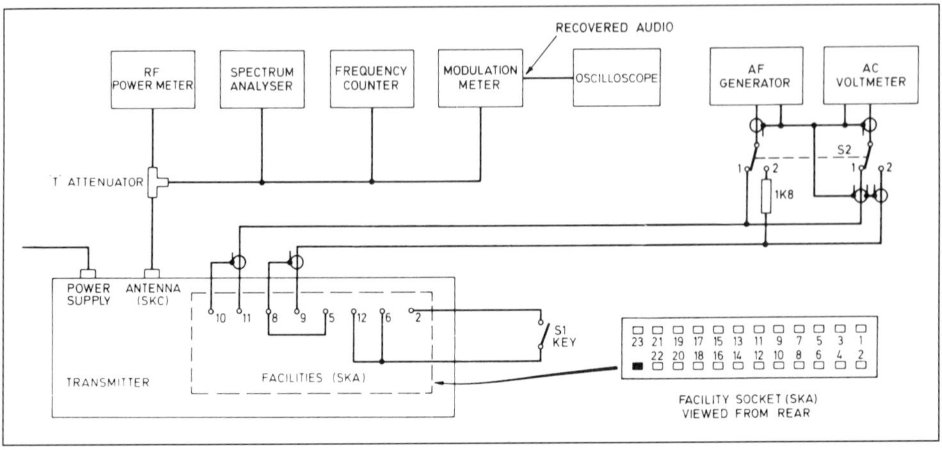

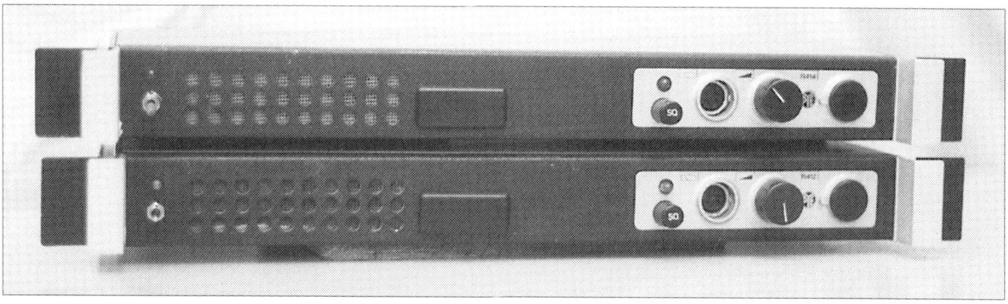

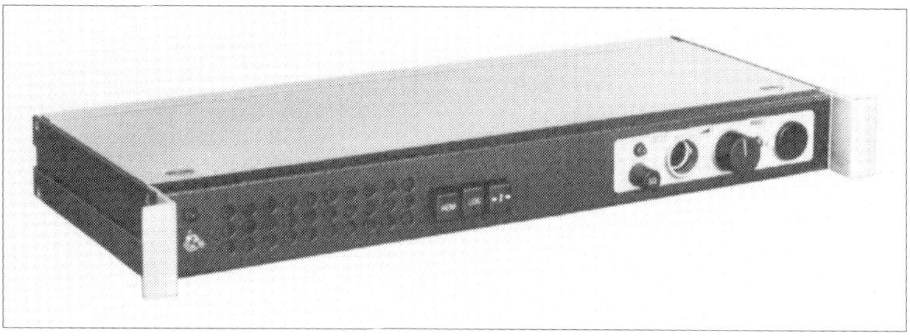

Top: **The R412 and R414 receivers**

Left: **The R412 receiver fitted with a Type 2 control module**

C16: maximum compression.
C17: maximum compression minus a quarter turn.

Refit the RF driver module screen lid, switch your power supply on and key the transmitter. Initially adjust RV1 on board 5 through approximately one-eighth of a turn. Now tune C5, C7 and C2 in that order for maximum reading on your in-line current meter, then tune C13 for maximum current. Now you should be seeing some RF power indication, so tune C16 for maximum power output, then adjust RV1 a further one-eighth of a turn. Now, watching your power meter, tune C16, C10 and C13 in that order, repeating the sequence as needed, until you get 15W RF output power. Then adjust C16 and C17 together for maximum power, followed by C10 and C13 together again for maximum power. Repeat this until you get at least 35W, readjusting RV1 to reduce this if you get over 35W, then finally adjust C5, C7 and C2 in order for maximum power output. Readjust RV1 for 30W output, and check your ammeter reads less than 3A at this output level.

Final presets

The peak deviation potentiometer is RV1, the 600Ω line control is RV2, and the mic gain control (ie from the engineer's handset) is RV3.

R412/R414

Identification

The equipment code on the rear label is as listed in Table 5.12.

Receiver alignment

Alignment diagrams and layouts are shown in Figs 5.24–5.28. First, after removing the top cover, check on PLC that links are made on

Table 5.12. Identification codes for R412/R414

Format:	**R41x aa bb cc d e ff g h i jj kk** with the following meanings:
R41x:	R412: (standard) or R414: (link version)
aa:	01: Standard production (UK specifications)
bb:	F3: 300–3400Hz audio bandwidth, R412 L3: 300Hz–3kHz audio bandwidth, R414 L6: 300Hz–6kHz audio bandwidth, R414 L9: 300Hz–9kHz audio bandwidth, R414
cc:	2A: TX/RX, loop or remote simplex 2B: TX/RX plus controlled talkthrough, local or remote simplex 2C: TX/RX plus receiver-call, local or remote simplex 2D: as 2C but two-wire 2E: TX/RX plus controlled talkthrough and receiver call 2F: TX/RX plus line-fail talkthrough, two-wire 2G: TX/RX plus power fail talkthrough 2H: TX/RX plus power fail talkthrough and receiver call 2J: TX/RX plus tone lock 2K: TX/RX plus controlled talkthrough and tone lock 2L: TX/RX plus power fail talkthrough and tone lock 2M: TX/RX, local simplex or duplex 2N: as 2M, with UED6 encode/decode as required 2P: as 2M, with UED6 encode/decode 3A: TX/RX plus automatic selection of receiver/transmitter
d:	0: Less crystals 1–6: Crystals for channels 1–6 fitted
e:	V: 25kHz channel spacing
ff:	T6: 375–440MHz U1: 420–470MHz W2: 470–512MHz
g:	1: Single-channel capability 6: Six-channel capability
h:	1: AC input, neg earth 7: 24V DC, neg earth 8: DC from associated TX, neg earth 9: 24V DC, pos earth A: DC from associated TX, pos earth
i:	0: No channel switch (single channel) 1: Locally switched channels 2: Channel switched from associated transmitter
jj:	00–69: Defines various mountings/supplied mating connectors
kk:	00: No secondary options 01: Tone lock decoder (R412) 03: Monitor loudspeaker 04: Tone lock decoder and monitor loudspeaker 30: UED6 encode and decode (R412) 31: 30 and 01 32: 30 and 03 34: 30 and 04

pins 1 and 2, and 5 and 6. Also, for single-channel equipments only, check on PLA that pins 2 and 3 are linked, and that PLB pins 1 and 2 are linked. Now, set the squelch adjustment preset RV126 fully clockwise. Depending on which control module your receiver has, connect up your alignment set-up as shown in the appropriate diagram. If you'd like to do a quick initial voltage check, then set your

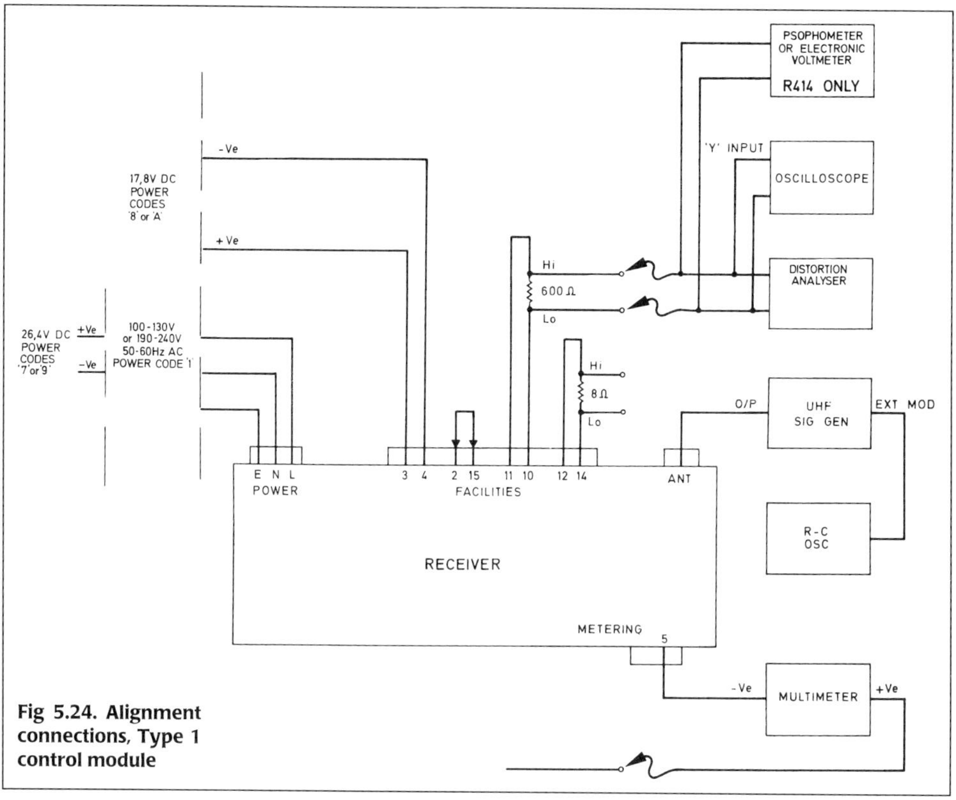

Fig 5.24. Alignment connections, Type 1 control module

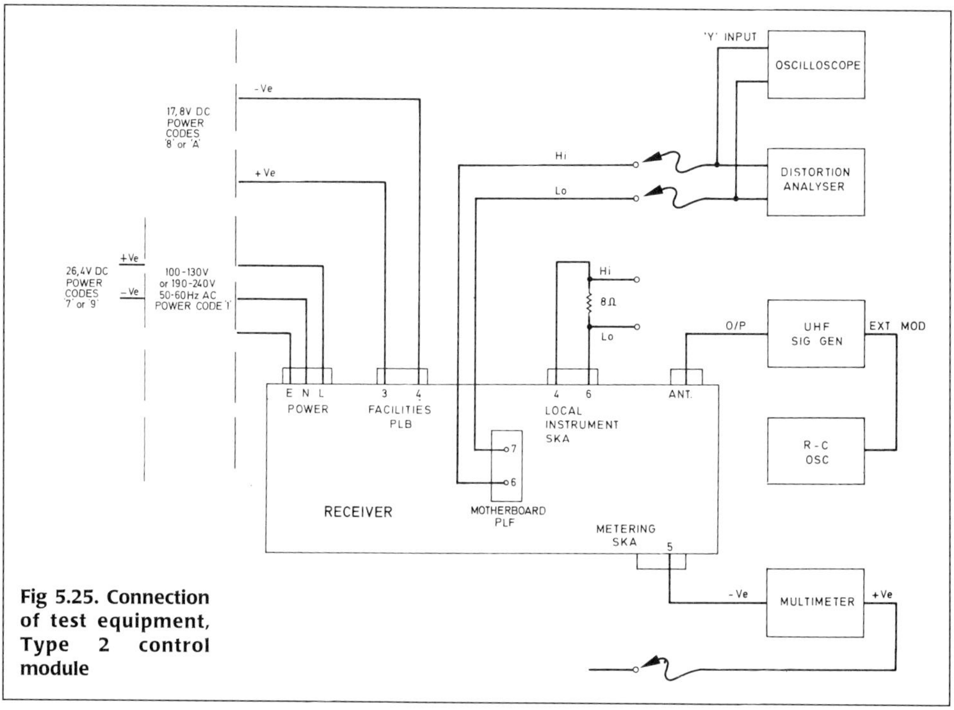

Fig 5.25. Connection of test equipment, Type 2 control module

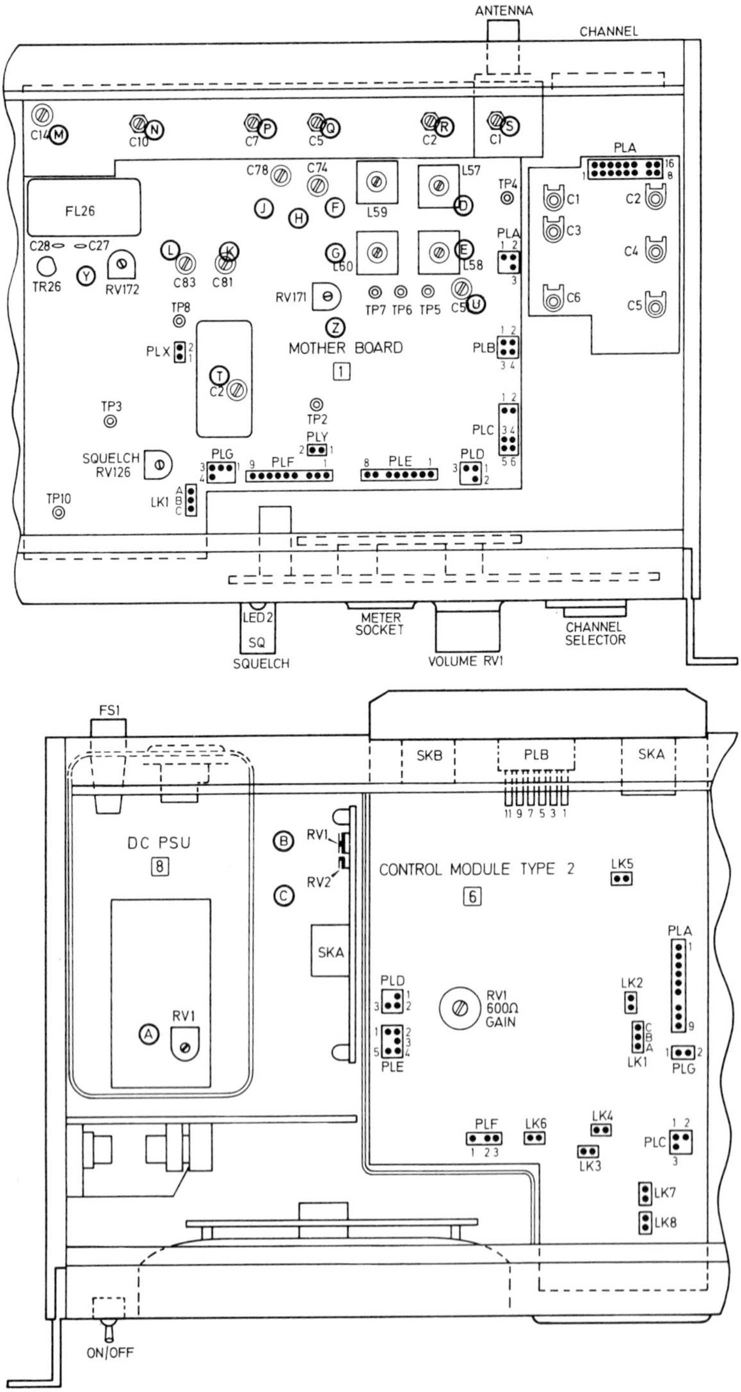

Fig 5.26. R412 internal layout

multimeter to the 30V DC range, and connect the positive lead in turn to PLG pin 2 (for a receiver powered from an external 26.4V DC source – you should read 23.5V here, RV1 on board 16 adjusts

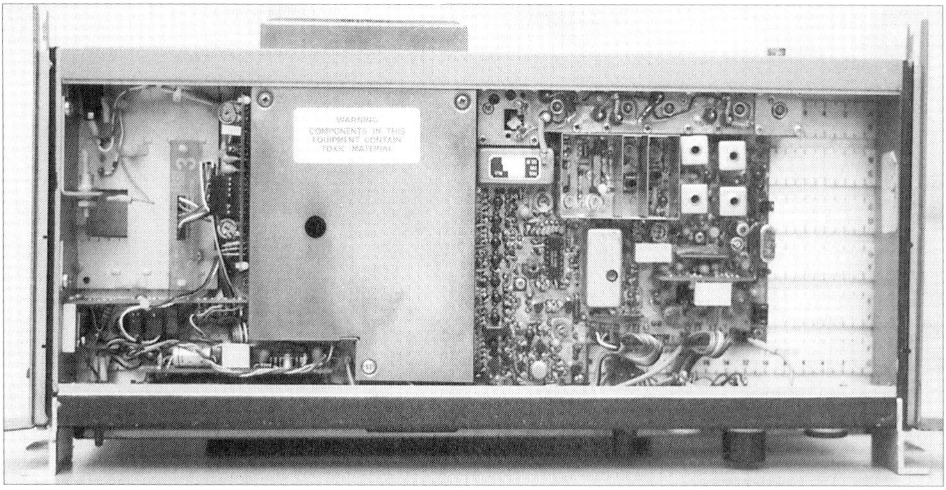

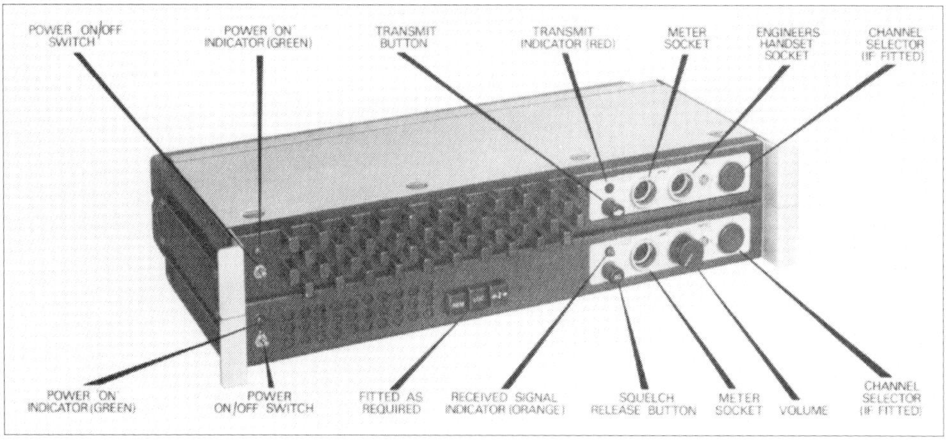

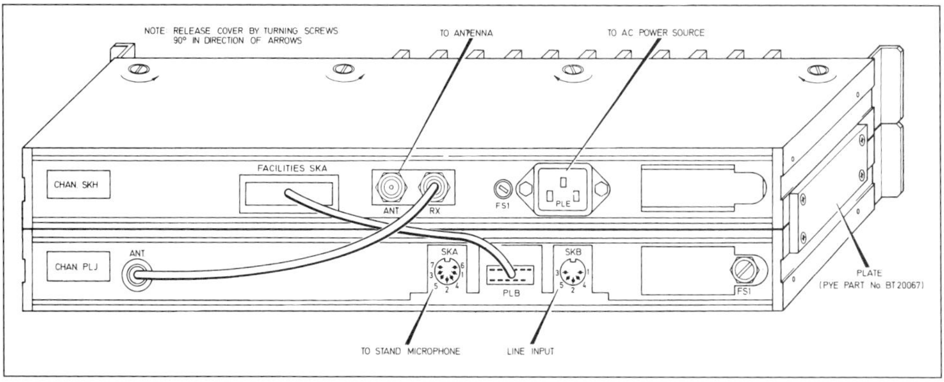

Top: **Inside the R412/ R414.** ***Middle:*** **Front-panel controls.** ***Bottom:*** **Fig 5.27. R412/ T412 rear-panel connections**

this), PLG pin 1 (12.5V, RV1 on board 10 adjusts this) and PLG pin 3 (8.5V, RV2 on board 10 adjusts this).

Now for the multiplier alignment. Set your multimeter to the 10V DC range, and connect the positive lead to TP5. Adjust L57 (D) for minimum reading (1.3-0.5V). Then transfer to TP6 and tune L58 (E)

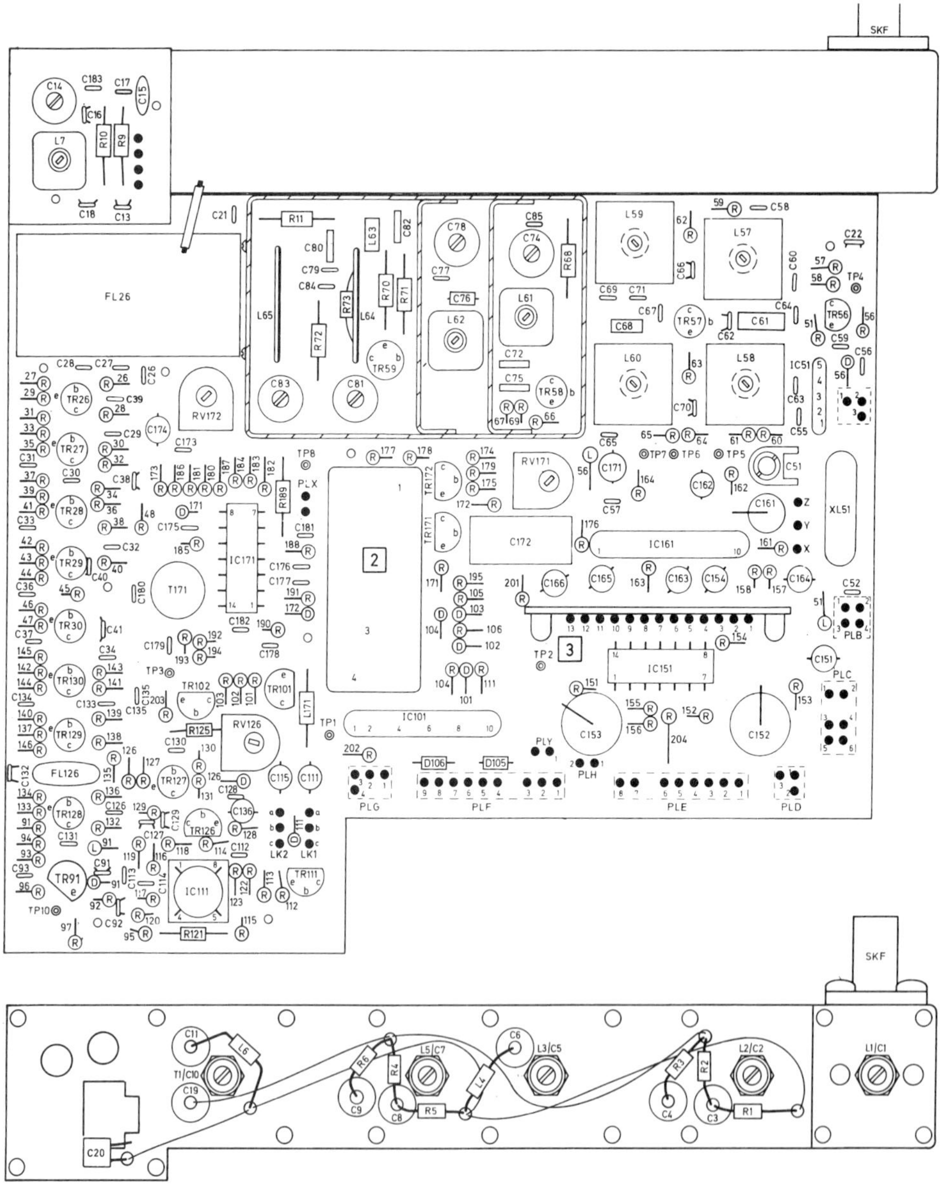

Fig 5.28. R412 component layout

Facing page: **Fig 5.29. R412 internal arrangement**

for maximum, then tune L57 and L58 together for maximum, followed by L59 (F) for minimum reading (2.5V–1.3V) – note the 'dip' here could be very shallow. Transfer your multimeter positive lead to TP7, and tune L60 (G) for maximum, then L59 and L60 together for maximum, then C74 (H) for minimum. Transfer your meter positive lead to TP8 and tune C78 (J) for maximum, then C74 and C78 together for maximum. Now, short-circuit L65 to negative, and tune C81 (K) for minimum. Remove the short-circuit from L65, and tune C83 for maximum – you should end up with a reading between 0.6V and 1.0V.

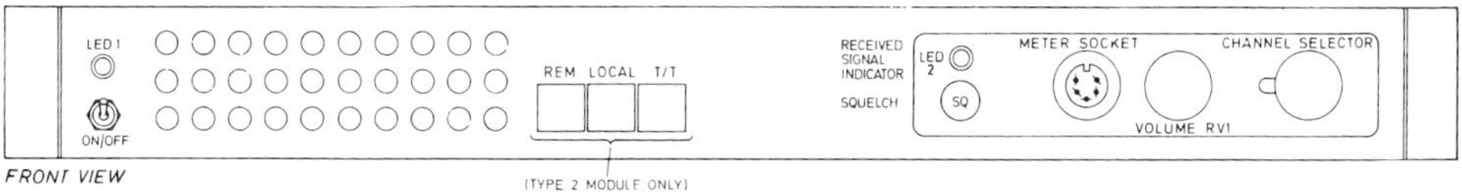

FRONT VIEW

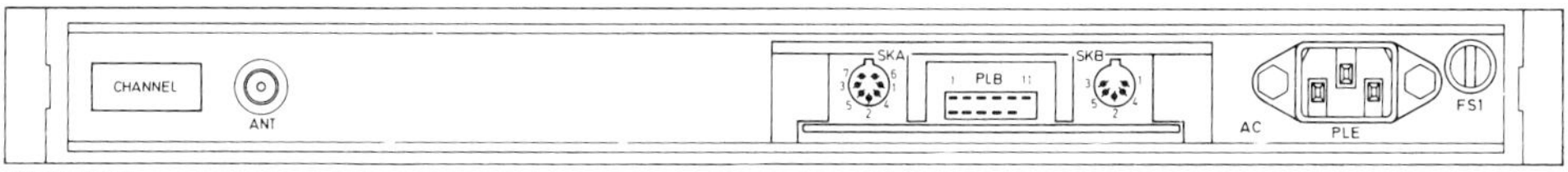

REAR VIEW

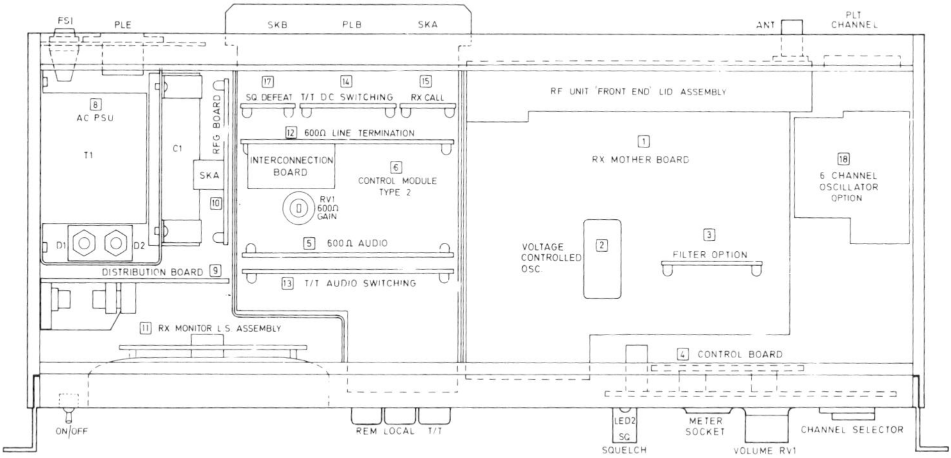

CHASSIS LAYOUT

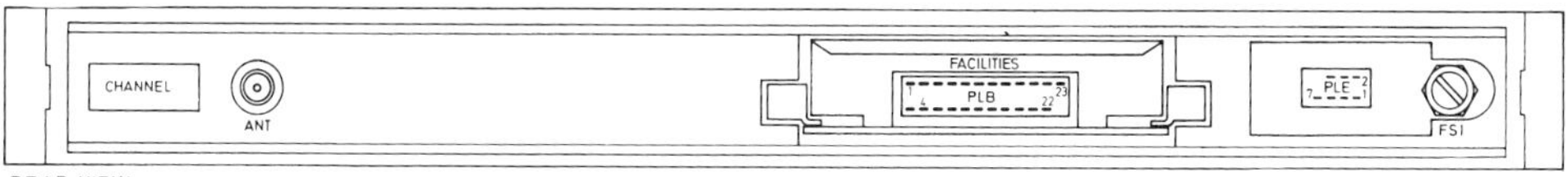

REAR VIEW

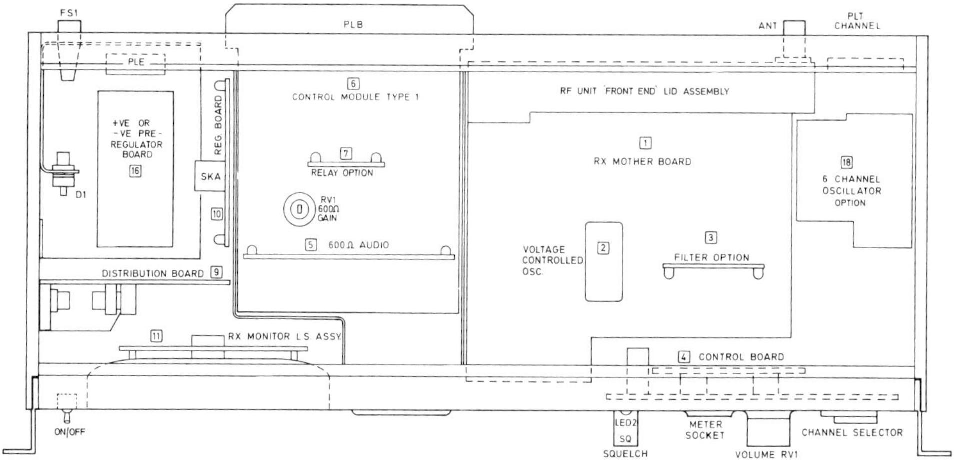

CHASSIS LAYOUT

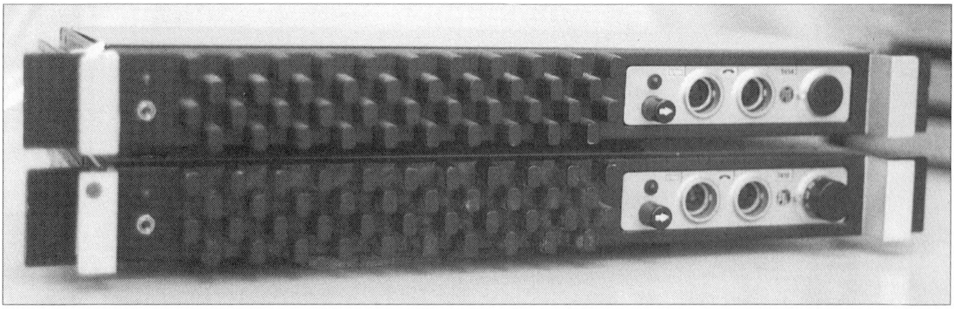

The T412 and T414 transmitters

The RF front end comes now. If you have a 100μA current range on your multimeter, connect the positive lead to TP10 and tune for maximum meter reading, reducing the RF signal level as needed to keep the reading below 100μA. Otherwise, tune for best received signal. On the front end board section, tune C14 (M), C10 (N), C7 (P), C5 (Q), C2 (R) and C1 (S) in turn for maximum multimeter reading or best signal as appropriate.

You can now reset the squelch preset to your preferred squelch opening level.

T412/T414

Identification

The equipment code is made up as listed in Table 5.13.

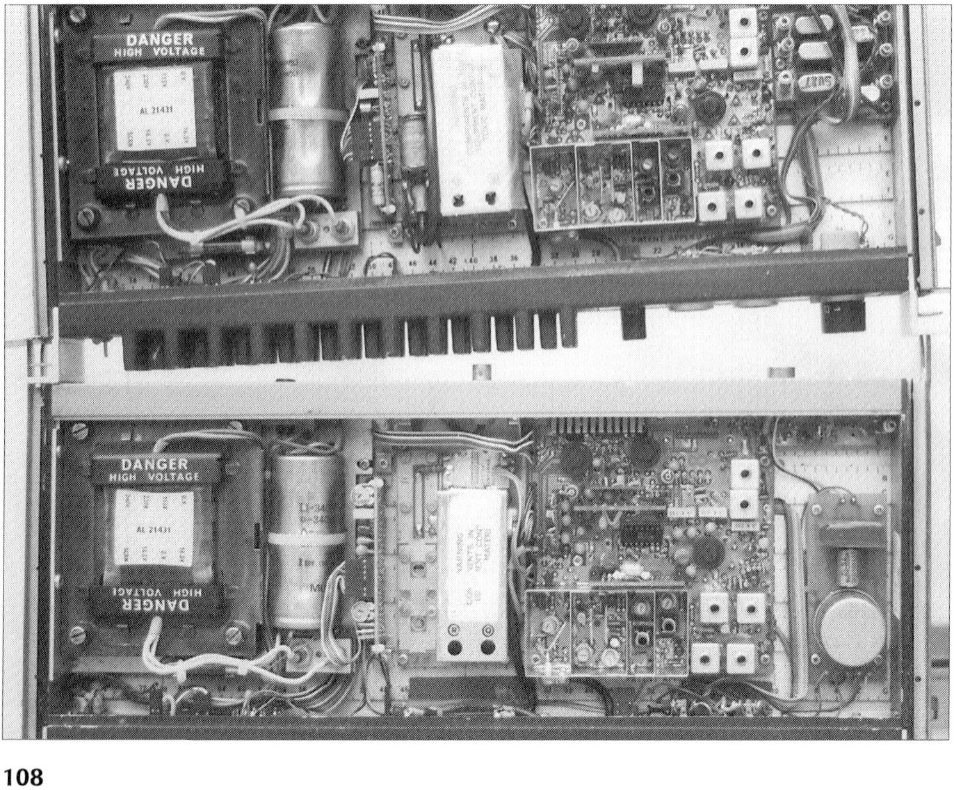

T412/T414 internal circuitry

Table 5.13. Identification codes for T412/T414

Format:	**T41x aa b cc d e f gg h i j kk ll** with the following meanings:
T41x:	T412: Standard, T414, link transmitter version
aa:	01: Standard production (UK specifications)
b:	2: Power output 2W, AC or DC input 3: Power output 5W, AC input only 4: Power output 5W, DC input only, with external regulator
cc:	F3: 300–3400Hz audio response (T412) L3: 300–3400Hz audio response (T414) L6: 300–6000Hz audio response (T414) L9: 300–9000Hz audio response (T414)
d:	A: Local and remote simplex operation B: Local and remote duplex and talkthrough operation C: As A but with 600Ω balanced inputs D: As B but with 600Ω balanced inputs
e:	0: Less crystals 1–6: Crystals for channels 1–6 fitted
f:	V: 25kHz channel spacing
gg:	T6: 375–440MHz U1: 420–470MHz W2: 470–512MHz
h:	1: Single-channel capability 6: Six-channel capability
i:	1: AC input, neg earth 7: 24DC, neg earth 9: 24V DC, pos earth
j:	0: No channel switch (single channel) 1: Locally switched, six channels
kk:	00–69: Defines various mountings/supplied mating connectors
ll:	00: No options 01: Tone lock encoder (T412 only) 02: Facility relay 06: Tone lock encoder plus facility relay

Transmitter alignment

Layouts and alignment diagrams are shown in Figs 5.30–5.33. Connect your dummy load / power meter to the antenna socket, and key the transmitter onto transmit by connecting rear-panel facilities socket SKA pins 6 and 12 to pin 8 (or if more convenient, the transmitter may be keyed using the engineer's handset connected to the front panel). Check that the antenna changeover and facility relays (if fitted) are energised. Note that, since the transmit indicator is controlled by the power monitoring circuit, it might not light at this stage.

Now, connect your multimeter, set to the 10V DC range, with the negative lead to the rear panel SKA pin 8, and the positive lead to the following test points in turn. Carry out the specified adjustment and check the multimeter reading in each case, reducing the range as necessary for accurate readings.

All inductors should be tuned to the peak, or null, obtained with the ferrite core nearest the printed circuit board of the set.

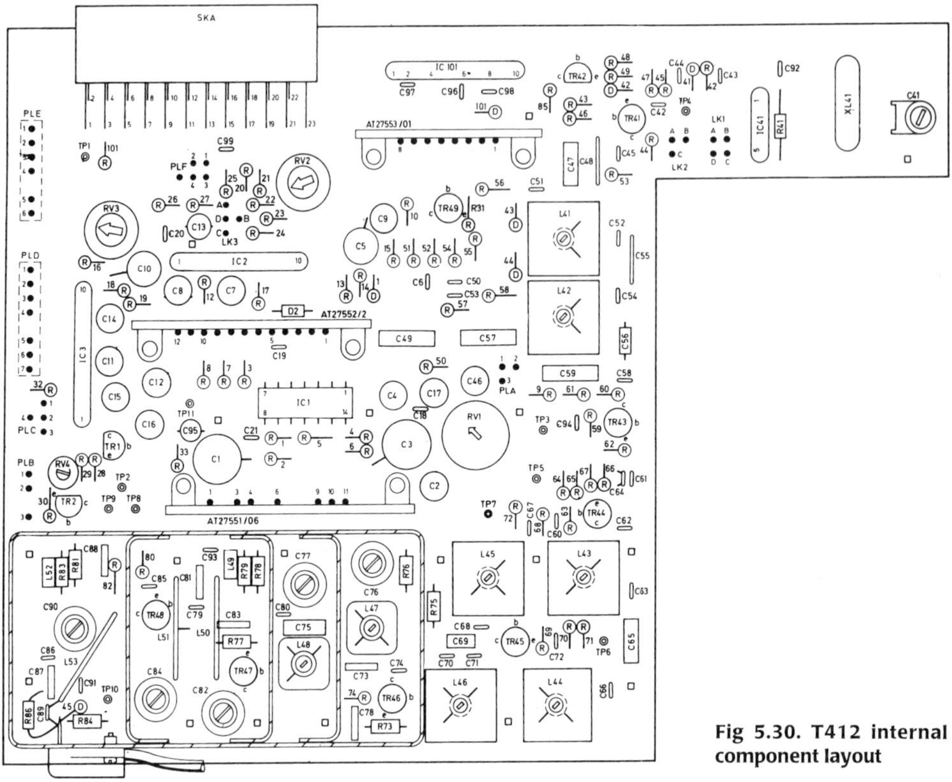

Fig 5.30. T412 internal component layout

With your multimeter's positive lead connected to test point TP1, tune L41 (D) for maximum (max 6.0V, min 3.7V). Transfer to TP5, and tune L41 (D) for maximum, then L42 (E) for maximum again,

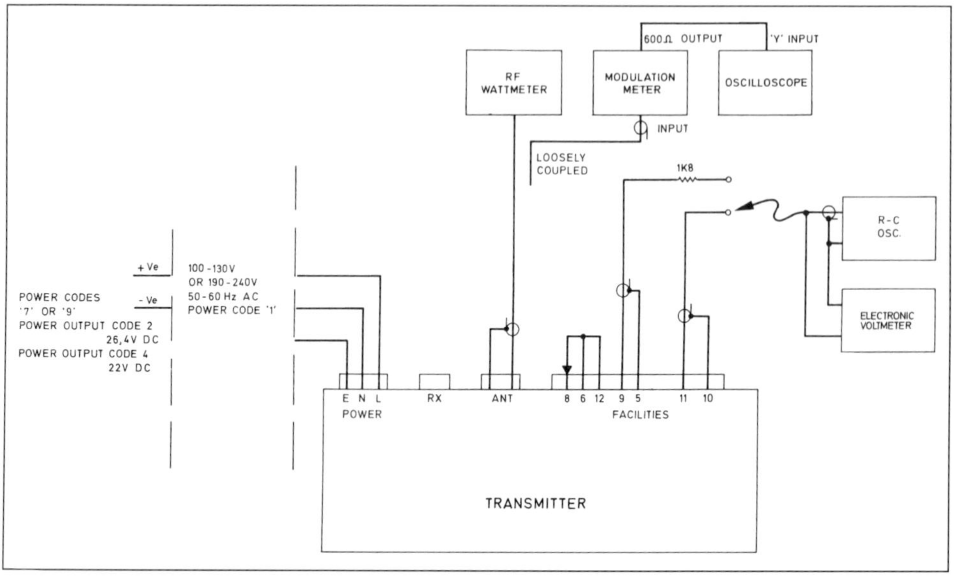

Fig 5.31. T412 alignment equipment connections

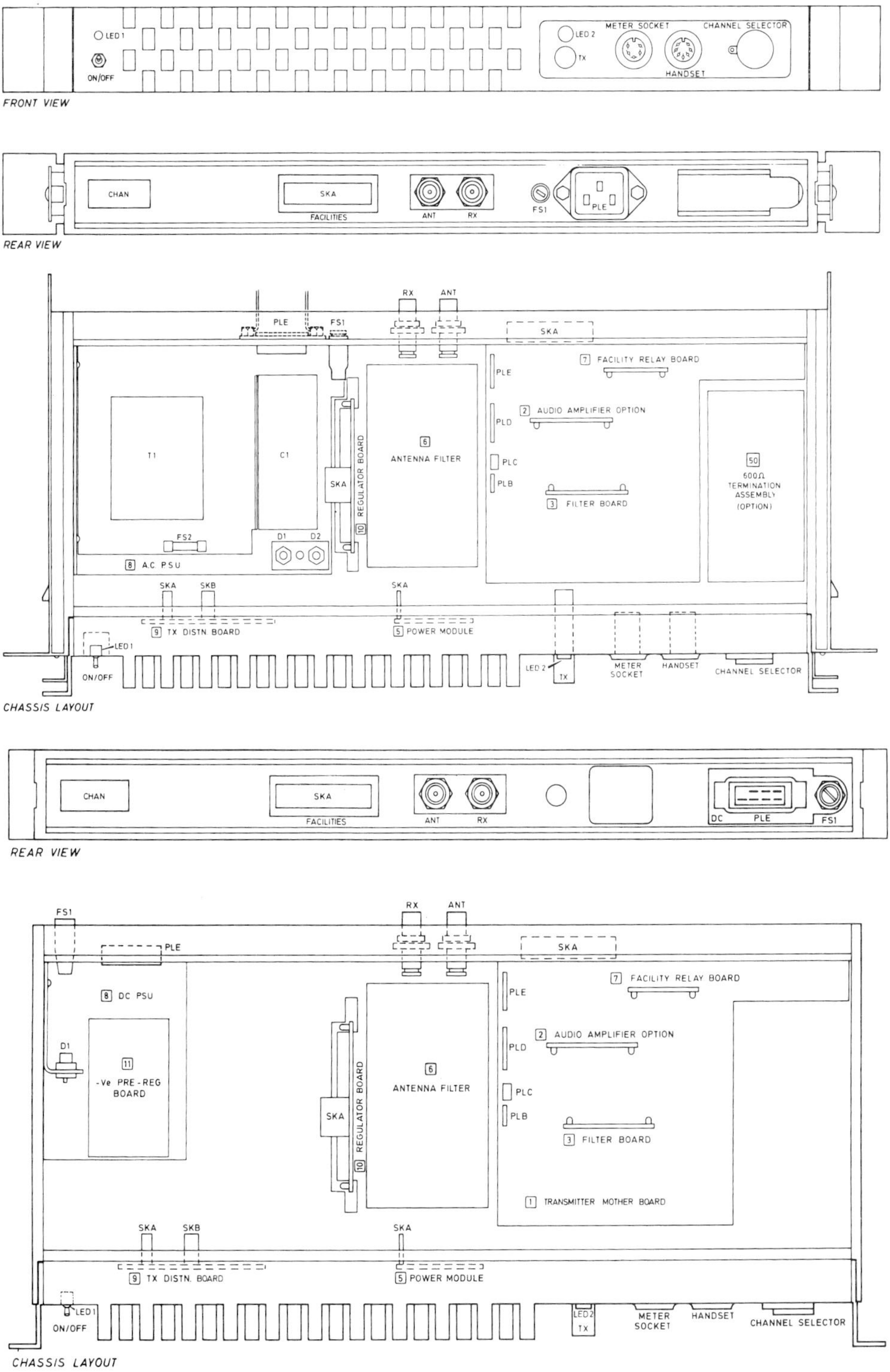

Fig 5.32. T412 internal arrangement

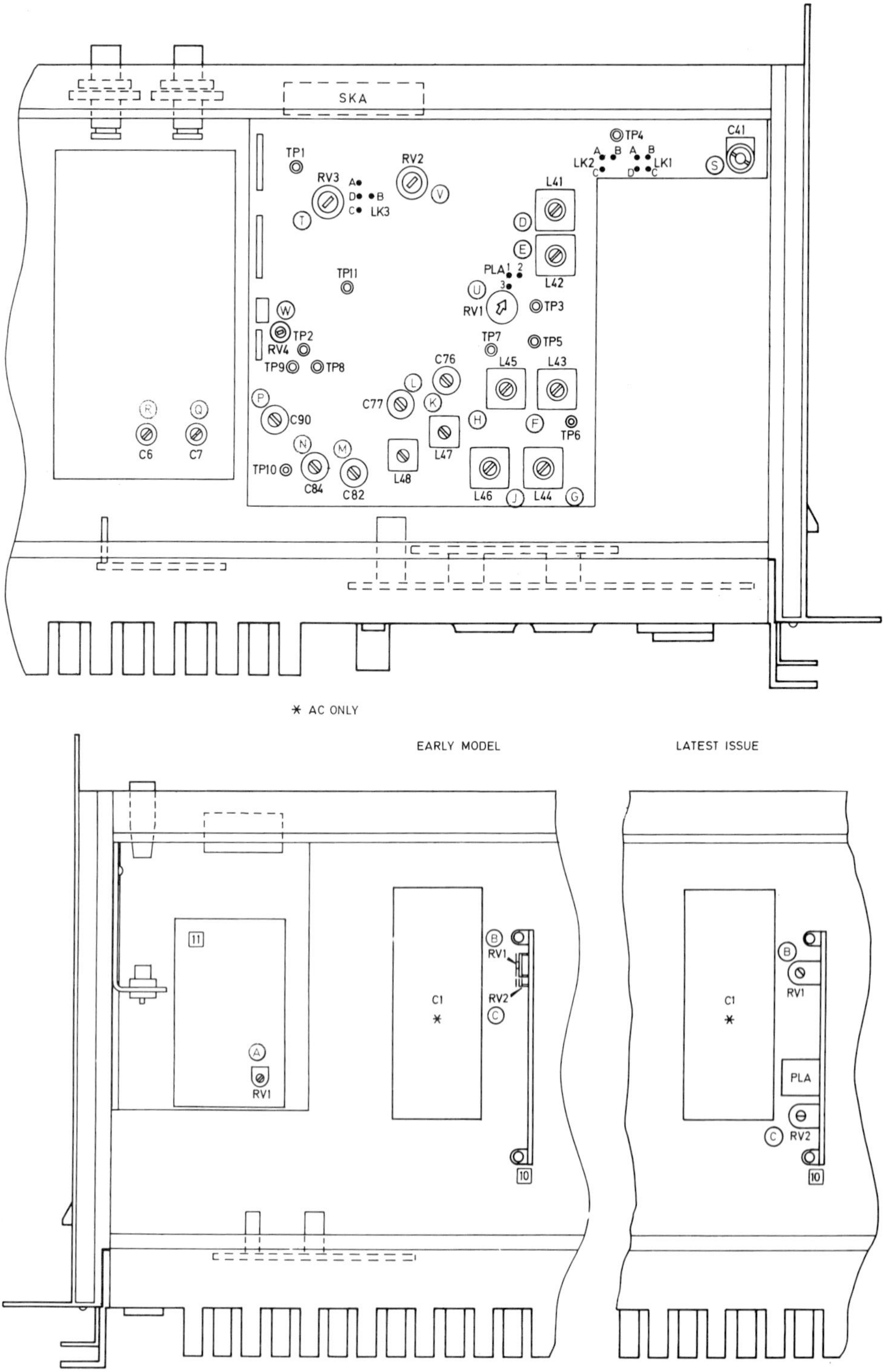

Fig 5.33. T412 alignment diagram

The L434 base station, comprising the R434 and T434

followed by L43 (F) but this time for minimum (max 2.0V, min 1.3V). Transfer to TP6, and tune L43 (F) for maximum, then L44 (G) for maximum again, followed by L45 (H) for minimum (max 2.5V, min 1.6V). Transfer to TP7, and tune L45 (H) for maximum, then L46 (J) for maximum again, followed by C76 (K) for minimum (max 2.5V, min 1.6V). Transfer to TP8, and tune C76 (K) for maximum, then C77 (L) for maximum again, followed by C82 (M) for minimum (max 1.6V, min 0.6V). Transfer to TP9, and tune C82 (M) for maximum, then C84 (N) again for maximum (max 0.45V, min 0.3V). Now measuring on TP10, adjust C90 (P) for maximum reading (max 2.0V, min 1.0V).

Finally, adjust C90 (P), plus on board 6 C6 (R) and C7 (Q) in turn for maximum reading on your RF power output meter. Now, rotate RV4 (W) clockwise until the red transmit indicator lights. If you'd like to set the power level indicator, temporarily detune C6 (R) for 1.5W output (power output code 2) or 3.0W (power output codes 3 and 4), then slowly rotate RV4 (W) until the transmit indicator is extinguished. Retune C6 (R) for maximum power, and check the transmit indicator is lit.

You can now adjust C41 (S) to set the transmitter to the correct frequency. The peak deviation potentiometer is RV1 (U), the 600Ω line control is RV2 (V) and the mic gain control (ie from the engineer's handset) is RV3 (T).

23cm EQUIPMENT – R434/T434

The R434 and T434 are a link receiver/transmitter pair, originally designed for operation in the frequency range 1450–1535MHz. The 'basic' receiver operates as an 'intermediate frequency' on UHF, and a separate down-converter unit attached to the receiver works in a similar manner to amateur receiver converters, ie down-converting 23cm to 70cm. On transmit, again a UHF transmitter is used, and a varactor diode tripler is used to triple the signal from 70cm to 23cm. I know of at least one 23cm UK voice repeater that uses the R434/T434 pair.

Identification

The identification here is a little less complex, as the set only operates in one band, and the 'added' section on the receiver is reasonably obvious! However, it's important to identify the power requirements etc as something like a positive DC earthed case doesn't go too kindly with a negatively earthed packet TNC unless you use appropriate isolation methods.

Full details of typical codes for the R434 are given in Table 5.14 and those for the T434 in Table 5.15.

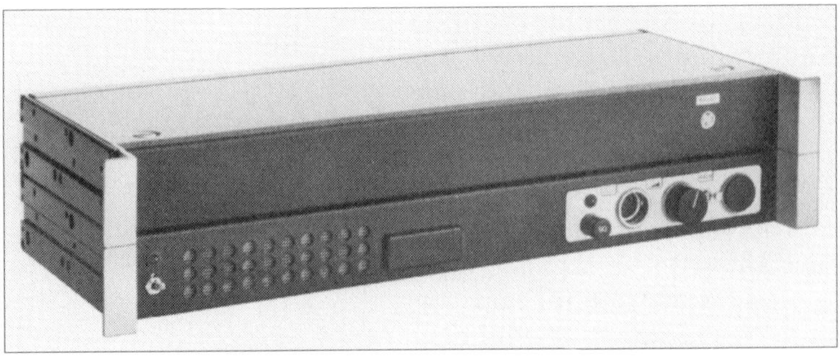

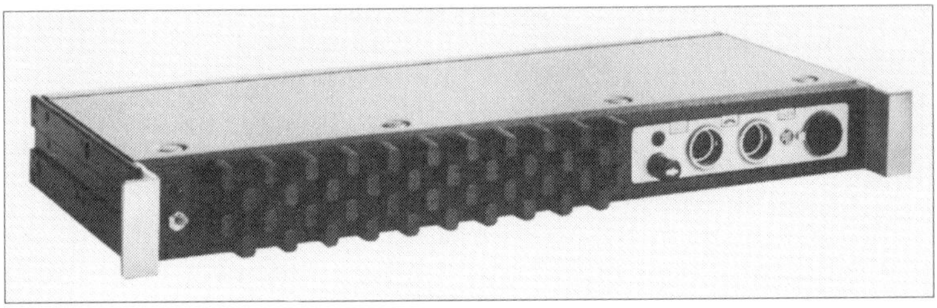

Top: **The R434 link receiver**

Bottom: **The T434 1400MHz link transmitter**

Receiver alignment

Connections, layouts and alignment details are given in Figs 5.34–5.39. First check that the following link assemblies are fitted as follows:

Control module Type 1:	LK1
600Ω audio PCB:	LK1 pins A and B
Receiver main PCB:	PLA pins 2 and 3
	PLB pins 1 and 2
	PLC pins 1 and 2, 5 and 6
	LK1 pins B and C

With the power switched off, set the squelch adjust control RV126 fully clockwise. Now connect your test equipment, as available (at least your DC multimeter), as shown in the accompanying diagram.

If you'd like to initially check the regulator, set your multimeter to the 25V DC range and connect the positive lead to PLG pin 2, and check you get between 17V and 25V. Then transfer to PLG pin 1 and you should read 13.5V – adjust RV1 (B) to set this if needed. Now

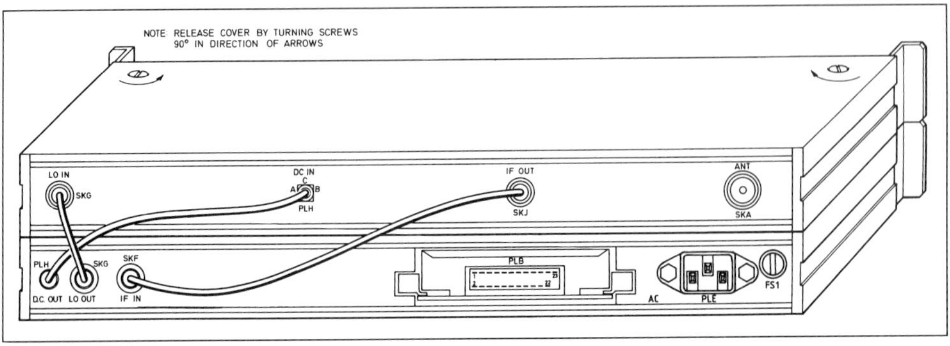

Fig 5.34. R434 rear-panel interconnections

Table 5.14. Identification codes for R434

Format:	**R434 01 L3 1A 0 N Y1 1 1 1 60 00** with the following meanings:
R434:	Equipment type
01:	Standard production
L3:	Audio response 300–3400Hz, (L6: Audio response 300–6000Hz) (L9: Audio response 300–9000Hz)
1A:	600Ω audio amplifier and squelch relay fitted (1B: 600Ω audio amplifier only)
N:	Channel spacing 50kHz
Y1:	Frequency band 1450–1535MHz
1:	AC input, neg ground (7: 24V DC, neg gnd) (8: DC from associated transmitter, neg gnd) (9: 24V DC, pos gnd) (A: DC from associated transmitter, pos gnd)
60:	Mating connectors supplied (00–69: various mounting options and supplied connectors)
00:	No options fitted (03: Monitor loudspeaker)

Table 5.15. Identification codes for T434

Format:	**T434 01 0 L3 C 1 N Y1 1 1 1 08 00** with the following meanings:
T434:	Equipment type
01:	Standard production
0:	Not used
L3:	Audio response 300–3400Hz, (L6: Audio response 300–6000Hz) (L9: Audio response 300–9000Hz)
C:	Link transmitter (D: As C but with 600Ω balanced input)
N:	Channel spacing 50kHz
Y1:	Frequency band 1450–1535MHz
1:	AC input, neg ground (1: AC input, neg gnd) (7: 24V DC, neg gnd) (9: 24V DC, pos gnd)
60:	Mating connectors supplied (00–09: various mounting options and supplied connectors)
00:	No options fitted (02: Facility relay)

transfer to PLG pin 3 and you should measure 9.0V – adjust RV2 if needed for this.

We'll now start with the multiplier alignment. With your multimeter set to the 10V DC range, connect the positive lead to TP5. Adjust L57 (D) for minimum reading (1.3–0.5V). Transfer to TP6 and tune L58 (E) for maximum, then tune L57 and L58 together for maximum, followed by L59 (F) for minimum reading (2.5V–1.3V) – note the 'dip' here could be very shallow. Transfer your multimeter

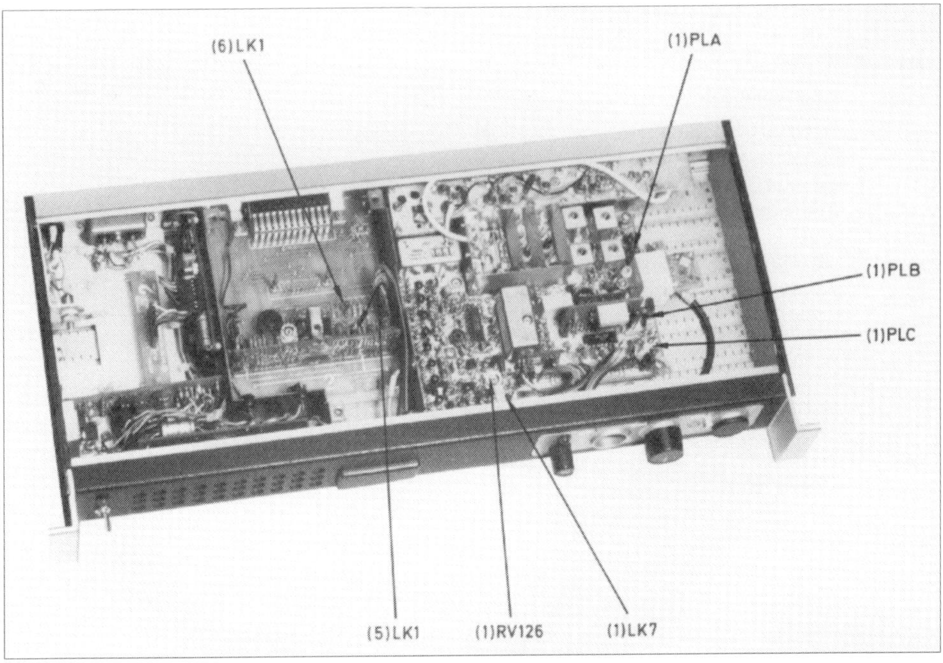

R434 internal view

positive lead to TP7, and tune L60 (G) for maximum, then L59 (F) and L60 (G) together for maximum, then C74 (H) for minimum (2.0V–0.7V). Transfer your meter positive lead to TP8 and tune C78 (J) for maximum, then C74 and C78 together for maximum. After this, short-circuit L65 to negative, and tune C81 (K) for minimum. Remove the short-circuit from L65, and tune C83 for maximum – you should end up with a reading between 0.6V and 1.0V.

The RF front end comes now. If you have a 100μA current range on your multimeter, connect the positive lead to TP10, and tune for maximum meter reading, reducing the RF signal level as needed to keep the reading below 100μA. Otherwise, tune for best received signal. On the front end board section, tune C14 (M), C10 (N), C7 (P), C5 (Q), C2 (R) and C1 (S) in turn for maximum multimeter reading or best signal as appropriate. You can now reset the squelch preset to your preferred squelch opening level.

RF amplifier alignment

Transfer your multimeter's positive lead to TP10 and select the 250μA DC range. Whilst receiving an off-air signal, adjusted so that the meter reading is around 75μA, tune C14 (M), C10 (N), C7 (P), C (Q), C2 (R) and C1 (S) in turn for maximum multimeter reading, reducing the RF signal level as needed to keep the multimeter reading below 100μA. Finally, readjust these for best reception of a weak signal. C51 is the crystal frequency trimmer.

You should find that the demodulator trimmers are correctly adjusted if the unit came out of working service, although C2 (T) and

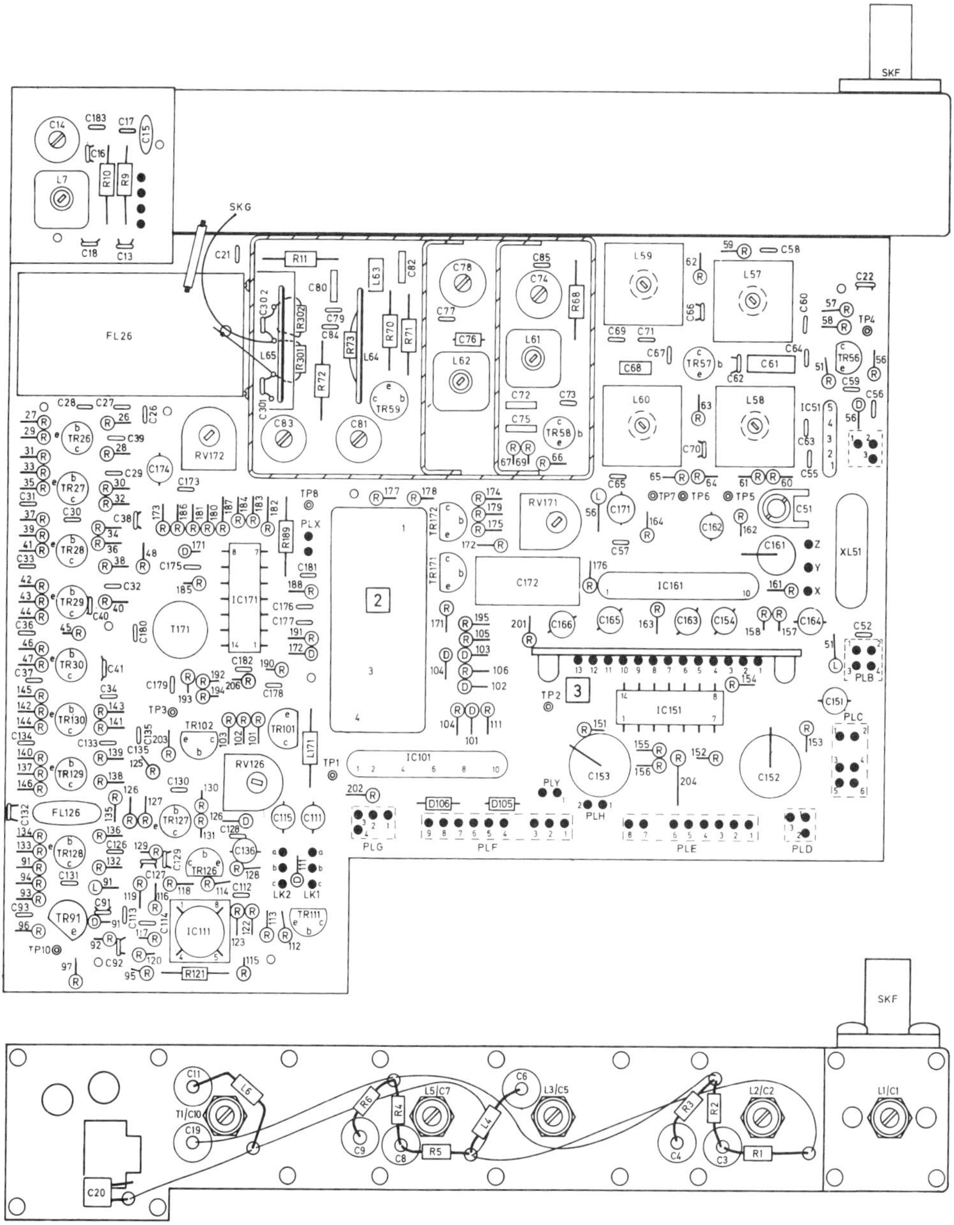

Fig 5.35. R434 component layout

C83 (L) can be fine-tuned for best received signal (least signal distortion) for critical applications, ie data, if needed.

RV1 is the 600Ω gain control – this is usually set to give 0dBm output.

Converter unit alignment

You'll need a sensitive RF power meter, or 50Ω load with a diode probe attached (or an off-air receiver with S-meter, tuning for

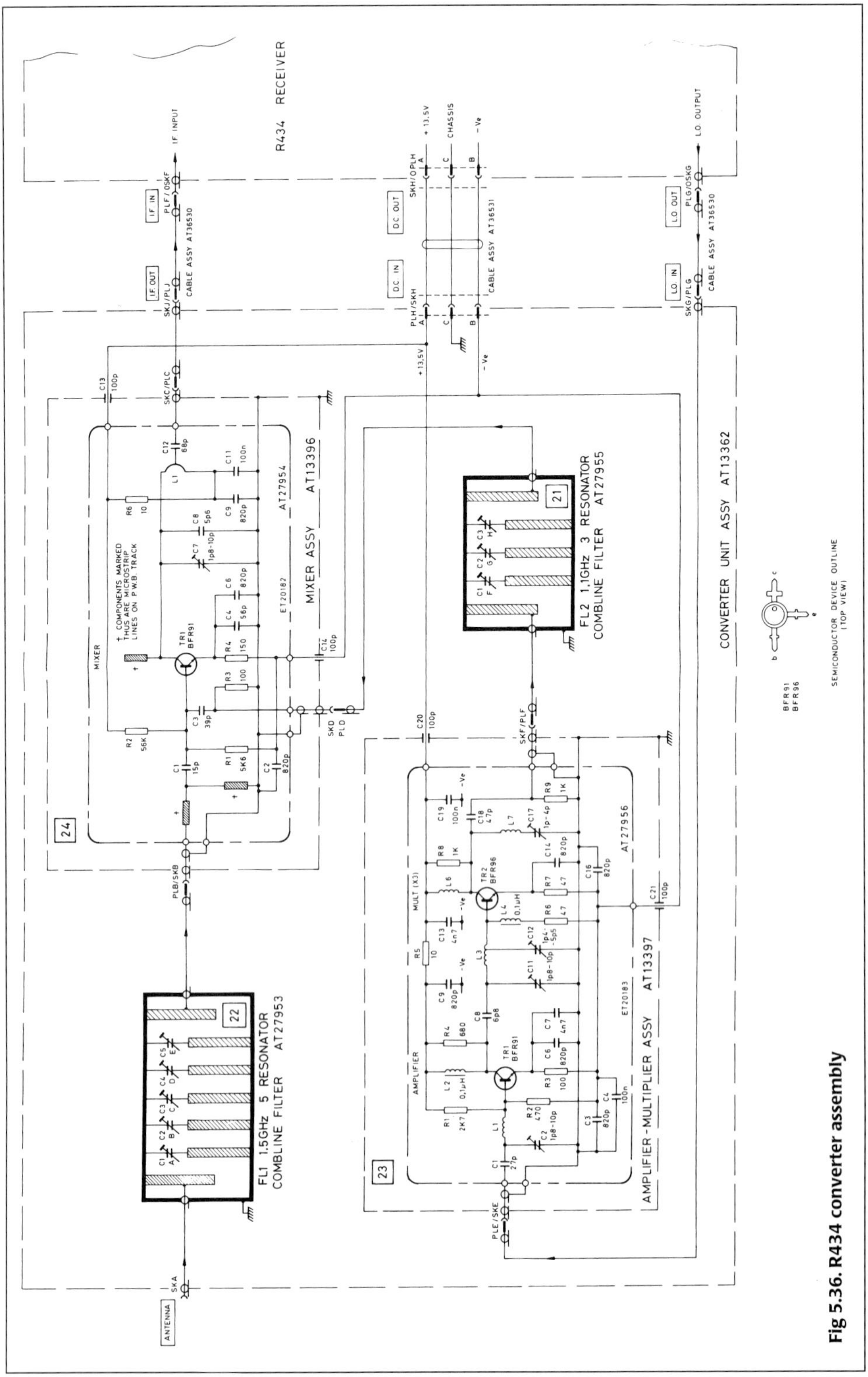

Fig 5.36. R434 converter assembly

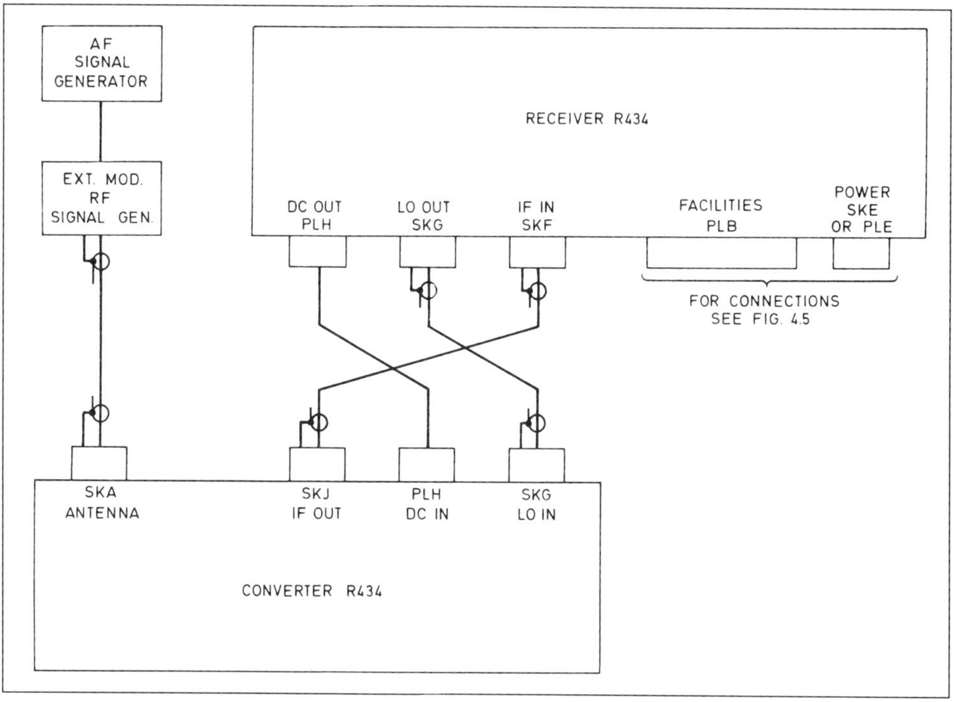

Fig 5.37. R434 overall test connections

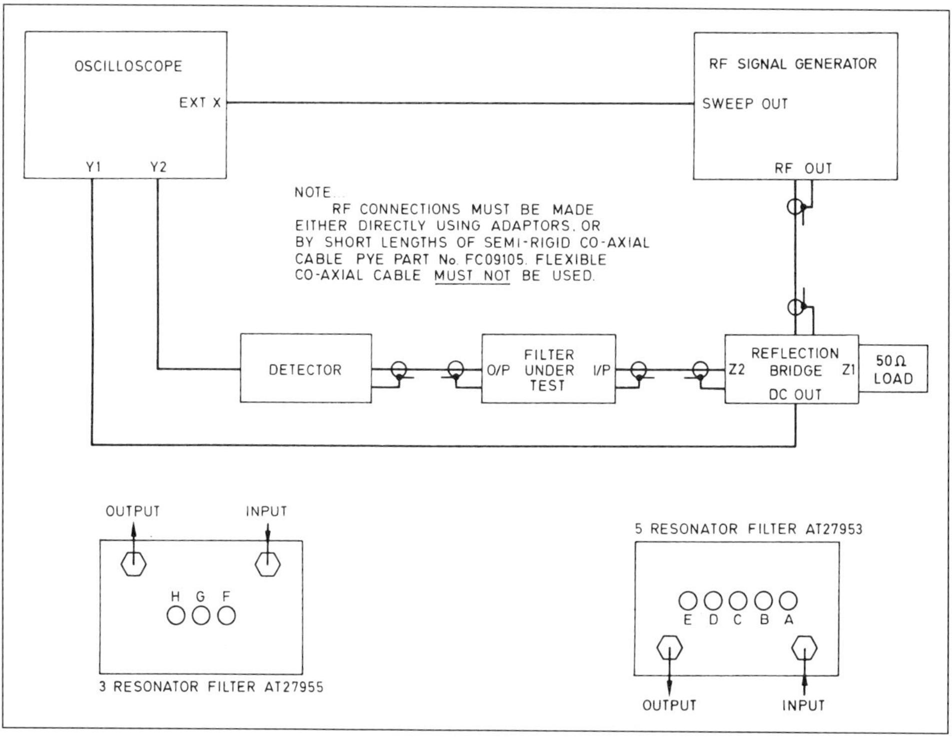

Fig 5.38. R434 converter filter alignment

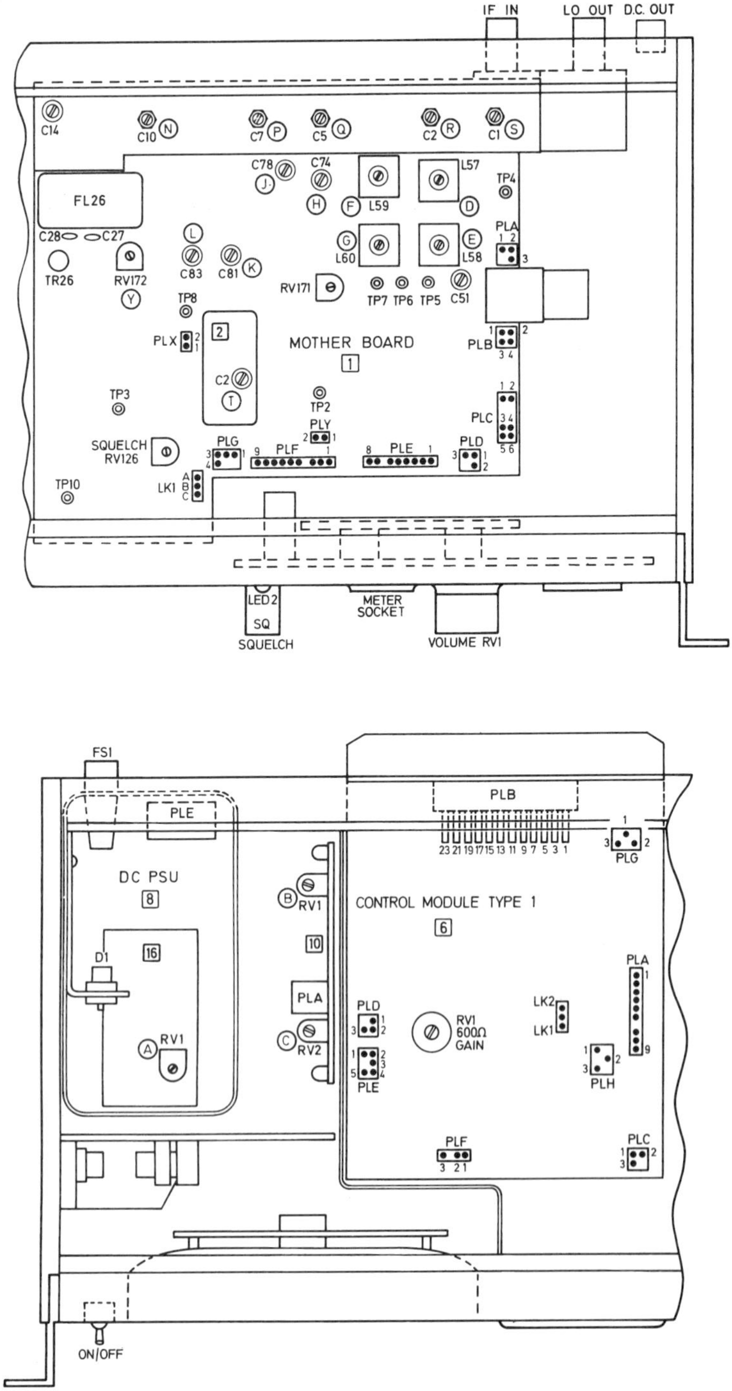

Fig 5.39. R434 receiver alignment diagram

maximum) for this stage. First, disconnect plug PLD from the mixer assembly and connect this to your RF power meter. Switch the receiver on, and adjust C2, C11, C12 and C17 in turn for maximum

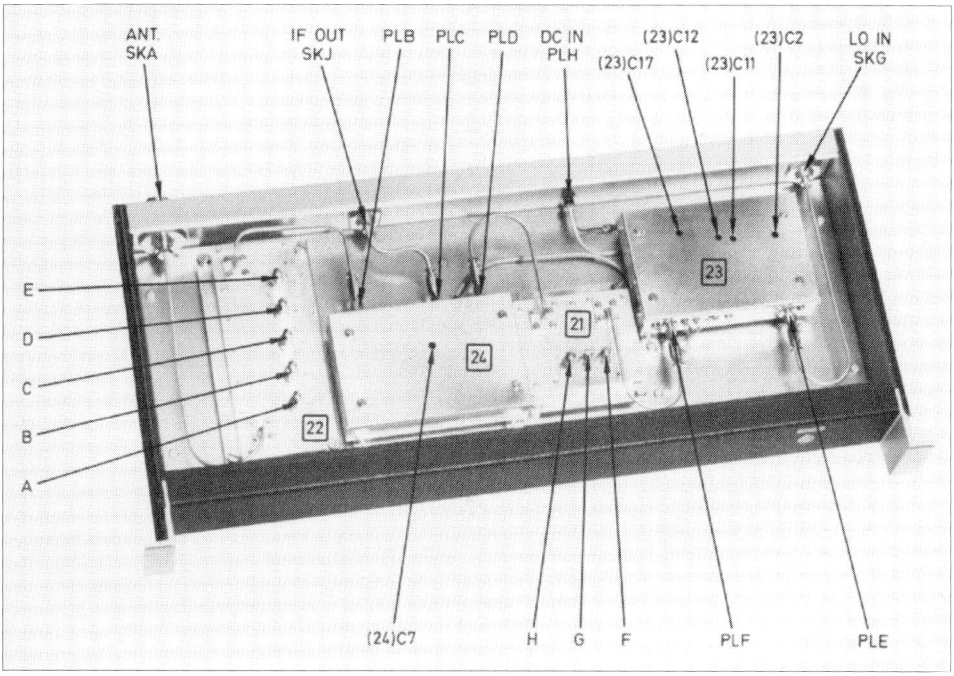

R434 converter, internal view

RF power meter reading – check this isn't less than 4mW. Now disconnect your power meter and reconnect the converter unit plug PLD to the mixer assembly. Check the converter unit 'IF Out' socket SKJ is connected to the receiver 'IF In' socket SKF.

Connect your multimeter, set to the 250μA DC current range, with the negative test lead to the receiver front-panel test socket SKA pin 5, and the positive lead to TP10. Whilst receiving an off-air signal, initially adjust the level of this for a reading of around 75μA, and adjust C7 for maximum reading, readjusting the RF level for a reading of below 100μA as needed.

Converter filter alignment

The set's technical manual says that alignment of the comb line filters used in the converter requires swept frequency measurement of return loss and insertion loss. The recommended alignment procedures use a reflection coefficient bridge and a synthesised signal generator providing an accurate frequency sweep.

However, where such equipment is not available, ie for the likes of you and me, just do the following:

Set your multimeter to the 250μA DC current range and connect the negative lead to the front-panel metering socket SKA pin 5, and the positive lead to TP10, as in the converter unit alignment above. Switch the receiver on, and again adjust the level of your off-air signal for a reading of around 75μA. Now, adjust the FL1 slugs in the sequence E, C, A, D, B for maximum multimeter reading, reducing the level of the RF signal as needed to keep the reading below

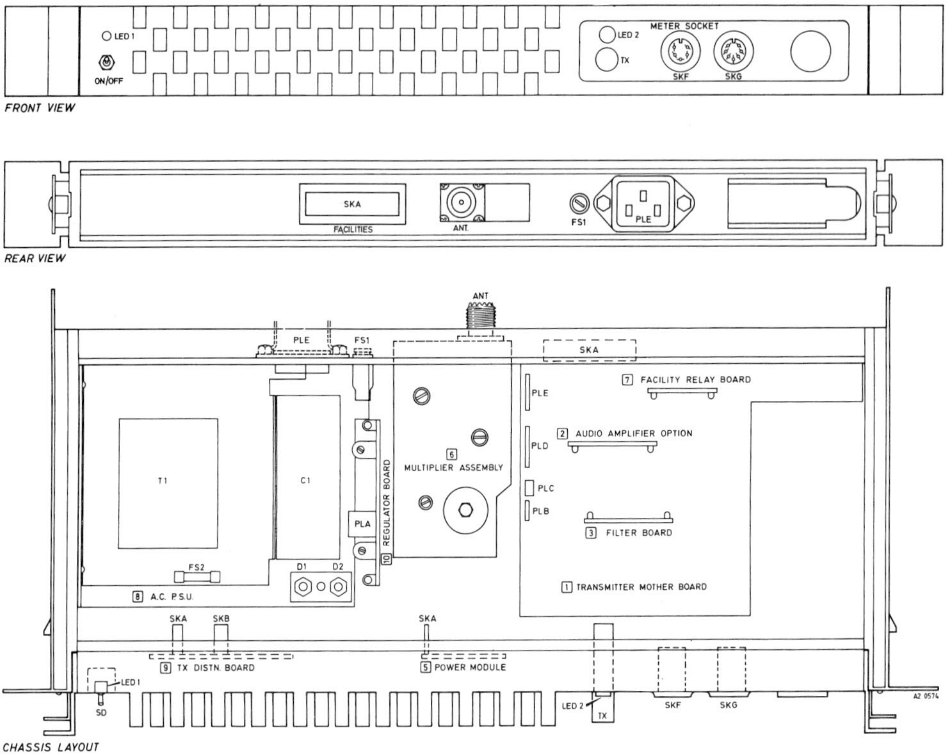

Fig 5.40. T434 transmitter layout

100μA. Repeat the above as needed, finally adjusting for best sensitivity from your off-air signal.

Transmitter alignment

Layouts and alignment details are given in Figs 5.40–5.44. Connect your RF power meter to the transmitter antenna socket, and key the TX by connecting the rear-panel facilities socket SKA pins 6 and 12 to pin 8 (the transmitter can alternatively be keyed using the engineer's handset connected to the front panel). Check that the antenna changeover and facility relays, if fitted, are energised.

Connect your multimeter, set to the 10V DC range, with the negative lead to the front-panel metering socket SKF pin 5, and the positive lead to the following test points in turn. Carry out the specified adjustments and check the multimeter reading in each case, reducing the range as necessary for accurate readings.

All inductors should be tuned to the peak or null obtained, with the ferrite core nearest the printed circuit board of the set. The initial alignment details are similar to those for the T412/T414, although with different voltage limit readings.

With your multimeter's positive lead connected to test point TP1, tune L41 (D) for maximum (max 6.0V, min 3.7V). Transfer to TP5, and tune L41 (D) for maximum, then L42 (E) for maximum again, followed by L43 (F) but this time for minimum (max 1.6V, min 0.8V).

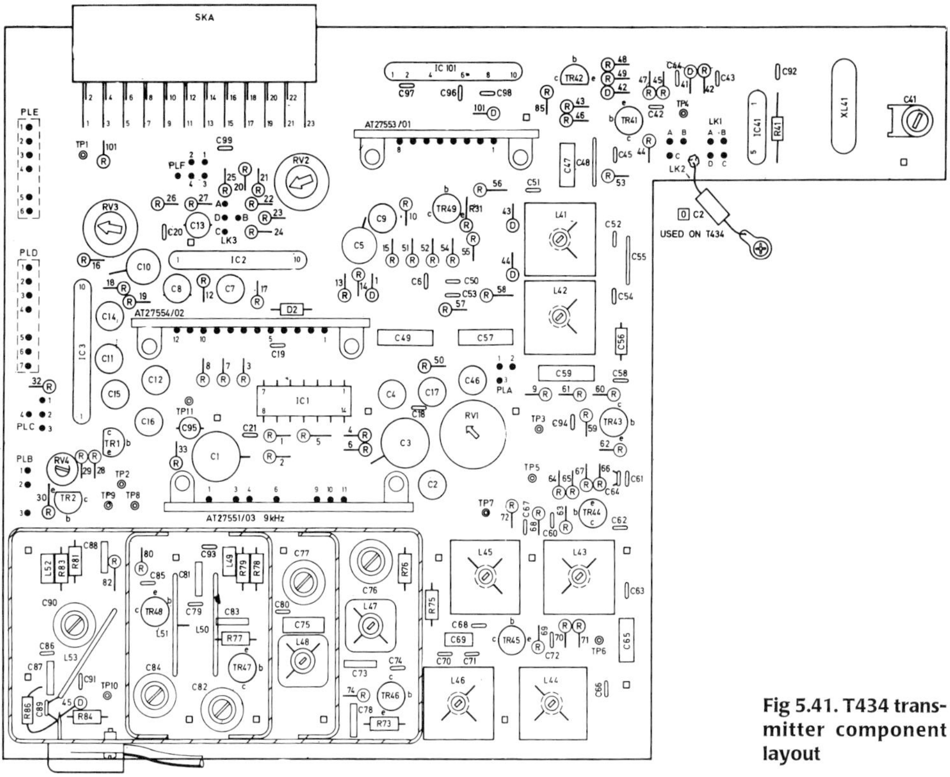

Fig 5.41. T434 transmitter component layout

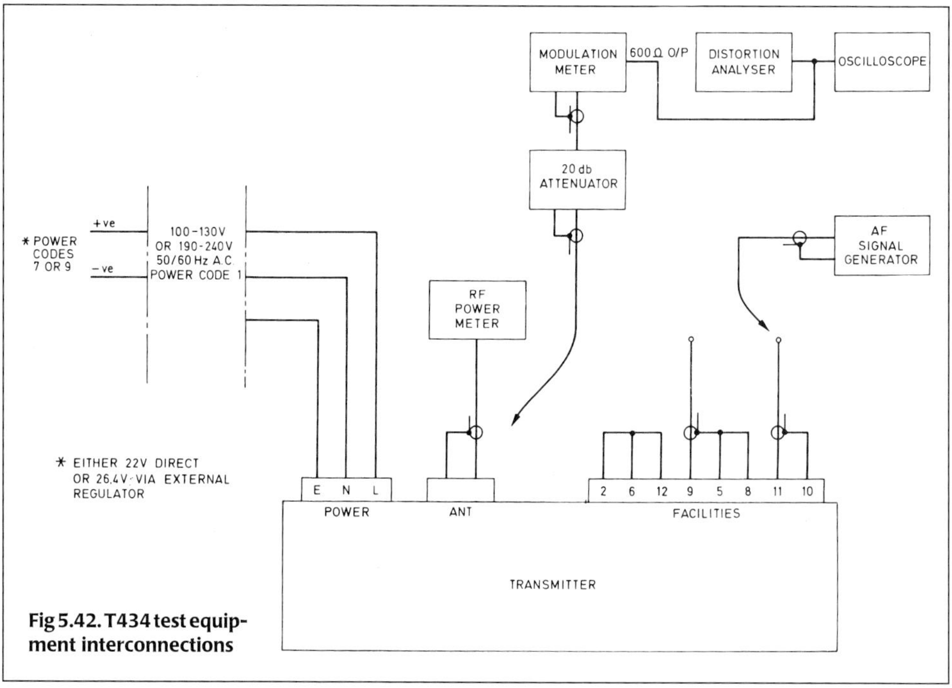

Fig 5.42. T434 test equipment interconnections

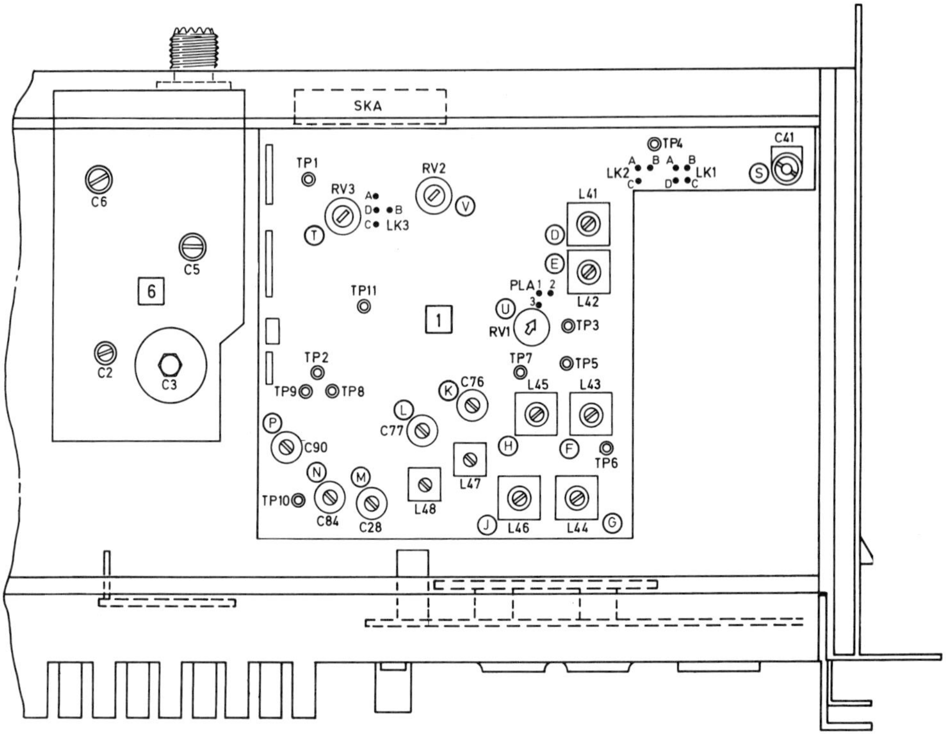

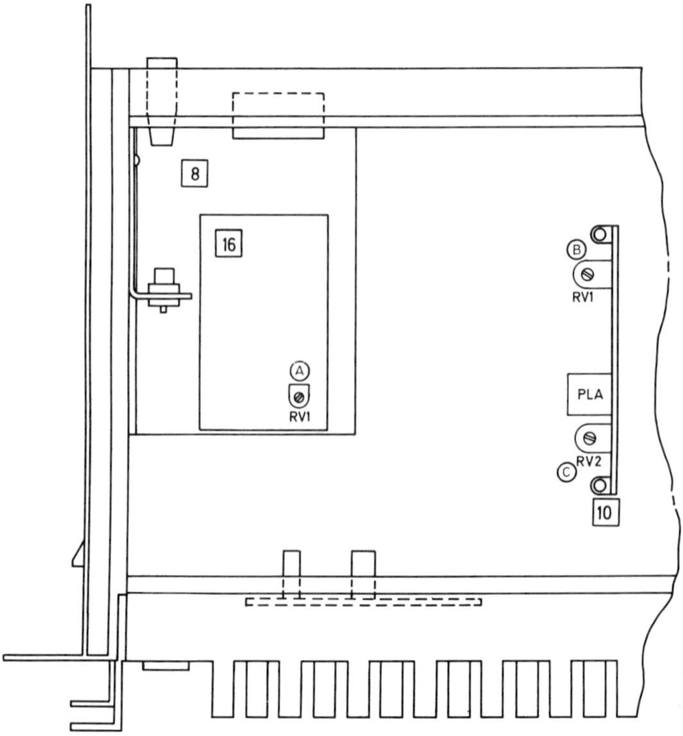

Fig 5.43. T434 transmitter alignment diagram

Transfer to TP6, and tune L43 (F) for maximum, then L44 (G) for maximum again, followed by L45 (H) for minimum (max 2.0V, min 0.9V). Transfer to TP7, and tune L45 (H) for maximum, then L46 (J) for maximum again, followed by C76 (K) for minimum (max 1.8V, min 0.8V). Transfer to TP8, and tune C76 (K) for maximum, then C77 (L) for maximum again, followed by C82 (M) for minimum (max 1.0V, min 0.4V). Transfer to TP9, and tune C82 (M) for maximum, then C84 (N) again for maximum (max 0.65V, min 0.3V). Now measuring on TP10, adjust C90 (P) for maximum reading (max 2.0V, min 0.85V).

Disconnect the rear-panel 'Facilities' socket SKA pins 6 and 12 from pin 2, and disconnect your multimeter. Now, if you've an RF power meter, connect this to 5PLH and operate the front panel 'transmit' button – you should see a power reading of around 7.5W here. Reconnect 5PLH to the multiplier unit, and connect your RF power meter to the antenna socket.

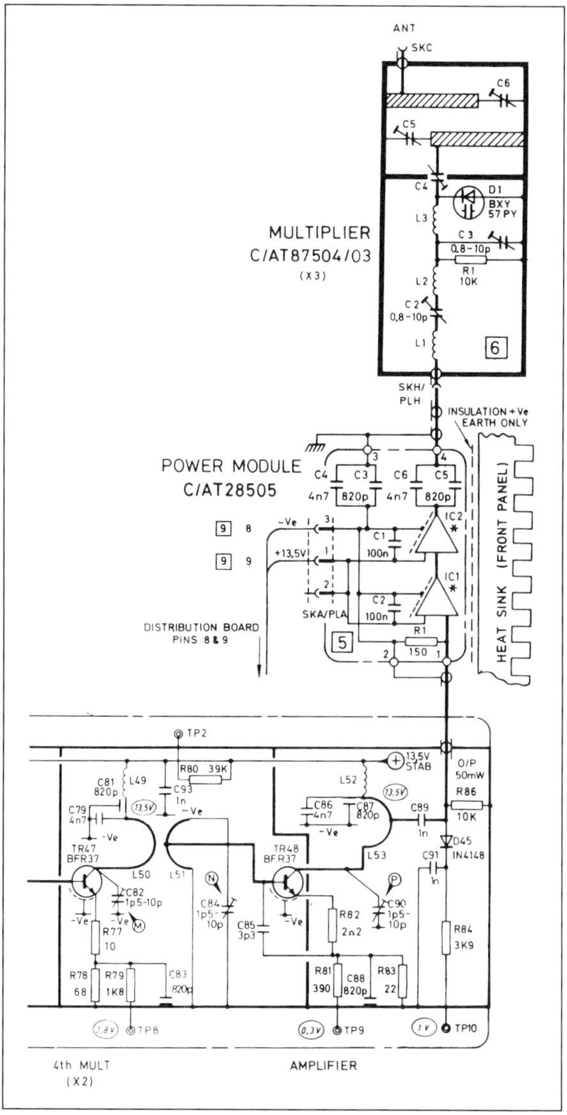

Fig 5.44. T434 transmitter output circuit

Key the transmitter again (ie connect the rear-panel 'Facilities' socket pins 6 and 12 to pin 2), remove the dust cap from C3 and adjust C5 and C6 alternately to give maximum power output reading, then C2 and C3 again alternately for maximum output. Readjust all the capacitors in the sequence C2, C3, C5, C6, C5 and again C6 for maximum output, repeating this procedure as needed until you achieve absolute maximum power output. Check the power output is at least 2.5W, and de-key the transmitter, remembering to refit the dust cap on C3.

C41 (S) is the transmitter crystal frequency adjuster, which you should set for the correct spot-on frequency. The peak deviation potentiometer is RV1 (U), the 600Ω line control is RV2 (V) and the mic gain control (ie from the engineer's handset) is RV3 (T).

6 Portable equipment

BURNDEPT BE470 UHF HANDHELD

These are very commonly found on the market, having been extensively used in the UK by police forces and the fire service. They come in a blue plastic outer case, with either a red or yellow PTT button fitted on the set's top panel. Early models had a red PTT button on the removable 'head', while later models had a yellow one. Although the set's RF circuitry is basically the same, it's the circuitry and the audio transducers in the head that are different. Type 'A' head has four transducers, together with a small reed switch which allows an external antenna to be connected if you use the optional mobile adapter.

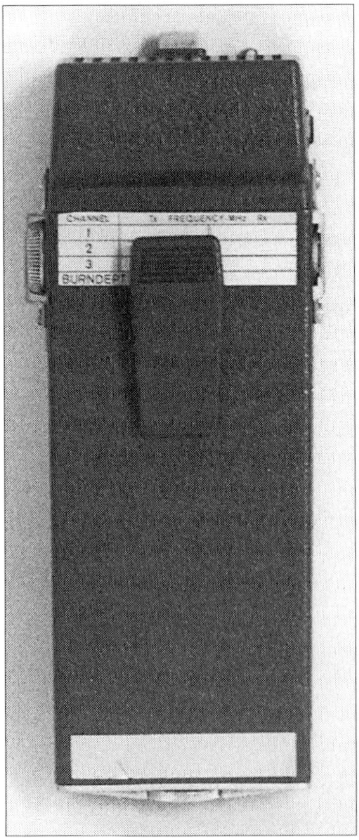

The Burndept BE470

Two frequency range variants are available, 420–450MHz and 450–470MHz, although most sets you'll see on the market are of the 450–470MHz type. The usual output power is around 300–500mW when used on the correct band, although you may find difficulty in getting over 250mW on 70cm, typically around 120mW, using the 450–470MHz type. However, I'll detail a simple modification later to overcome this.

The set uses two 9V batteries, similar to the PF1 receive batteries (see the BE600 conversion information in this chapter for more details).

Opening up

First unscrew the battery compartment tray by the screw at the bottom of the set (that's if it's an early version – the later version doesn't uses a screw here), then on the back remove the centre screw, followed by the two small screws at the side. You should now be able to slide the set's inner chassis out of the case, ready for alignment.

Crystals

The crystals are third-overtone types – the frequencies required are as shown below:

$$\text{RX xtal freq} = \frac{\text{RX freq} + 10.7\text{MHz}}{9}$$

$$\text{TX xtal freq} = \frac{\text{TX freq}}{9}$$

When ordering, make sure you state the crystals are for the Burndept BE470 transceiver to your crystal supplier, to ensure you obtain the correct type for the set's oscillator loading parameters. Otherwise, you may find your set operates with a final frequency offset of around 10kHz or so high if fitted with 'normal' crystals.

Alignment

Details of the set's internal layout and the head units are given in Figs 6.1 and 6.2.

The PTT switch, besides changing the DC from receive to transmit modes, also acts as the antenna changeover. The set-top antenna is connected to this via a 5.6pF series matching capacitor, so for alignment you can temporarily disconnect the antenna feed at the switch and substitute a short length of coaxial cable.

We'll first start with the transmitter. First, if you have a couple of variable power supplies connected in place of the 8.4V nicads, set these initially to 4.0V each, and check the current – you should find around 5mA is drawn. Now, carefully adjust coil L2 on the TX oscillator and multiplier (accessible from the side of the chassis), and you'll find the current will increase by around 0.5mA when the oscillator starts. Leave L2 at this position, and vary the position of trimmer capacitor C8 for an increase in current. If there isn't any increase, change the setting of C11 very slightly and repeat the tuning of C8. Keep changing the C11 setting by increments and varying C8 until you see an increase in current and RF power appearing. Then adjust

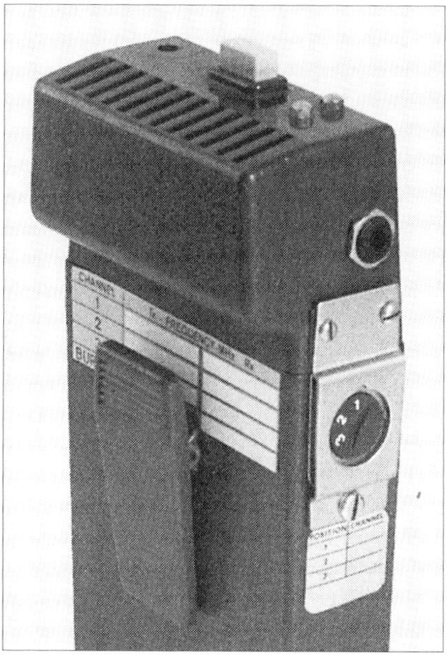

Top: **The BE470 controls**

Above: **A rectangular top-panel PTT button is used**

Below: **Inside the BE470**

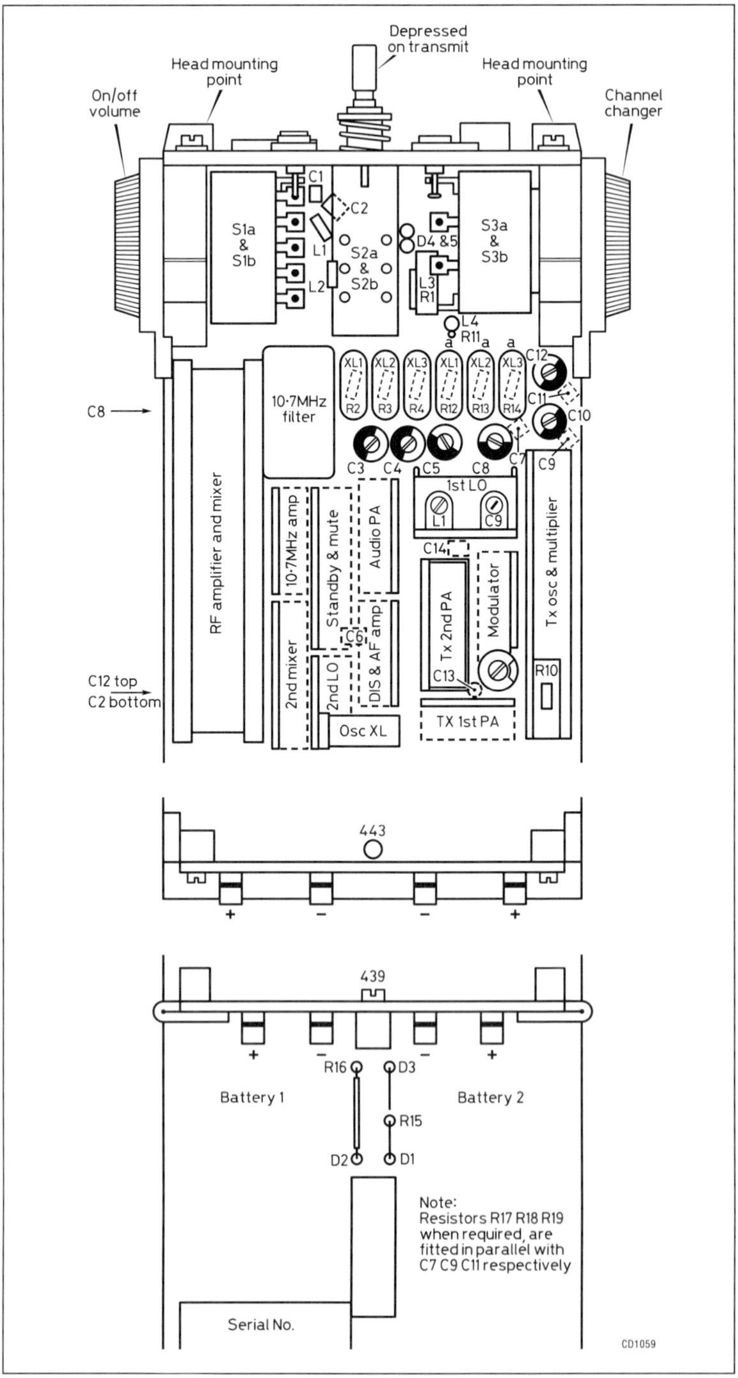

Fig 6.1. BE470 Internal layout

C8, C11, C13 and C16 all for maximum RF power output. Now increase the DC voltage to 9.75V from each supply, and readjust the trimmers all for maximum RF output, and readjust the appropriate

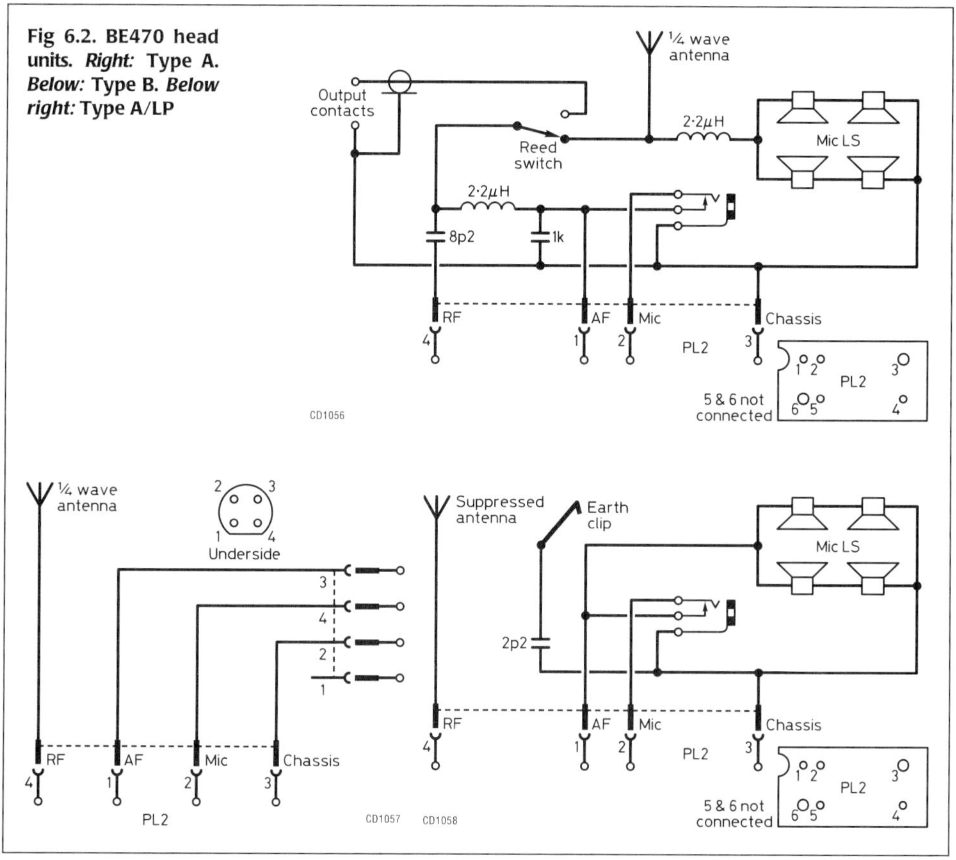

Fig 6.2. BE470 head units. *Right:* Type A. *Below:* Type B. *Below right:* Type A/LP

transmit crystal trimmer to get the correct frequency. R15 is the small trimmer potentiometer next to the modulator – this is the deviation control which you should adjust to give the required 5kHz peak deviation.

For the receiver alignment, first connect a DC current meter in series with the supply to the set, and adjust the core of L1 for an increase in current – this will show the oscillator is working OK. Now adjust the crystal trimmer for the centre frequency of your received alignment signal, and adjust C9 for best reception, carefully retuning L1 as necessary, again for best reception. Then tune in sequence the antenna, 1st and 2nd RF trimmers for best reception, repeating all the above for absolute best sensitivity.

The squelch opening point is set by the value of C6, which is in the centre of the track side of the set's motherboard. You can change the value of this to change the preset squelch level – greater capacitance means a 'tighter' squelch, although most amateurs will probably want to reduce the level – try values of 68pF or 82pF to start with. You might also find it useful to temporarily disconnect one leg of C6 to keep the squelch open to help you when aligning the receiver.

Transmitter PA circuit modification

First, take a look at the transmitter 1st PA board, and you'll see capacitor C5, which is connected in parallel between the output of the stage (PCB pin 1) and ground (PCB pin 2). Add a further 10pF capacitor in parallel across these pins, keeping the capacitor leads as short as possible.

Now, go to the TX 2nd PA, and you'll see capacitor C4 at the middle of the top of the PCB. You should add a 1.8pF capacitor in parallel across this, soldered to the existing pads of C4 on the track side of the PCB, again using the shortest leads possible. There will be a Melinex insulator strip next to the board – be careful you don't burn this with your soldering iron. If you temporarily remove the insulator, then *do* make sure you replace it after you've added the capacitor, otherwise you might quickly find you have a non-working set the next time you switch it on!

After these modifications, you should retune the transmitter oscillator/multiplier trimmer capacitors, particularly C16 and C13, for maximum power output, which you should now find is a rather higher level.

The BE600 is a handy-sized 70cm portable

BURNDEPT BE600 HANDHELDS

The BE600 is a reasonably sized portable transceiver, sets typically found in the UK having often seen use in areas such as the energy and government services. The set can operate on up to six crystal-controlled channels, and models are available for VHF in 136–150MHz plus 150–174MHz bands, and UHF in the 420–470MHz range. However, all those I've seen on sale in the UK have been UHF sets.

The VHF sets are typically 25kHz channel spacing when found in the 136–150MHz range, and if you can find one of the 141MHz or 147MHz crystalled sets (having crystals to spec EDSK930 fitted) you're in luck! The 150–174MHz sets are invariably 12.5kHz spacing (crystal spec EDSK929). The sets appear quite similar from the outside, and internally, self-contained screened modules make frequency identification a little difficult. Some sets that I've seen, ie UHF sets having come from ex-government service, have had no external identification whatsoever or any remaining crystals. However others have had the manufacturer, type number, and even the operational frequencies marked in large letters on the outer case of

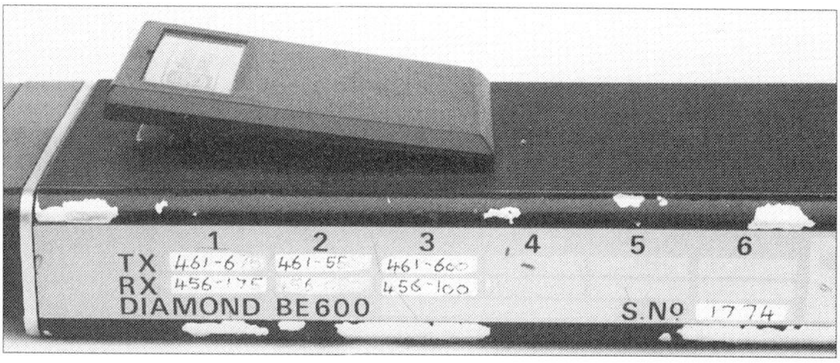

Identify your set

the set. If your set hasn't any apparent identification, or if it's suffered the effects of wear and tear, then you can check which band it's operating on (without transmitting with it and checking with a frequency counter!), by looking at the frequency marked on one of the transmit crystals if these are still fitted. A 'six times' multiplication is used on VHF, and a 'nine times' multiplication on UHF. Thus a VHF set will have a TX crystal between 22.6MHz and 29.0MHz, and a UHF set will have a TX crystal between 46.6MHz and 52.2MHz.

Controls

A ribbed, extruded metal alloy outer case is used, which is painted black (you'll usually see the paint flaking off in surplus sets – all those I've seen have this), and a large sprung clip is fitted to the case as a carrying aid. Small edgewise controls are used for volume adjustment and channel change, and the top of the set has two red buttons – one for transmit PTT and the other acting as a 'monitor' squelch override. A small internal combined mic / speaker is used, and a side-mounted 2.5mm jack socket lets you plug in an external earphone if you wish.

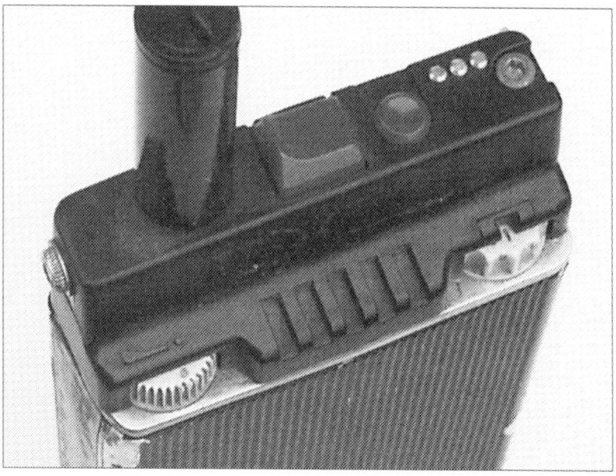
Top-panel controls of the BE600

The three small rounded metal studs on the set top are to allow the use of an vehicle adaptor – these carry contacts for chassis, external mic/ speaker (which is the centre contact), and external PTT (connect this to the chassis pin for transmit).

Finally, a screw-in, stud-mounted helical antenna is used – make sure your set is fitted with one of these to save having to fit a replacement.

Internal nicads

The set uses a pair of 8.4V PP3-sized nicads which fit into the lower section of the set's case. Although similar in size to the PP3 cell, the nicads use three flat connections for power, rather than the two 'clip' type connectors as found on standard PP3 batteries. The nicads used in the BE600 are identical to those used in the Pye PF1 receivers. They're usually yellow in colour with a black plastic top, and you may see them at rallies at quite low prices (the last batch I bought from a rally stand were priced at £1.00 for 10 – quite a bargain!). The

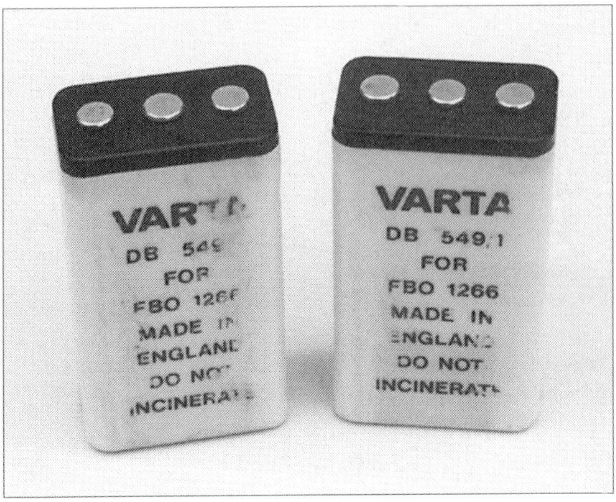

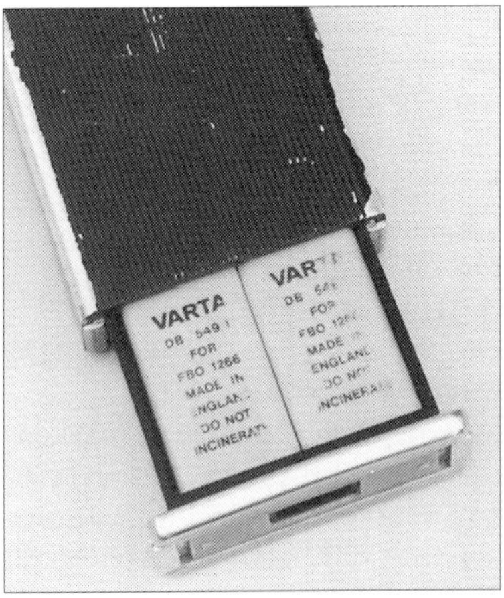

Above: **The 9V nicads have three connections – the centre is positive, the two outer contacts are negative**

Top right: **The BE600 batteries fit into the lower section of the case**

Below: **The circuitry is accessed by removing two screws inside the battery compartment**

centre contact on the battery is positive, and the two outer contacts are internally connected together to the battery negative.

If you can't manage to find any surplus nicads that are still usable, then a pair of standard PP3 nicad batteries, available from several high street sources, can be wired into the set. The typical capacity of the original nicads is 80mAh, so the charging rate should be 8mA for 14 hours.

Disassembly

At the bottom of the set's case, press the two small spring-loaded catches together to release the battery compartment and pull this down. Once this is down as far as it will go, if you're *very* careful you can gently squeeze the top side sections of plastic together to remove the battery compartment completely, in order to make the next operation a little easier.

In either case, looking into the set from the battery section you'll see two screws on either side of the centre of the inner set's chassis. Unscrew these (using a long screwdriver if the battery tray is still in place) (they're fitted with captive washers so they won't fall out) and you'll now find that you can pull the body of the set out from the top of the case.

If you need to remove the top panel, maybe to clean the volume and channel knob legends as they do tend to get grubby in use, first unscrew the set-top antenna then, using a suitable Allen key, unscrew the small hexagonal fixing bolt on the opposite side of the top

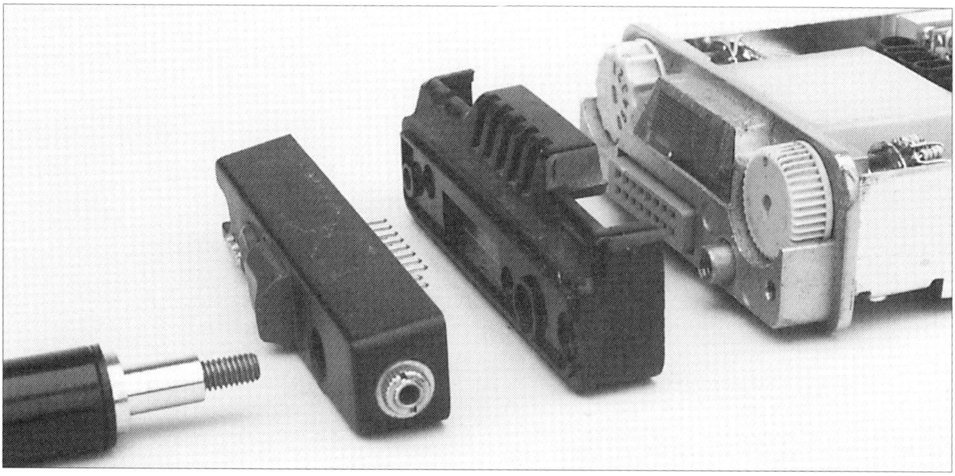

Top: **The top panel sections can easily be removed**

Right: **The modules are plainly identified**

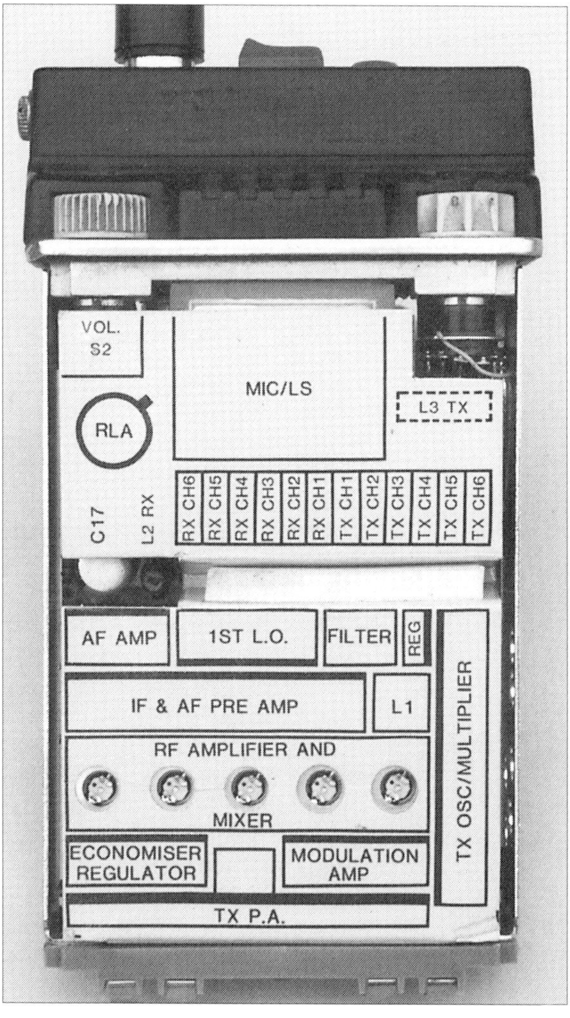

panel. Lift off the upper section of the top panel, which plugs into the body of the set via a 16-way connector, then undo the further screw you'll see to remove the lower section of the top panel.

Crystals

These are series-resonant, third-overtone types on both transmit and receive. When ordering your crystals, note these are HC-45/U types, which are wire-ended crystals with a smaller height than the 'usual' HC-18/U types. If you're only fitting one or two channels, you'll find you can use HC-18/U types, which are usually cheaper, by bending the crystals over to fit inside the available space. It's only when you fill the set up to its crystal limit that you'll need to ensure you obtain the correct physical types. In either case, quote the specifications given below or state they're for the BE600 to ensure you obtain the correct loading capacitances etc.

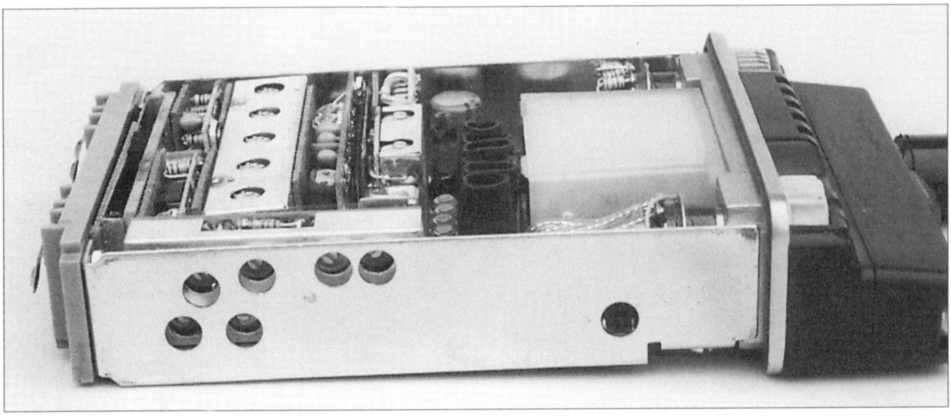

Some of the alignment points are accessible through the side panel

The crystals required are:

2m (specification: EDSK930)

$$\text{RX xtal freq} = \frac{\text{RX freq} - 21.4\text{MHz}}{3}$$

$$\text{TX xtal freq} = \frac{\text{TX freq}}{6}$$

70cm (specification: EDSK906)

$$\text{RX xtal freq} = \frac{\text{RX freq} - 21.4\text{MHz}}{9}$$

$$\text{TX xtal freq} = \frac{\text{TX freq}}{9}$$

Alignment

You can connect an external coaxial lead for alignment by first removing the very thin coaxial lead from the PCB-mounted antenna relay to the internal antenna connector stud bolt (the lead is on the PCB track side, not the relay side) and carefully soldering your coaxial cable to the PCB pad where the coaxial lead was originally connected.

First, for the receive alignment, initially adjust the small trimmer capacitor adjacent to your receive crystal to accurately place the receiver on frequency. Note there's also an adjustable ferrite-cored coil L2 to the left of the crystal bank which affects the frequency of oscillation of the entire receiver bank of crystals. If you get no receive oscillation at all, it's worth adjusting this to see if your crystal bursts into life with the different load inductance. Once 'netted' on frequency, adjust the two capacitors on the 1st local oscillator module, then the five capacitors on the RF front end, all for best received signal.

As on receive, on transmit there's also an adjustable ferrite-cored coil L3 (next to the channel switch and beneath the ribbon wire link), which this time affects the frequency of oscillation of the entire transmit bank of crystals, as well as individual channel adjustments made by the trimmer capacitors adjacent to each crystal. You can adjust this via a small hole at the *side* of the inner chassis, near to the channel switch. To align for transmit power, whilst keying the PTT, adjust the six trimmer capacitors at the side of the set for maximum power, starting with those nearest to the top of the set and progressing to those nearest the bottom of the set. You may find it helpful to first listen to the strength of the initially very weak signal off-air on an adjacent receiver, to help you tune the multiplier stages for maximum. Alternatively, connect a DC ammeter in line with the battery supply and carefully initially tune for maximum current drawn. Then finally retune all the six trimmers for maximum transmit power. After checking for accurate frequency of your signal, the small potentiometer at the top-right of the modulation amp board is the transmit deviation preset control.

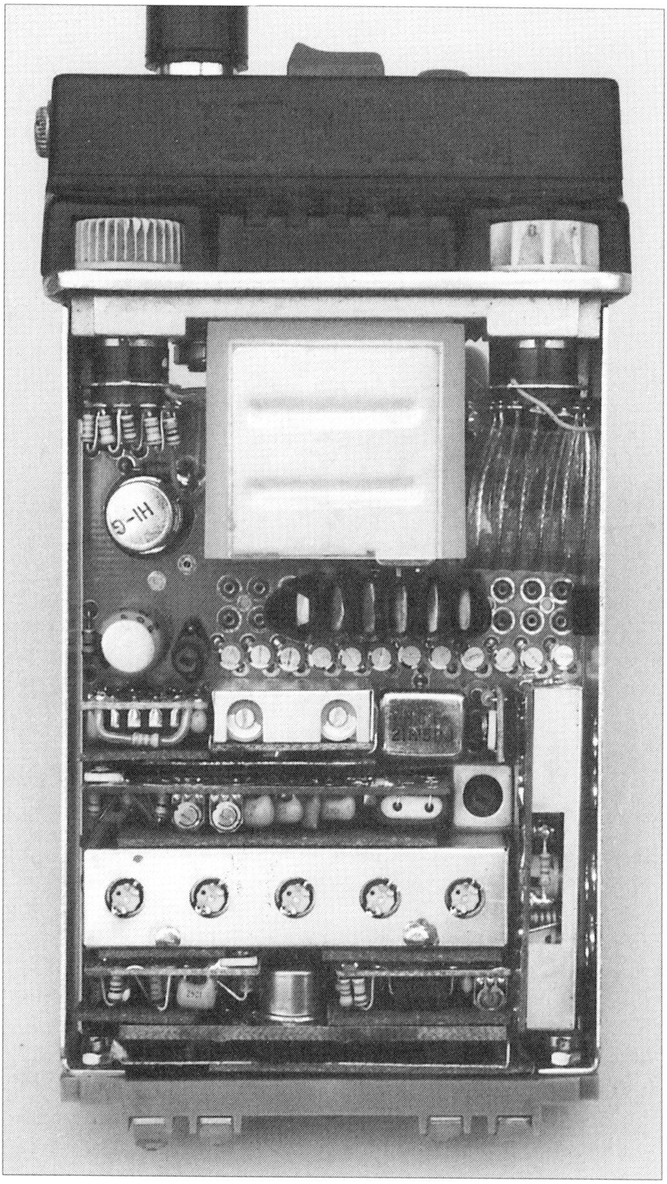

The BE600's inner circuitry

MOTOROLA MT700

The MT700 is a reasonably neat handheld, which comes in either a 'slimline' or 'omni' case configuration. The usual transmit power output is 1W, although a 4W output option is available for the omni version. The slimline set is 40mm thick, and can come in either a 'short' case (177mm × 69mm) or 'extended' case (193mm × 69mm). Each slimline set is 40mm thick, the omni version having an extended case and being 47mm thick.

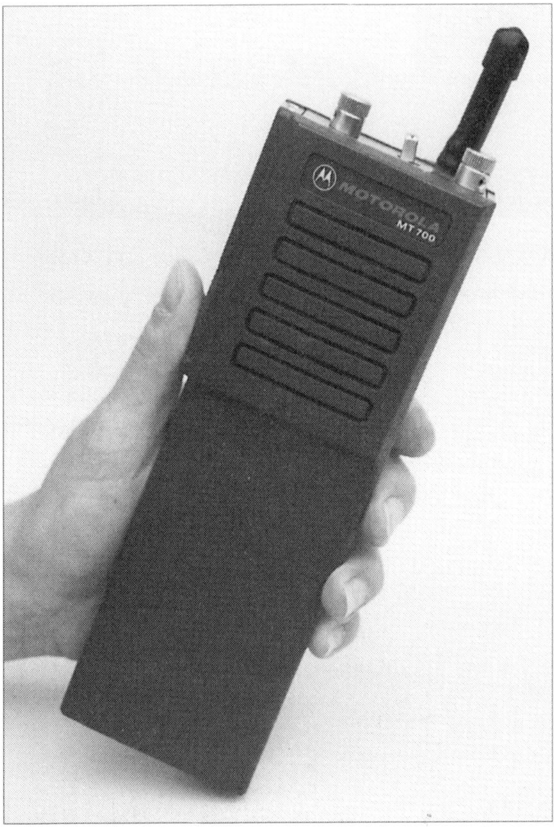

Above: **The Motorola MT700.** ***Below:*** **The MT700 comes in single-channel, two-channel, and six-channel combinations**

A screw-in helical antenna is commonly used, although the set allows room for a telescopic whip. All the sets I've seen have had a helical attached – telescopic whips undoubtedly don't last very long in PMR use! However, this facility is worth noting, because an alternative full-sized quarter-wave whip for 2m or 70cm, screwed in when needed in place of the short helical, could give you that bit extra communication range when conditions demand.

The single-channel and two-channel MT700 slimline sets are the types I've mainly seen on sale at rallies in the UK, the six-channel omni being fairly rare. I have also seen the MT500, which is externally virtually identical to the MT700 apart from the model number on the case. But inside the set (at least, in the three UHF MT500s I have here) the set uses plug-in crystal oscillator *modules*, and *not* discrete crystals, together with completely different internal RF circuits. You may be able to

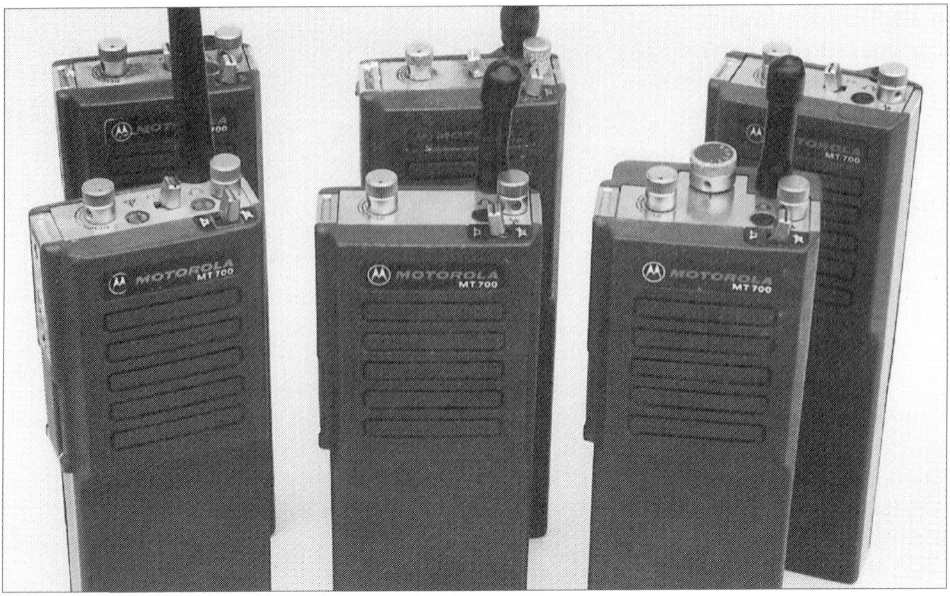

realign the sets, but obtaining replacement oscillator modules, or opening them up to fit alternative crystals, could be an expensive and rather tricky, if not impossible, matter.

Identification

The set comes in VHF and UHF versions, and you'll see an identification plate on the rear of the set which gives details on the crystalled channels. So identification shouldn't be too much of a problem. If it's had the serial number/identification plate removed, then leave *well* alone!

The MT500 and MT700 use a specially made, removable, sealed 15V nicad pack which fits inside the set. The battery compartment opens up with a coin-sized slotted screw at the bottom rear of the set's case, although some sets have two small holes in this which usually require a special tool – a pair of fine-nosed pliers can act as a temporary measure. Ensure your set is fitted with a battery when you buy it – you'll probably have a hard job in squeezing 12 individual nicads into the space available. If you see additional nicads on sale, an extra one or two are well worth purchasing. All the nicads I've seen are rapid-charge types, bright orange in colour, and are marked as type no NLN4462B.

Flat recessed connections are used on the battery terminals, which make 'home' charging of the nicads rather difficult – you can't connect croc-clip leads or whatever to them. Also, the two charger connections at the bottom of the set's case are flush with the case body, again making connection difficult. So, if you also see a charger on sale, then grab it if it's a reasonable price. Even if it doesn't work, the charger

Above: **The basic two-channel MT700 without CTCSS fitted.** ***Below:*** **Look at the rear panel ID label to see what's inside the set**

Below left: **Check your MT700 has a battery fitted before buying it.** ***Below right:*** **The MT700 uses a specialised battery – buy a spare if you can**

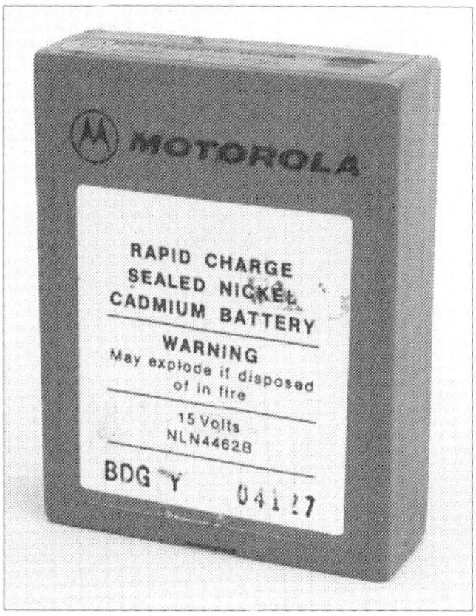

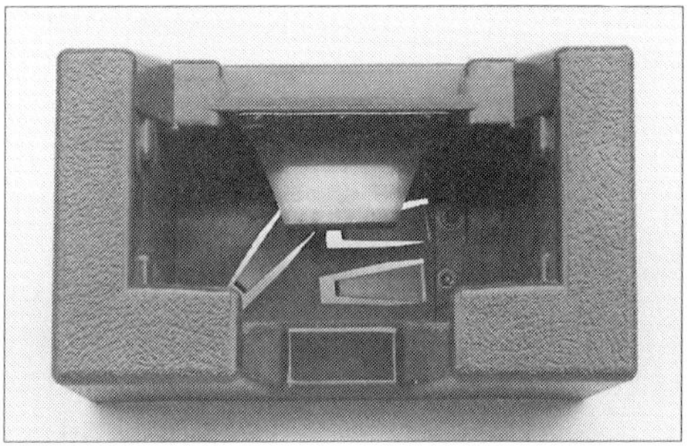

Above: **A dedicated charger is available.** ***Top right:*** **If you can't get a charger, then a charging pod is useful.** ***Right:*** **Spring contacts are used to connect to the flush battery contacts**

'pod', which the set slips into with the built-in sprung contacts, will allow you to use your own charger circuit.

Controls

The set's top case has a couple of small silver-coloured knobs – the left-hand one is on/off/volume, the right-hand one is the squelch control. Some models have an internal CTCSS unit (which Motorola call 'PL') fitted; here you'll see a small toggle switch at the top of the set, just in front of the squelch knob, which can be used to defeat the CTCSS if needed – very handy for amateur use. The other toggle switch, in between the volume and squelch knobs, is used for channel select, toggling between 'F1' and 'F2' channels – the single

Below: **The six-channel top-panel controls.** ***Below right:*** **Top-panel controls include volume and squelch controls plus channel and CTCSS defeat switches.**

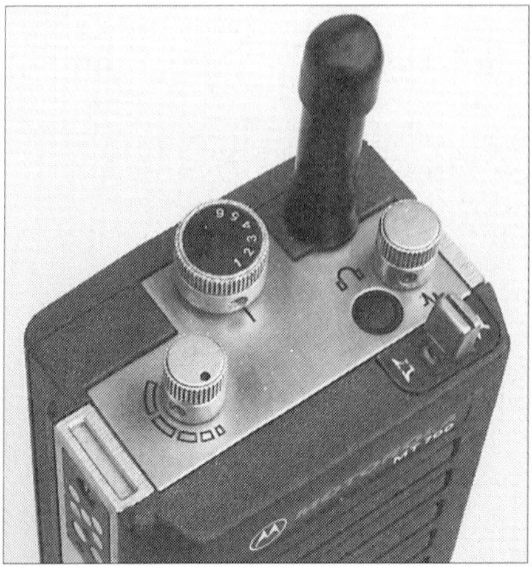

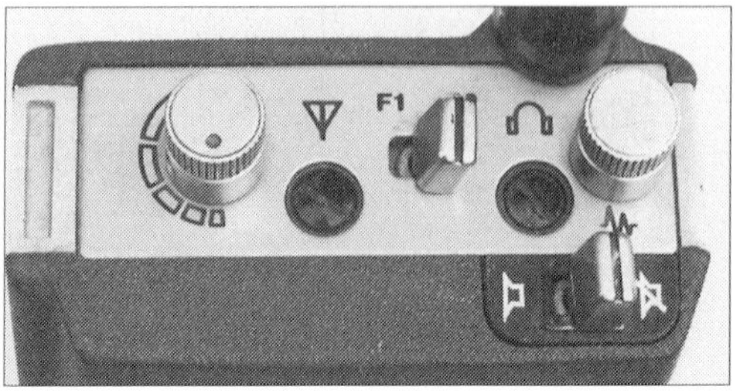

channel set omits this of course. The 'omni' model of the MT700 adds a channel selector knob in the 'extended' part of the set's case.

Connectors

On each model, next to the squelch knob you'll see a small black plastic screw – removing this reveals a 2.5mm jack for an external earphone. Depending upon the model variant, you may also find a similar screw near the volume knob, this being a further 2.5mm jack which you can use for connecting an external antenna – the set-top antenna is internally disconnected when a jack plug is plugged in.

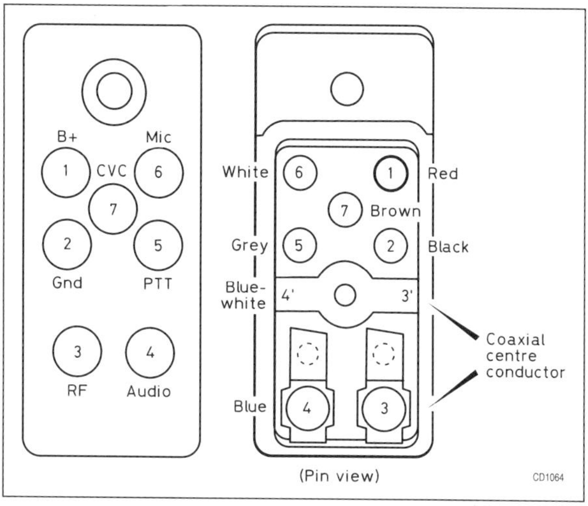

Fig 6.3. MT700 accessory connector

Each set uses similar multi-way side connectors for an external speaker-mic, with connections for mic, PTT, DC voltage, receive audio and external antenna. The receive audio and external antenna connections are spring loaded – a suitable plug with pins in these positions will disconnect the internal speaker and/or antenna as needed. Again, if you see some speaker-microphones on sale with the sets (ie with the valuable mating side connectors!), one of these may be worthwhile purchasing, especially if you'd like to use the set at home, or for packet, or out in the car.

Inside the MT700

To open the case for alignment, first remove the battery cover, then

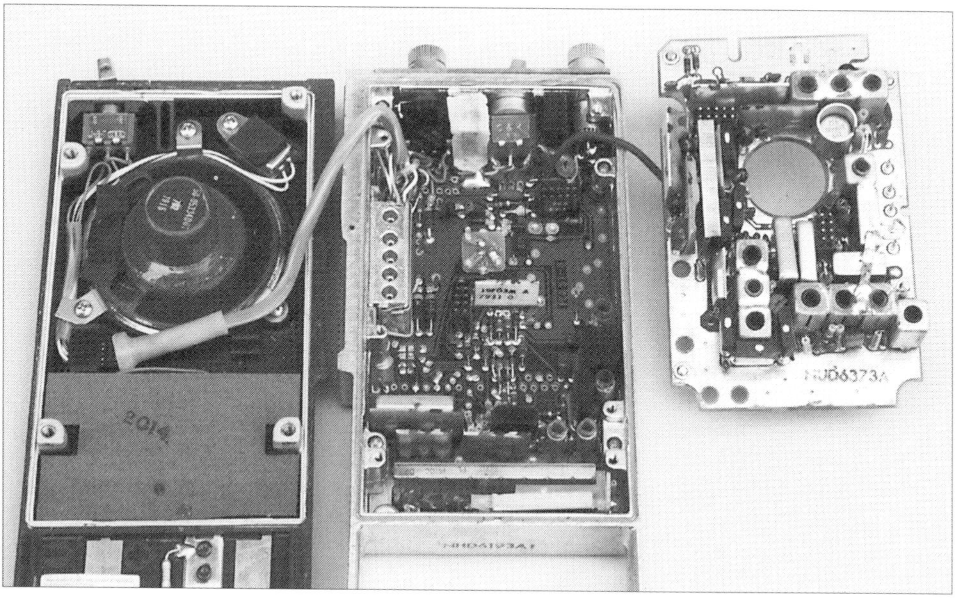

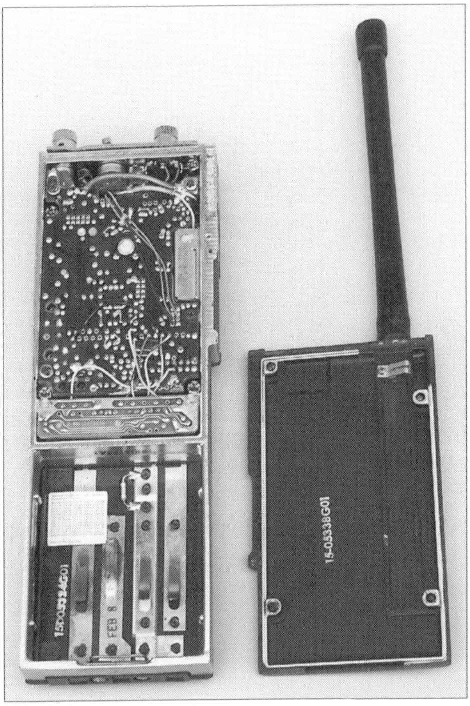

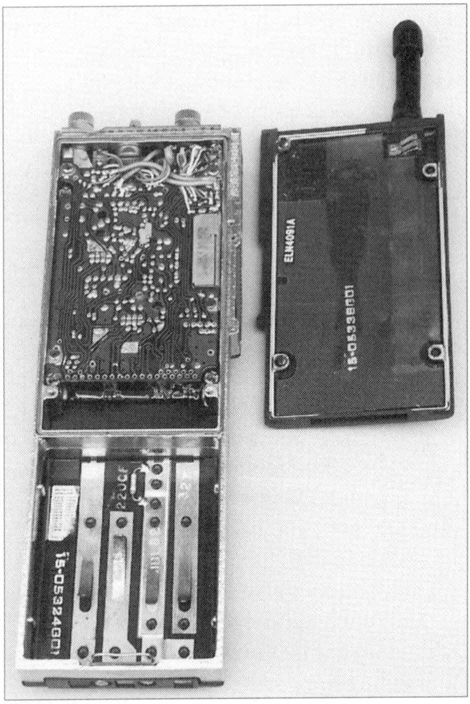

Ready for alignment. *Left:* The VHF MT700; *right:* the UHF MT700

Below: **Ensure you don't damage the wire loom when removing the front panel**

undo the four captive cross-head screws securing the rear panel and remove this. Inside, at roughly the four corners of the main PCB, you'll see four pillars with cross-head cut-outs. Use a suitable

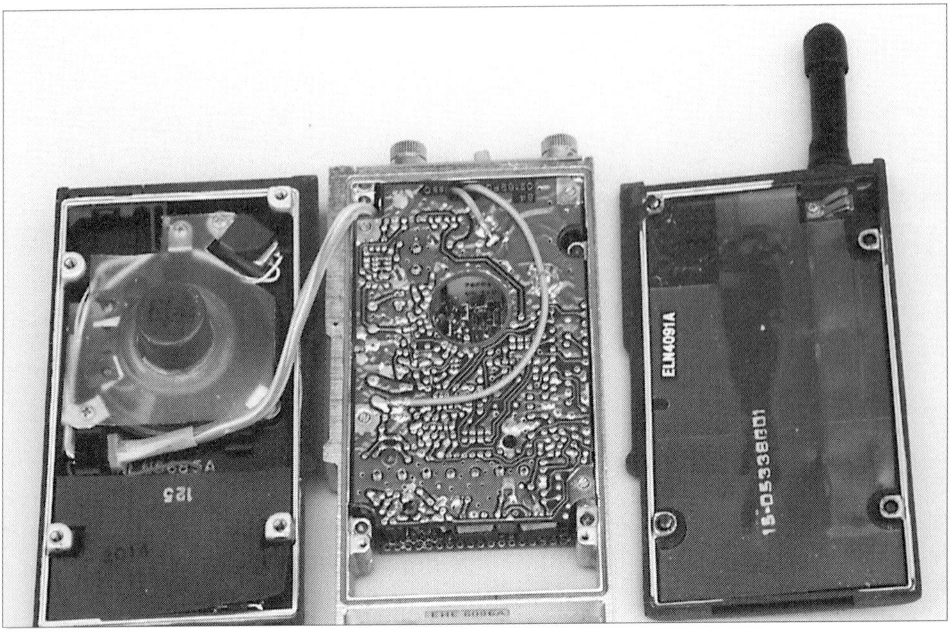

The main board

screwdriver to undo these, and you'll now be able to remove the front panel of the set, being careful not to damage or break the attached wire loom to the speaker, mic and CTCSS override switch.

You can get to all the alignment points now but, if you need to access the circuitry, then, using a very small flat-bladed screwdriver, undo the four small screws, again at roughly the four corners of the PCB. These are 'captive' screws so just undo them until they revolve freely. Now you can remove this PCB, which plugs into the other PCB via a board-mounted multi-way plug and socket. The internal layouts of the set are shown in Figs 6.4 and 6.5.

CTCSS unit

The PCB at the lower section of the set, if fitted, is the CTCSS unit. Don't bother removing it if you don't need it as you can easily 'defeat' it using the set-top toggle switch, and adjust the TX CTCSS deviation to zero by turning the potentiometer on the CTCSS board (at the bottom left) fully anticlockwise.

The CTCSS tone frequency is controlled by a plug-in resonant reed unit – you'll see the tone frequency marked on this. Unfortunately it's not variable or programmable – for a different tone you plug in a different reed module. I was quite fortunate in finding a batch of UHF MT700s with 71.9Hz fitted, which is my 'regional' CTCSS tone and used by my local 70cm repeater. However, if yours is a two-channel set and fitted with CTCSS, you may find the 'other' channel could be useful for club or group purposes with the CTCSS enabled for 'quiet'

The CTCSS ('PL') unit is fitted in the lower section of the inner circuitry

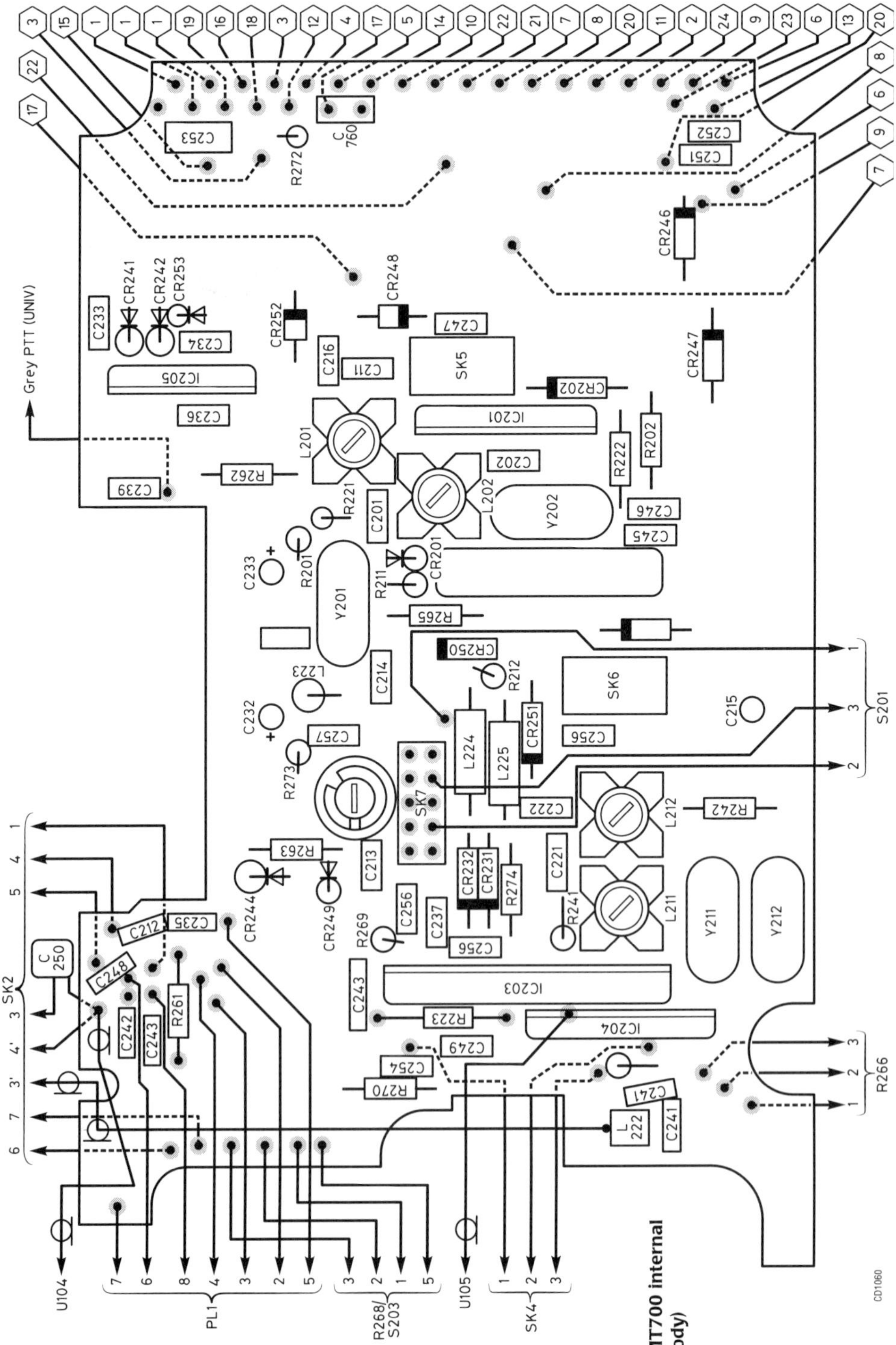

Fig 6.4. MT700 internal layout (body)

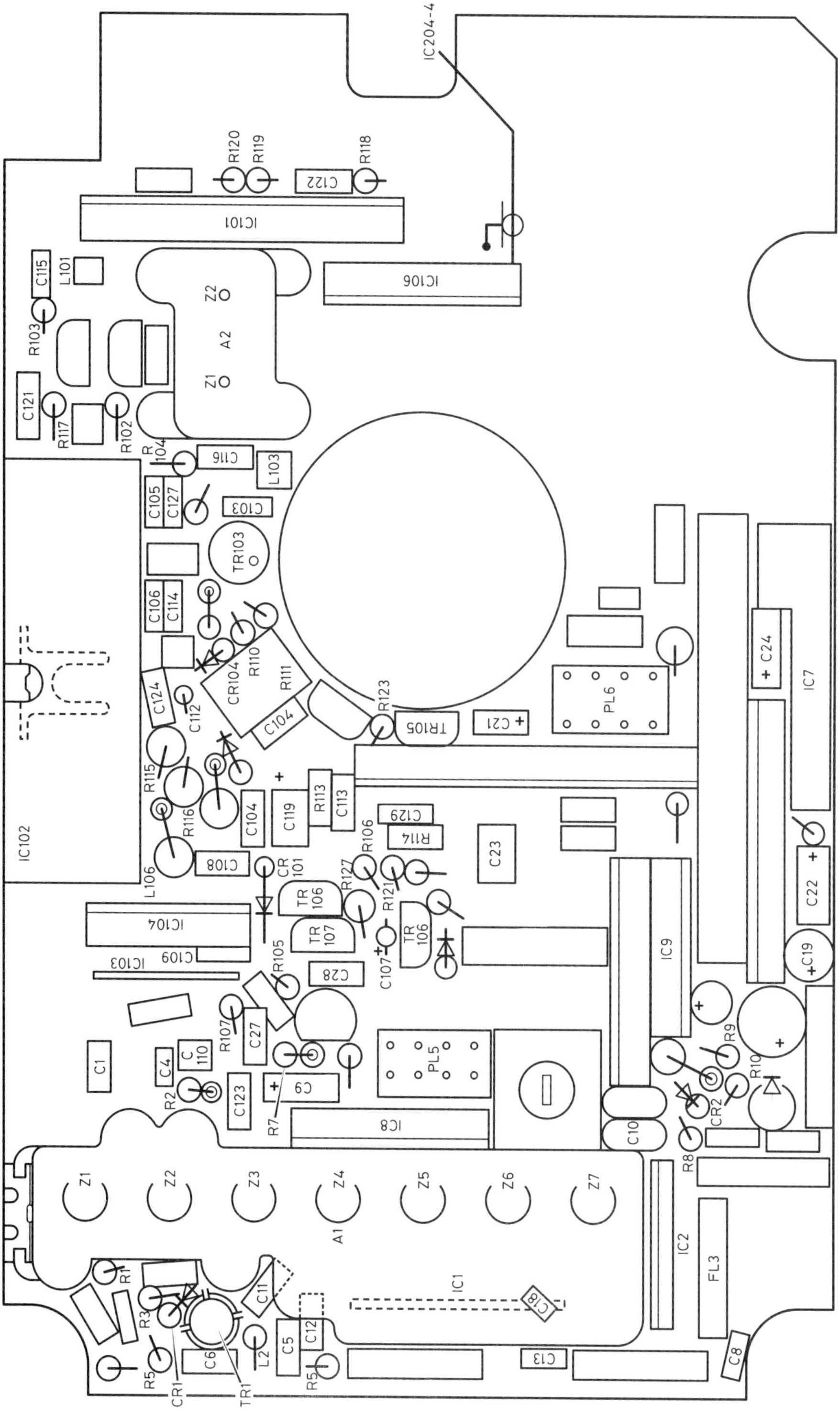

Fig 6.5. MT700 internal layout (case front)

monitoring, regardless of what the actual tone frequency is (especially if a batch of sets from the same user are purchased as a 'job lot').

Crystals

Both VHF and UHF band sets use a receiver with a 17.9MHz IF, and use 'short'-cased crystals – state the MT700 to your supplier when ordering. The crystal frequencies required are:

2m

$$\text{RX xtal freq} = \frac{\text{RX freq} - 17.9\text{MHz}}{3}$$

$$\text{TX xtal freq} = \frac{\text{TX freq}}{9}$$

70cm

$$\text{RX xtal freq} = \frac{\text{RX freq} - 17.9\text{MHz}}{8}$$

$$\text{TX xtal freq} = \frac{\text{TX freq}}{24}$$

VHF alignment

To align the receiver, switch the CTCSS ('PL') off if fitted, using the set-top switch, and adjust the squelch control to minimum so you hear receiver noise from the speaker. First tune the appropriate crystal trimmer (L251 for channel 1, L253 for channel 2) to correctly receive a strong signal. Then adjust the oscillator multiplier coils L6, L7, and then the receiver front-end coils L1, L2, L3, L4 and L5, all for best signal, reducing the signal level as needed.

To align the transmitter, with your power supply set to 15.0V (or with a fully charged nicad in place), press the transmitter PTT and tune L101, L102, L103 and L104, and then the variable capacitor and inductor (L107) in the transmitter PA, for maximum transmit power output. Finally, carefully adjust the relevant transmitter crystal oscillator coil for spot-on frequency (L252 for channel 1, L254 for channel 2).

UHF alignment

To align the receiver, switch the 'PL' (CTCSS) off if fitted, and adjust the squelch control to minimum so that you can hear receiver noise from the speaker. First tune the appropriate crystal trimmer to correctly receive a strong signal, then adjust L6, Z7, Z6, Z1, Z2, Z3 and Z5 for best signal, reducing the signal level as needed.

To align the transmitter, first set R111 fully clockwise – this is the transmit power level control. Now, with your power supply set to 15.0V (or a fully charged nicad in place), press the transmitter PTT and tune Z1 and Z2 of the A2 transmitter stage, in that order, for maximum transmit power output. Once you've achieved maximum, you can if you wish adjust R111 to set the transmit power to a lower

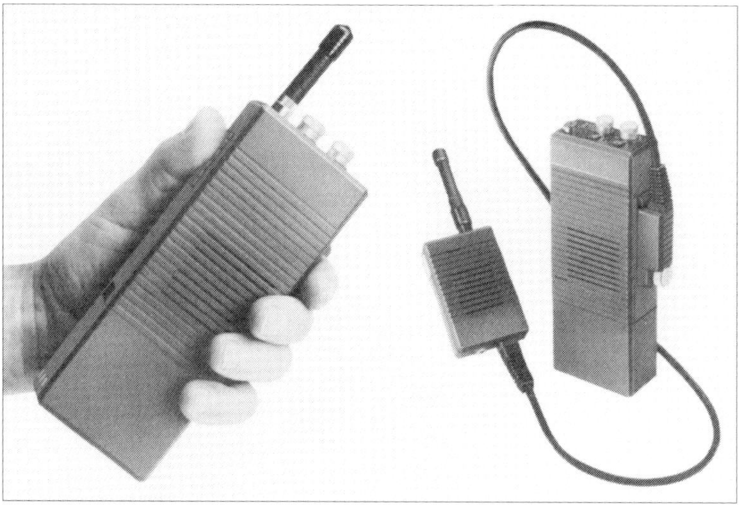

The PF85

The PFX

level if you prefer. Finally, carefully adjust the relevant transmitter crystal oscillator coil for spot-on frequency. The deviation is adjusted by trimmer potentiometer R264.

PF85 AND PFX HANDHELDS

The PF85 is a crystal-controlled handheld for VHF or UHF, and is found in either single-channel or three-channel versions. The PFX is in a similar-sized case and can use the same accessories, but is a synthesised set with up to 99 channels with push-button rather than rotary set-top controls.

At the time of writing, the PFX is a fairly rare 'find' on the surplus market, but there are literally thousands of the UHF version of these in current government use in the UK, and if past performance

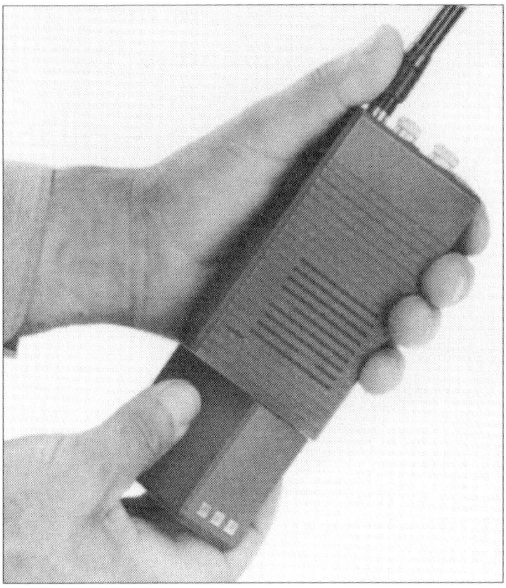

Fitting the battery

is typical these may well in the near future be released onto the surplus market. Hence the UHF PFX will also be dealt with in this chapter.

Battery pack

Each set uses a purpose-designed 9.6V nicad pack, which fits onto the lower part of the set's case via a 'twist and clip' arrangement. Make sure you get a battery with your set, possibly a spare or two if there are some available. However, inside the standard battery you'll find eight AA-sized nicad cells, so if you do find you have a faulty nicad a cell replacement may be possible if you're careful in opening the battery case. A higher-capacity battery is also available, which uses elongated cells. The battery is released by pressing in the small rectangular spring-loaded button at the lower side of the set, just above the battery, and twisting the battery off. There's a small in-line 2.5A fuse at the bottom of the set – you'll be able to get to this with the battery removed, using a small screwdriver blade to slide open the plastic retaining clip for the fuse (Fig 6.6). If your set is totally dead, even with a fully charged battery, check the condition, or even the presence, of this fuse. A common fault is the internal regulator board, which is a three-pin plug-in unit. A brown burn mark in the lower corner signifies prior misuse and the only cure here is replacement.

The most common replacement requirement, however, is that of a new helical set-top antenna, these usually receiving rather a 'battering' in commercial use. You can buy new replacements from companies such as Panorama Antennas in London, or remodel the case

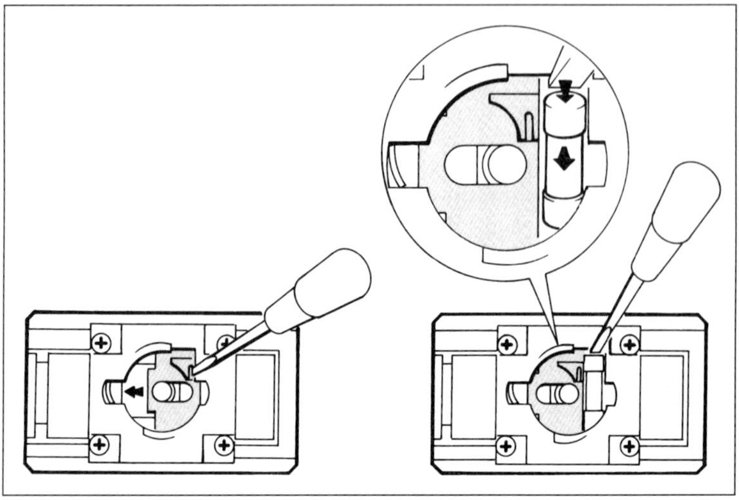

Fig 6.6. Removal of fuse

(be very careful if you attempt to do this!) to fit a coaxial connector such as a single-hole mounting BNC socket.

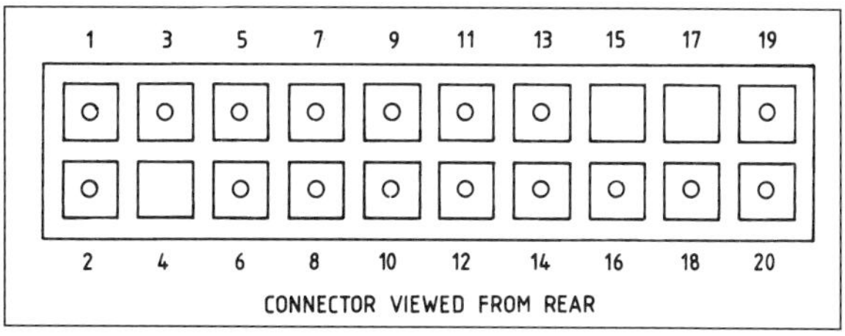

Fig 6.7. PF85/PFX selective calling option connector

Circuitry

Each set uses a number of plug-in and soldered-in thick and thin film modules. Faultfinding and repair is often down to replacing the module itself, so be careful to check the set is working first before attempting conversion. The transmitter PA module is particularly expensive, however the set-top transmit LED is only lit (or the LCD 'chevrons' displayed in case of earlier PFX equipments) if RF power is present, which can be a useful check. Two power output versions are available, depending on which type of PA module is plugged in – either 1.5W (VHF and UHF sets, you'll find this power is the most commonly available) or 5W (VHF) and 4W (UHF). The PAs are common between PF85 and PFX sets – simply replacing the PA gives a different maximum power level, and an internal power output preset lets you set the power level as needed. A PA module with 'FU00700/...' marked on it is a 1.5W module, an 'FU00710/...' type is a 5W module, the number following the oblique indicating the band segment.

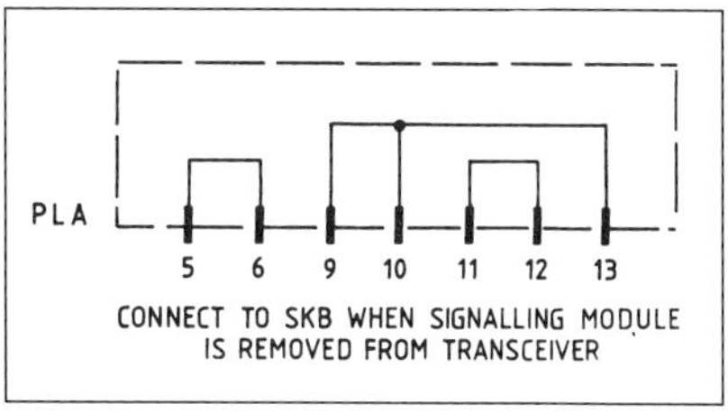

Fig 6.8. These are the links to make if your set has been fitted with a selective calling unit

The set's case length is determined by which, if any, selective calling options are installed, either CTCSS, five-tone, or both. However, all the sets I've seen on the surplus market haven't had any of these fitted. Details of the selective calling option connector and suitable links are shown in Figs 6.7 and 6.8.

Facility connector

As well as handheld use with the internal mic and speaker, a facility connector at the side of the case allows use of an external speaker/mic (Figs 6.9–6.12). Two of the contacts are spring loaded – these are change-over contacts for the speaker and antenna connector, which can be rather handy for base and mobile use. If you're lucky, you might find an external speaker/microphone is also available – some of these also have a short helical antenna fitted on the top of the speaker/mic case for better TX/RX range when used in this bodyworn fashion. In any case, the plug connected at the base of the speaker/microphone is extremely useful for connection of external accessories. You'll find the speaker pin and the external antenna pin (if fitted) on this connector are tiny screw-in types, to mate with the spring-loaded connectors on the set – you can unscrew these as

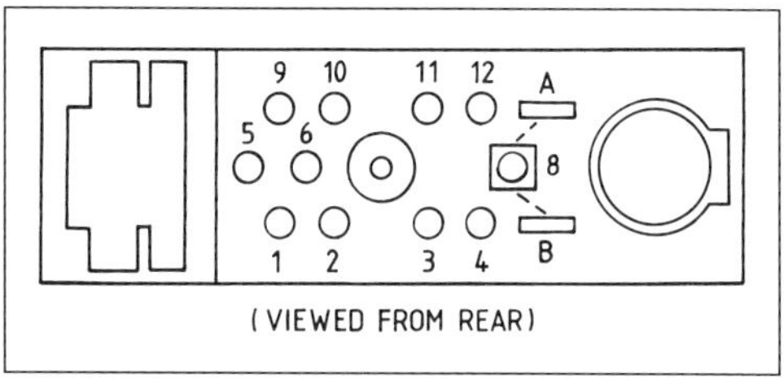

Fig 6.9. PF85/PFX facility plug connections

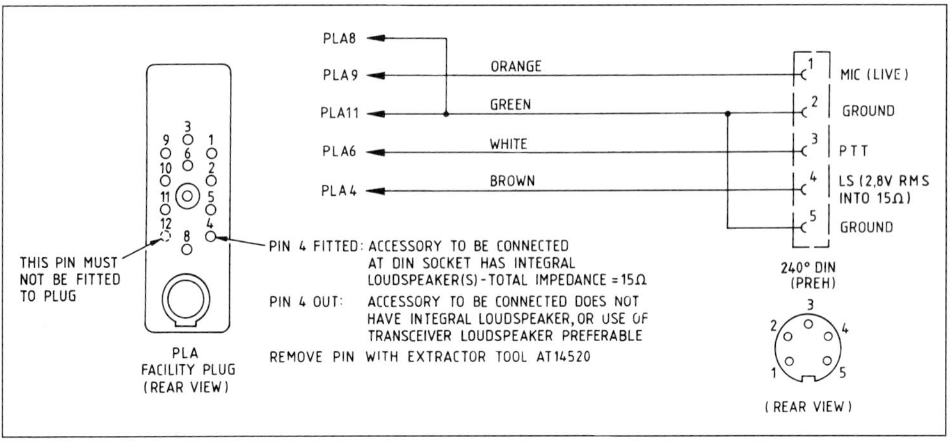

Above: **Fig 6.10. PF85/PFX audio connections to the facility connector**

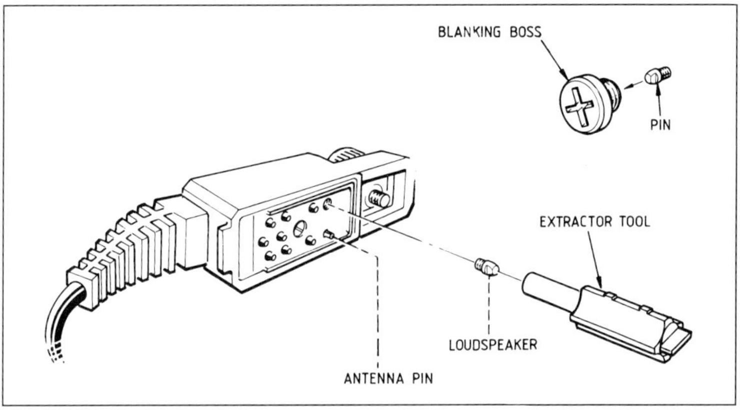

Fig 6.11. The facility connector has the option of removable antenna and loudspeaker changeover connections

needed (but don't lose the pins!). The facility connector also allows the set to be used with a mobile adapter. You'll usually find the connector on the side of the set's case, beneath a thin plastic clip-on or (on later models) a screw-on cover. If the plastic cover over the facility module is missing, you may find that the antenna changeover could become intermittent – you might even get an RF burn on your finger when transmitting.

Table 6.1. Band designators for the PF85 and PFX

A1	148–162MHz
A2	160–174MHz
B1	132–146MHz
B2	142–156MHz
E1	68–79MHz
E2	77–88MHz
TP	405–447MHz
TL	405–425MHz
TH	412–447MHz
UP	438–472MHz
WP	466–512MHz

Bands

The rear panel serial number plate gives you the usual information on the set's band, ie A0, E0, T1, U0 etc, in order of the transmit band first followed by the receive band. Immediately prior to the transmit band designator, you'll see either an 'S' (12.5kHz channel spacing), 'R' (20kHz channel spacing) or 'V' (25kHz channel spacing).

The band designators are shown in Table 6.1.

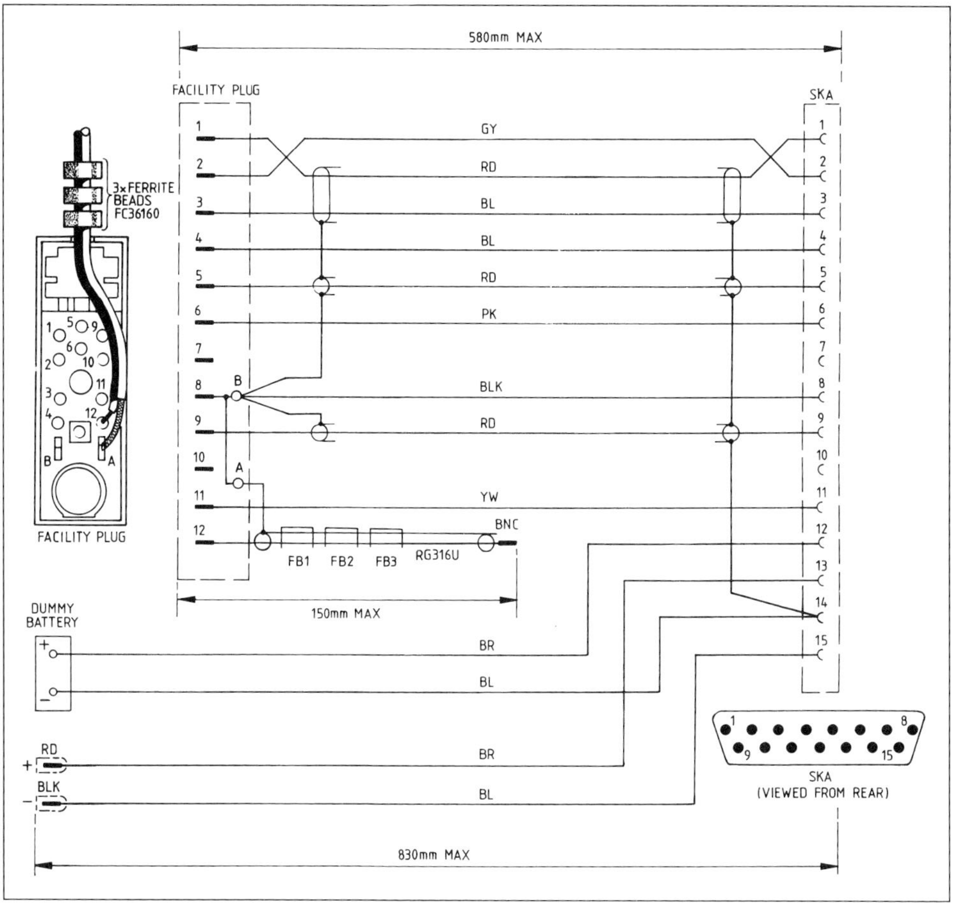

Fig 6.12. PF85/PFX test lead wiring diagram

PF85

Controls

The top panel of the set has a combined rotary on/off/volume switch, plus, for three-channel versions, a rotary channel switch. Other push buttons are used for optional squelch defeat and tone-call options.

Crystals

The crystals used are reduced-height HC-18/U types. The commercial receive crystal specifications are T306S or E306S for VHF, and T307S or P307S for UHF. Likewise, the commercial transmit crystal specifications are T305S or E305S for VHF, and T307S or P307S for UHF.

The frequencies required are:

Receiver

A1, A2 band: Xtal freq = (RX freq – 10.7MHz) ÷ 3
B1, B2 band: Xtal freq = (RX freq – 10.7MHz) ÷ 3
E1, E2 band: Xtal freq = (RX freq + 10.7MHz) ÷ 2

PF85 controls and indicators

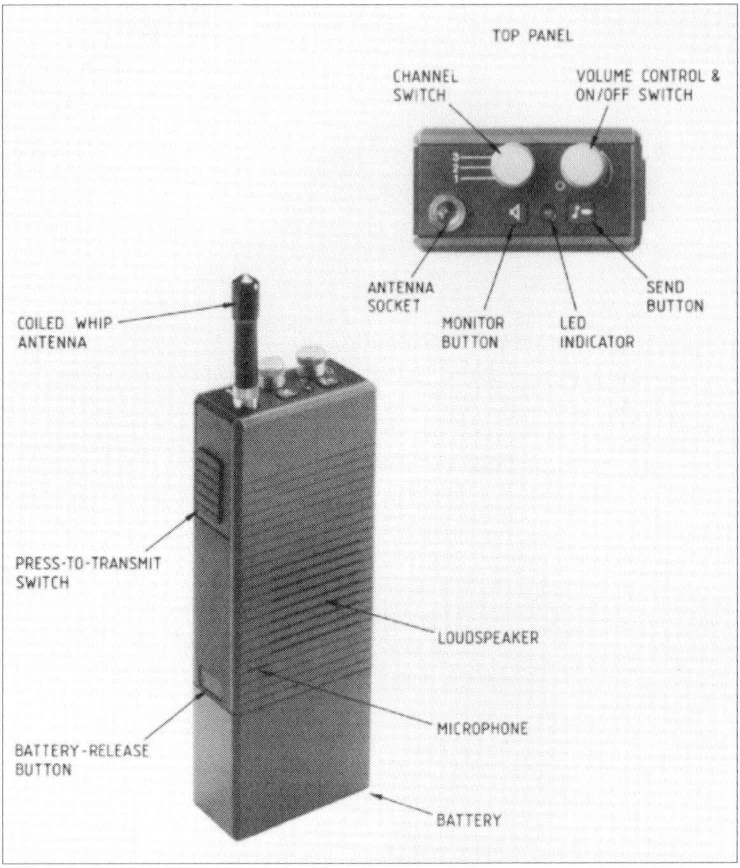

Below: **Internal view of the PF85**

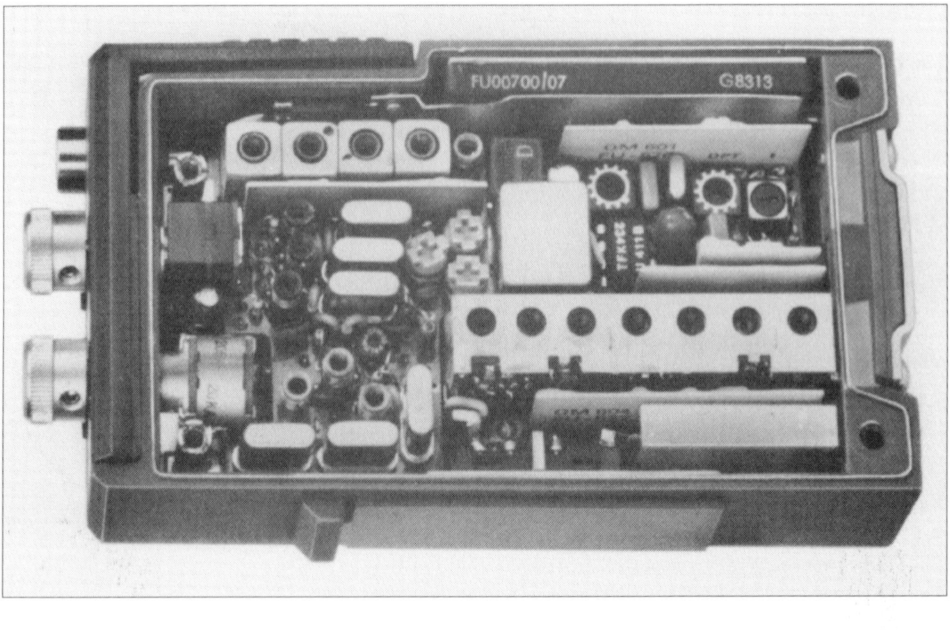

TL, TH band: Xtal freq = (RX freq + 21.4MHz) ÷ 9
UP, UW band: Xtal freq = (RX freq – 21.4MHz) ÷ 9

Transmitter

A1, A2 band: Xtal freq = TX freq ÷ 8
B1, B2 band: Xtal freq = TX freq ÷ 8
E1, E2 band: Xtal freq = TX freq ÷ 4
TL, TH band: Xtal freq = TX freq ÷ 9
UP, UW band: Xtal freq = TX freq ÷ 9

VHF receiver alignment

An alignment diagram is shown in Fig 6.13. With your crystals installed, first adjust the preset squelch potentiometer RV7 until you can hear received squelch noise, and adjust the relevant crystal trimmer for the correct receive frequency. L1 adjusts channel 1, L3 adjusts channel 3, and L5 adjusts channel 3. Then, whilst receiving an off-air signal, adjust L6, L1, L2, L3, L4 and L5 in sequence for best signal, finally repeaking on a weak received signal. Reset RV7, and that's it. L1 is the discriminator coil, which shouldn't need adjustment, although this is adjusted for maximum demodulated audio output.

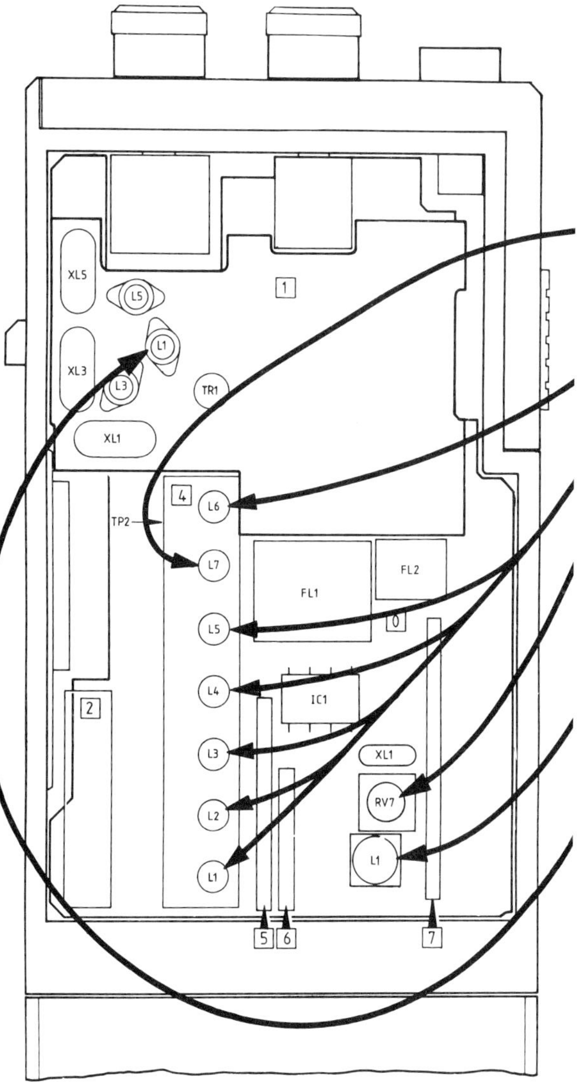

Fig 6.13. PF85 VHF receiver alignment points

VHF transmitter alignment

An alignment diagram is shown in Fig 6.14. If you've a diode probe, connect this to the TP1 test point, otherwise tune for maximum RF output power, measured into a 50Ω dummy load. Temporarily disconnect the set-top antenna for this, replacing it with a short coaxial lead to your meter or use a facility connector if you have one. Initially adjust RV5 fully clockwise to give maximum transmit output power.

Tune L7, L8, L9, L10 and L11 all for maximum output

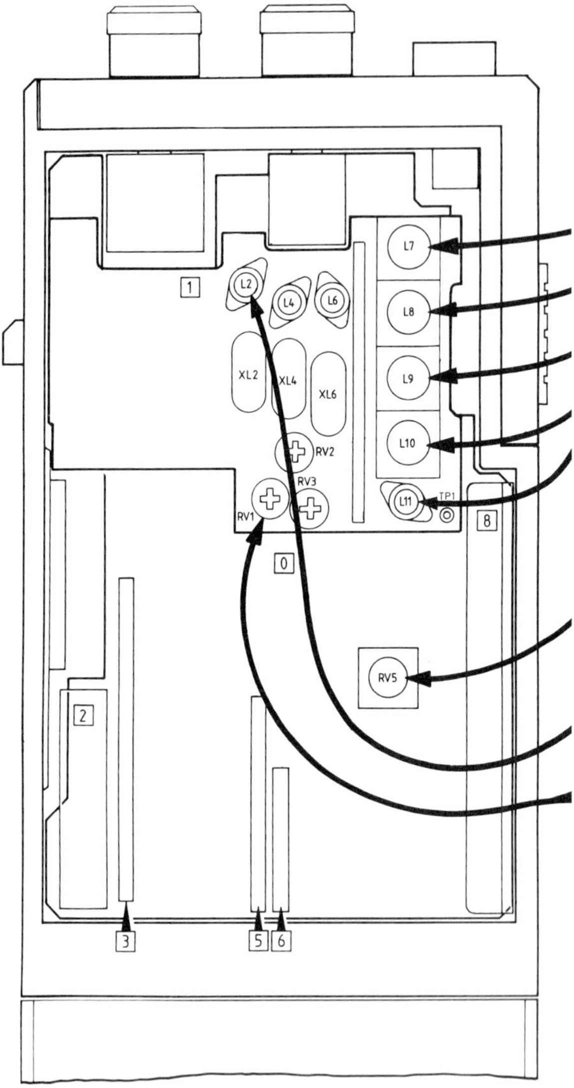

Fig 6.14. PF85 VHF transmitter alignment points

reading, finally readjusting the appropriate crystal trimmer for the correct frequency. L2 adjusts channel 1, L4 adjusts channel 2, and L6 adjusts channel 3. The transmit deviation is individually set on a channel-by-channel basis, with RV1 adjusting channel 1, RV2 adjusting channel 2, and RV3 adjusting channel 3. RV5 is the transmit power potentiometer, which you can set for the desired power level.

UHF receiver alignment

An alignment diagram is shown in Fig 6.15. With your crystals installed, first adjust the preset squelch potentiometer RV7 until you can hear received squelch noise, and adjust the relevant crystal trimmer for the correct receive frequency. L1 adjusts channel 1, L3 adjusts channel 3, and L5 adjusts channel 3. Then, whilst receiving an off-air signal, adjust L7 on the crystal board, and L6 and L7 on the main receiver board, for best received signal, readjusting as needed. Then adjust L8 on the crystal board, followed by L1, L2, L3 and L4 on the main board, all for best signal. Finally, on the main board, readjust in sequence L6, L7, L1, L2, L3 and L4 all for best signal, finally repeaking on a weak received signal. L5 will usually already be adjusted – this is tuned for least distortion on a strong received signal.

L1 is the discriminator coil, which shouldn't need adjustment, although this is set for maximum demodulated audio output. Finally, reset the squelch preset RV7 to just close the receiver squelch.

UHF transmitter alignment

An alignment diagram is shown in Fig 6.16. If you've a diode probe, as with the VHF alignment, connect this to the TP1 test point, otherwise tune for maximum RF output power, measured into a 50Ω dummy load. Temporarily disconnect the set-top antenna for this, replacing it with a short coaxial lead to your meter or use a facility connector if you have one. Initially adjust RV5 fully clockwise to give maximum transmit output power. Tune L9, L10, L11, L12 and L13 all for maximum output reading, then adjust L12 and L13, followed by L9, again for maximum. Now retune L10, L11, L12 and L13 again for absolute maximum. Finally adjust the appropriate crystal trimmer for the correct frequency. L2 adjusts channel 1, L4 adjusts channel 2, and L6 adjusts channel 3. The transmit deviation is again individually set on a channel-by-channel basis, with RV1 adjusting channel 1, RV2 adjusting channel 2, and RV3 adjusting channel 3. RV5 controls the transmit power. Reset RV5 to give you the required power level if you want to lower this from the maximum output.

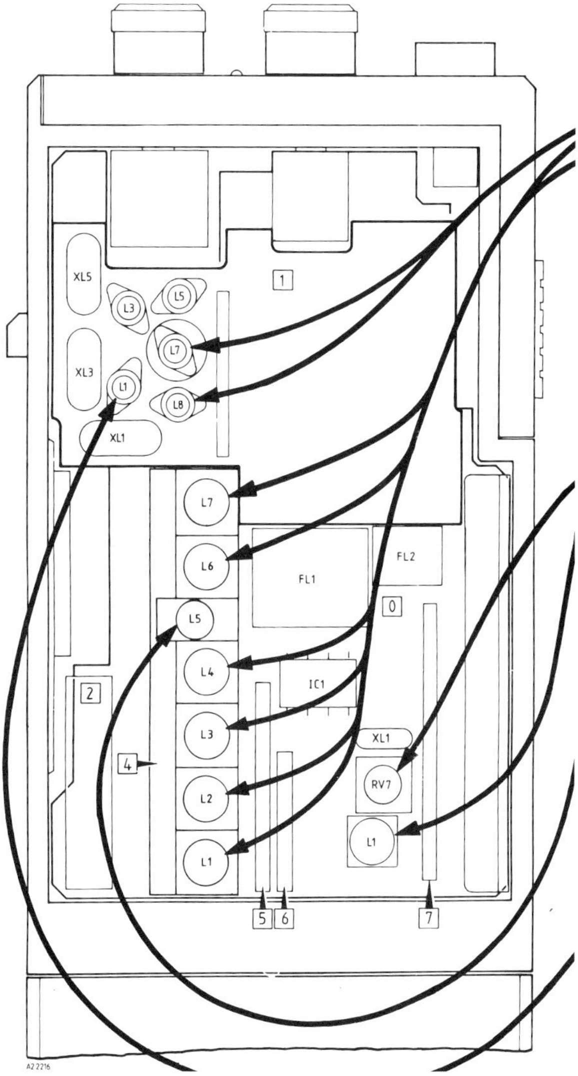

Fig 6.15. PF85 UHF receiver alignment points

UHF PFX

The PFX on/off power switch is a rectangular button at the lower side section of the radio, on the opposite side to the battery release catch. A plug-in TTL PROM is needed, which is an 82S185 (similar to the type used for the MX290 series). You'll need to have this suitably programmed for your required 70cm channels.

The set uses an LCD for channel and volume indication. The LCD normally indicates the selected volume setting, and pressing the set-top '+' and '–' buttons changes the volume in levels between 1 and 8. Pressing the 'M' button switches to channel change mode, the LCD then indicating 'Channel' in place of 'Volume', and the '+' and '–' buttons now changing channel with the set automatically reverting to volume set mode after a few seconds. Further buttons include an LCD backlight button, a squelch defeat button, and a 'tone' button used for selective calling options. Pressing the PTT will, on early sets, cause the LCD to display a line of chevrons, but note this isn't a relative power output bargraph. On later sets the

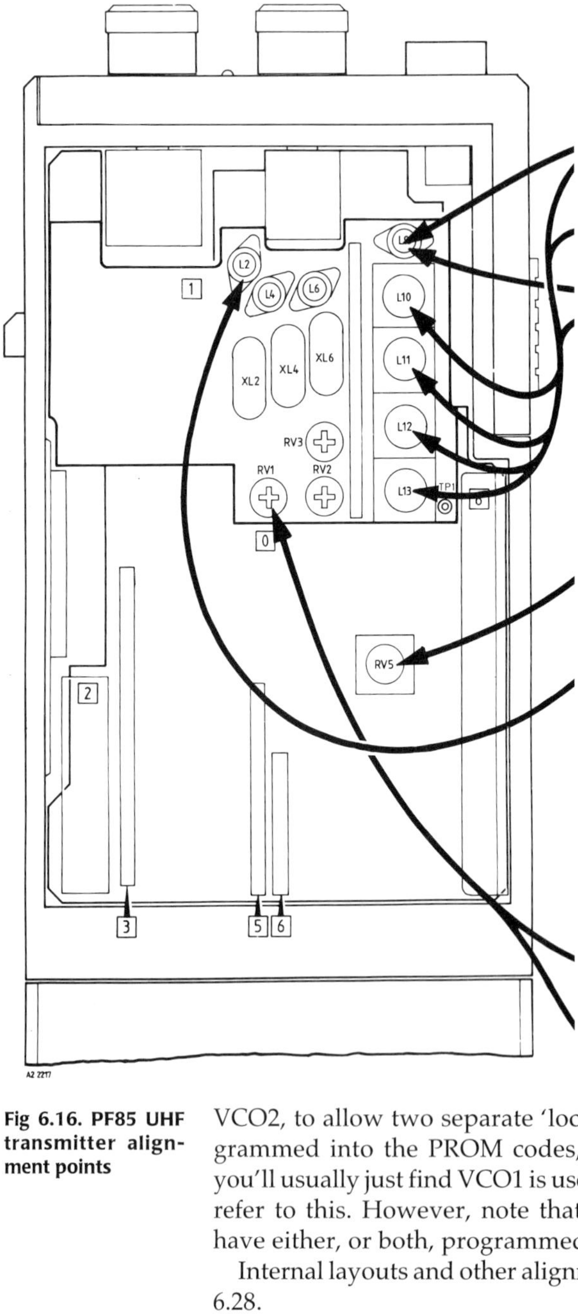

Fig 6.16. PF85 UHF transmitter alignment points

LCD will go totally blank on transmit, with a small red LED used to provide TX indication.

The transceiver frame assemblies and top-panel controls are shown in Figs 6.17 and 6.18.

Preliminaries

Inside the set, two internal round, silver-coloured lithium cells provide a constant supply for the logic board. If you find your set is faulty, then check whether you can switch to unprogrammed channels, ie all 100 channels including channel 00 which can't normally be accessed, and if so then check the voltage of these cells. Each cell should measure at least 2.6V, their normal voltage being 3.3V, so replace these if needed. A further common fault is that the plug-in reference oscillator, which operates at 8.4MHz, can sometimes 'lose' one of its three plug-in pins through vibration, such as the set being dropped. Unplug this and check if you find the VCO doesn't lock up with a correctly programmed PROM.

The set uses one VCO (voltage controlled oscillator) for receive, but two independent VCOs for transmit, VCO1 and VCO2, to allow two separate 'lock ranges'. The VCO range is programmed into the PROM codes, although for amateur purposes you'll usually just find VCO1 is used, and the code calculations given refer to this. However, note that equipment out of service could have either, or both, programmed. See Fig 6.19.

Internal layouts and other alignment details are given in Figs 6.20–6.28.

Transmitter alignment

The transmitter *must always* be aligned before you start the receiver alignment. First set the transmit power level control RV5 fully counter-clockwise, and with your PROM fitted, select the channel with the highest transmit frequency in the VCO TX1 range. Switch to

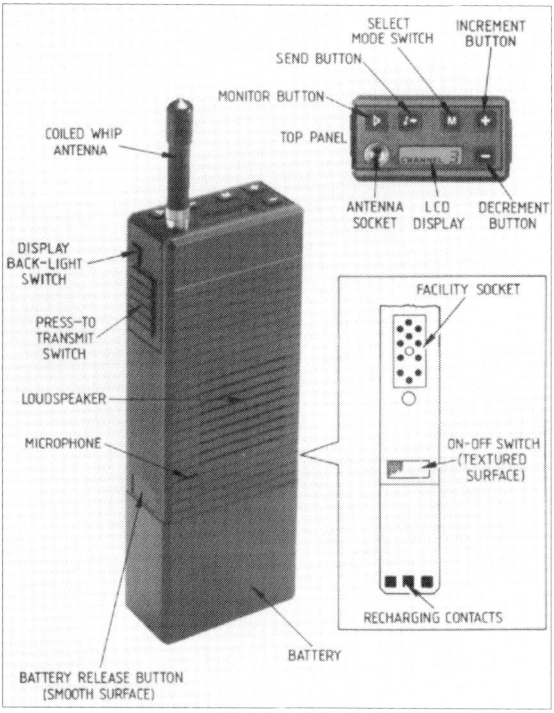

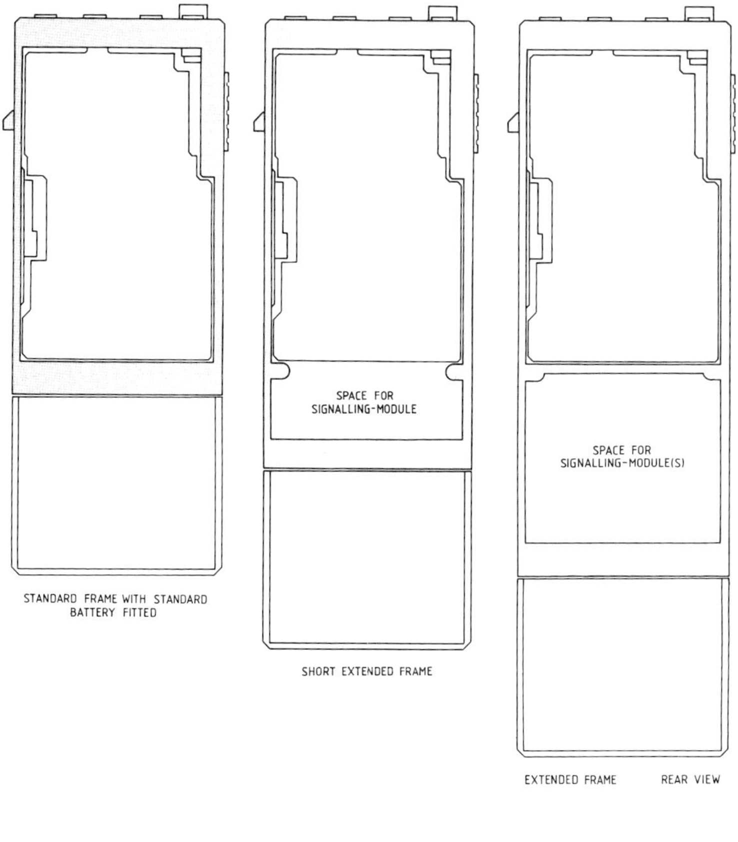

Above left: **PFX controls and indicators**

Above: **The PFX, like the PF85, comes in three different case lengths depending upon the selective call options fitted**

Fig 6.17. PFX transceiver frame assemblies

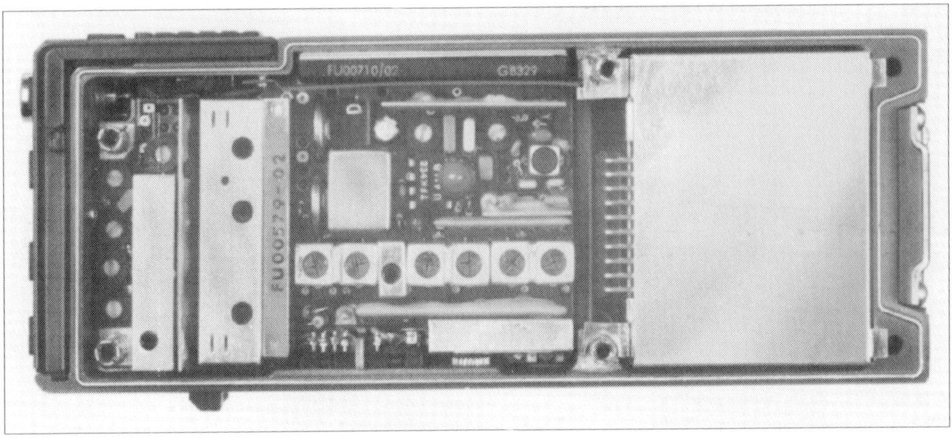

Inside the PFX

transmit, and adjust L2 on the VCO (module 3) to give the highest possible voltage between 2.0–5.0V on test point TP4. A steady voltage of 7V here indicates the VCO isn't in lock. Now select the channel with the lowest transmit frequency in the VCO TX1 range, and check the voltage on TP4 is greater than 2.0V – this checks the VCO is still in lock. Now, if you've any channels programmed on the TX VCO2 range, select the highest transmit frequency in this range and whilst on transmit adjust L4 on the VCO again to give the highest possible voltage between 2.0–5.0V on test point TP4. Now select the channel with the lowest transmit frequency in the VCO TX2 range, and again check the voltage on TP4 is greater than 2.0V.

You'll now need to set the analogue phase detector gain – an oscilloscope and audio generator if you have these are handy here,

Below: Fig 6.18. Top-panel controls

Bottom: Fig 6.19. Example of VCO grouping

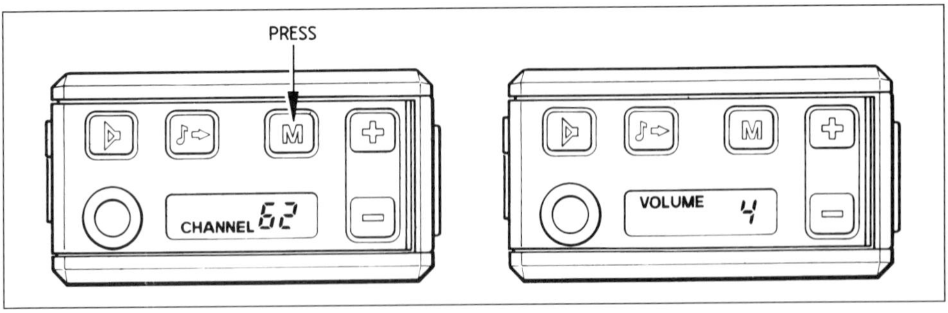

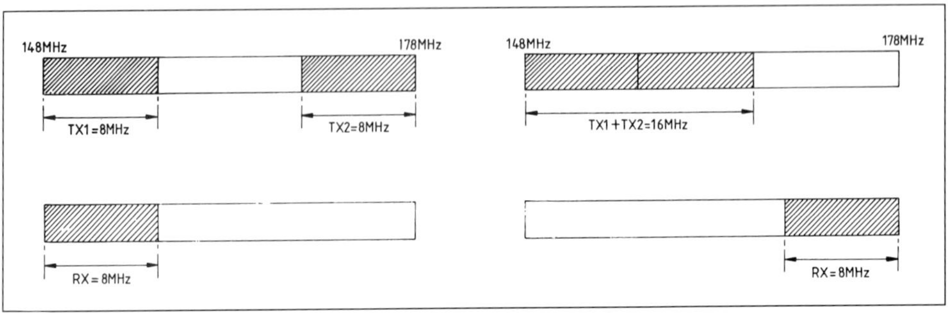

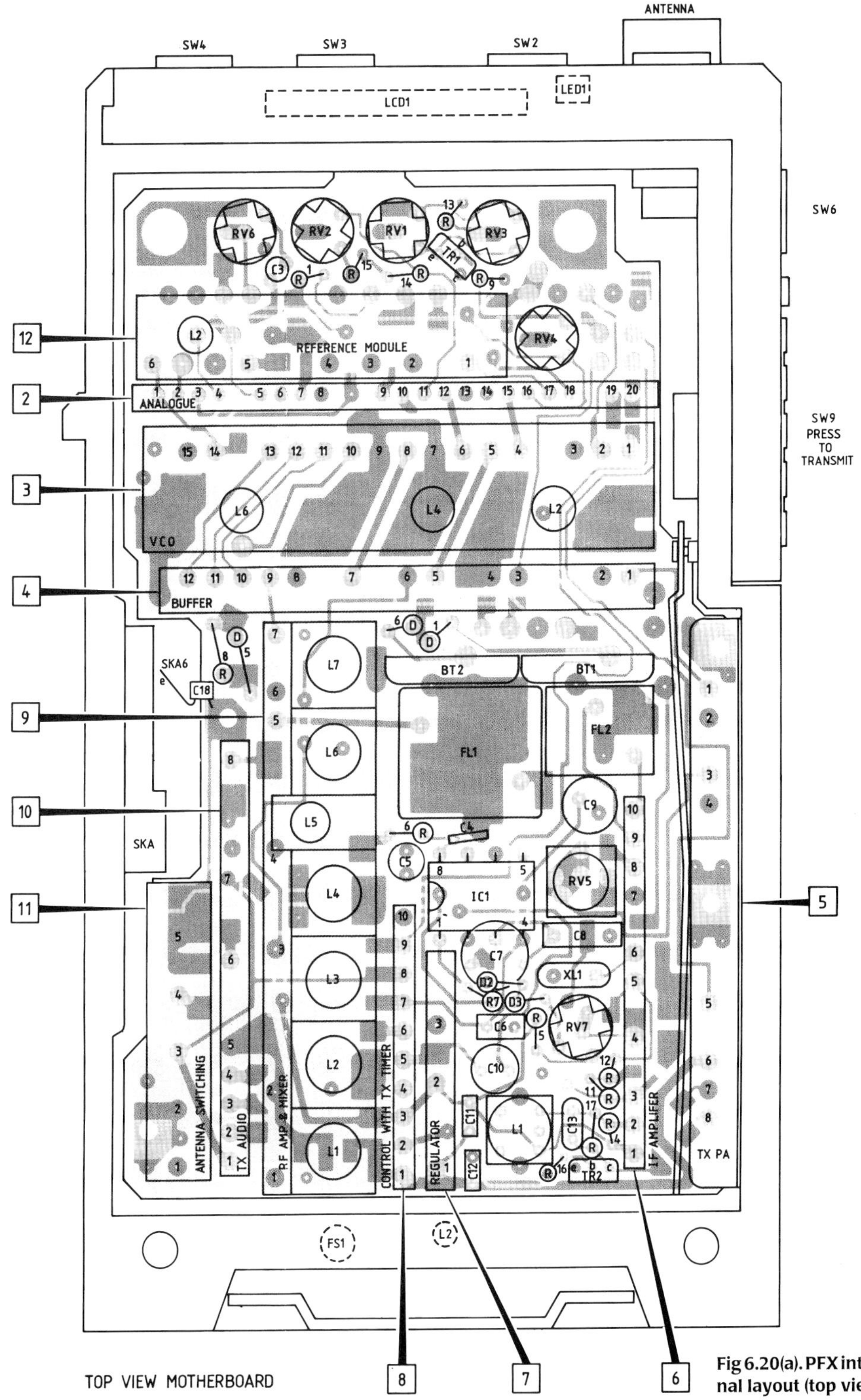

Fig 6.20(a). PFX internal layout (top view)

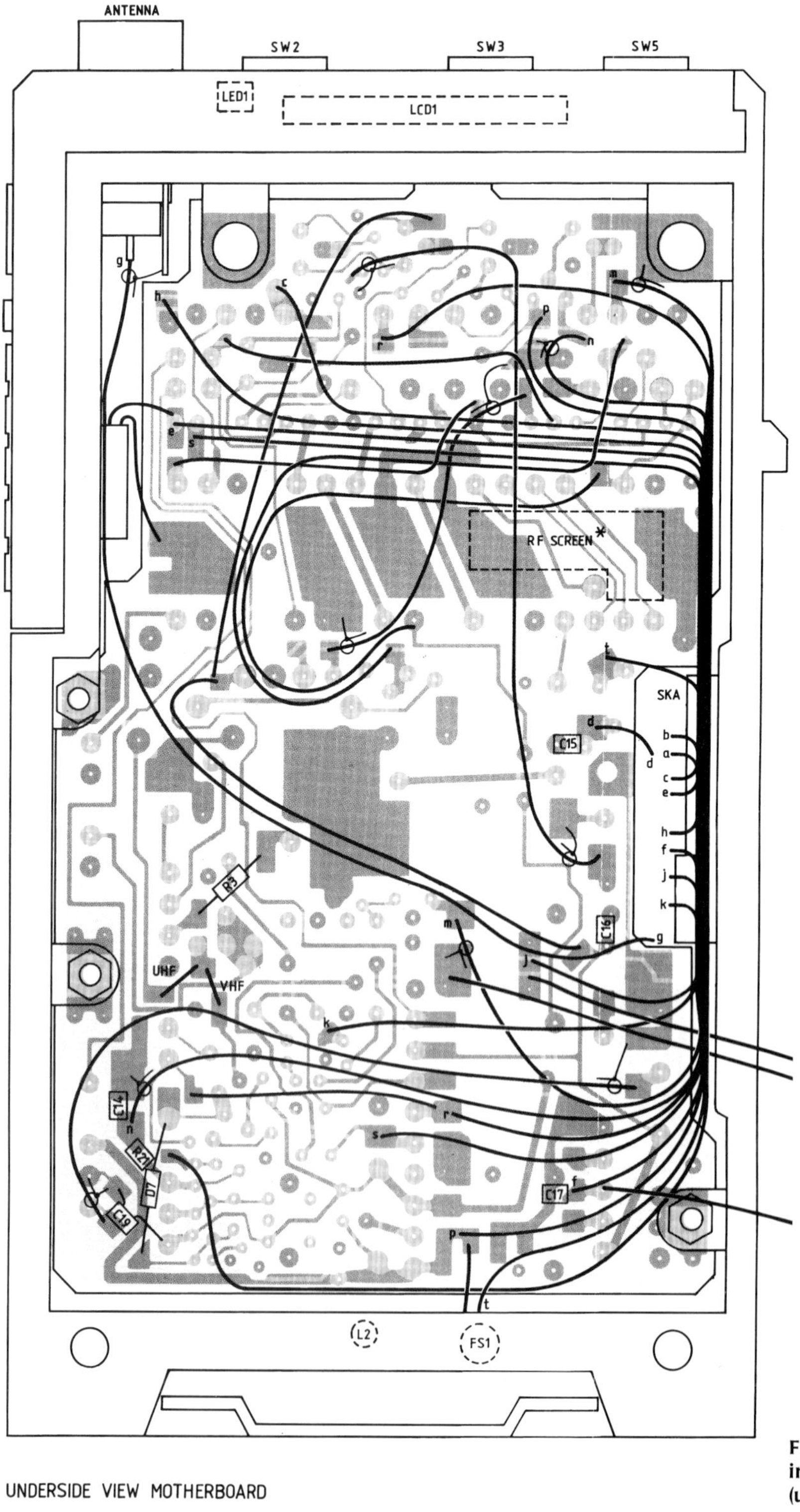

Fig 6.20(b). PFX internal layout (underside view)

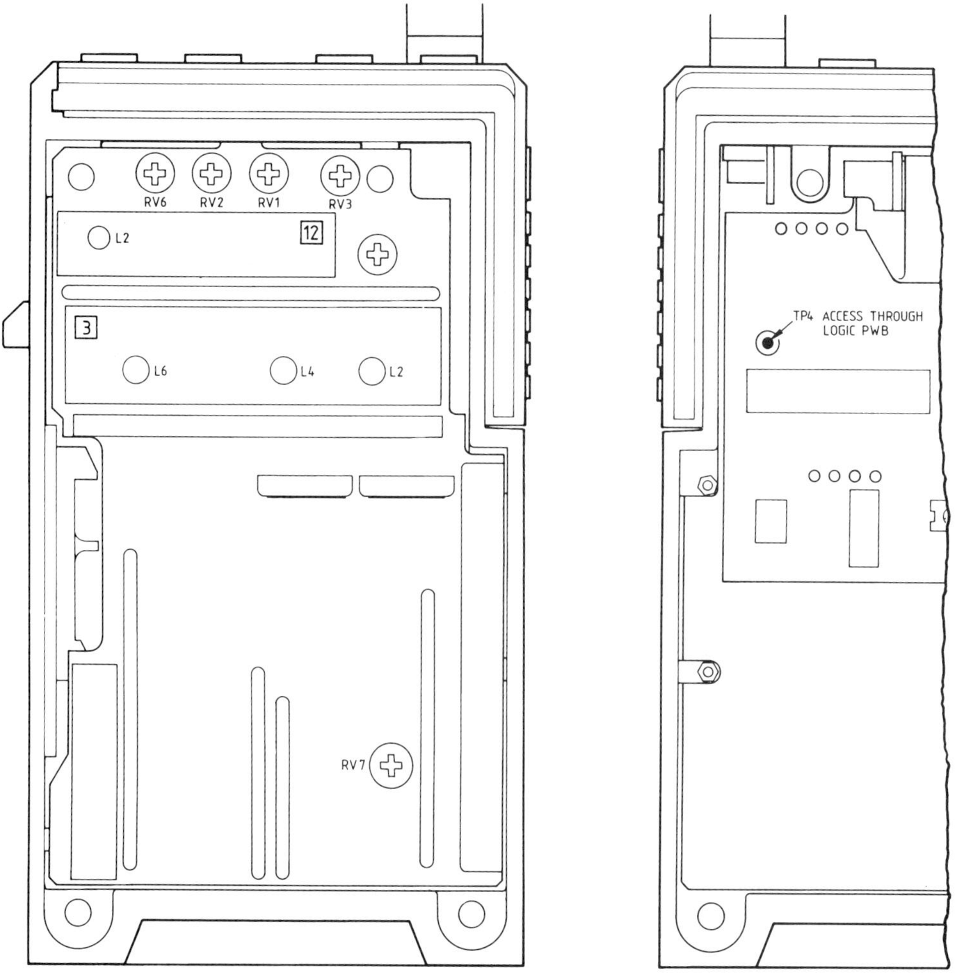

Fig 6.21. PFX preliminary adjustments to receiver

otherwise I'd advise leaving this part well alone. Connect your scope probe to TP3, socket 19 of the logic module. First adjust RV1, RV3 (mod level), RV2 and RV4 (balance) on the main board all to their fully counter-clockwise positions. Set the AF generator output to 500Hz and connect this to the set's TX audio input, switch to transmit, and adjust the output level to gain 2.8–3.2kHz transmit deviation. Now, adjust RV1 on the logic board (this is a smaller board on the other side of the set, not RV1 next to the VCO on the set's main board) so that the sine wave on the scope display is between 78–96mV p/p, or 63–75mV p/p for a 5kHz reference frequency. Reset the audio level again for 2.8–3.2kHz deviation and readjust RV1, repeating this as needed to get the required level on the scope.

To set the peak deviation, choose the lowest frequency on TX VCO1 range, and whilst on transmit with audio applied, adjust RV2 for minimum signal level on the scope, still connected as above. Now adjust RV1 on the main board (next to the VCO module) for

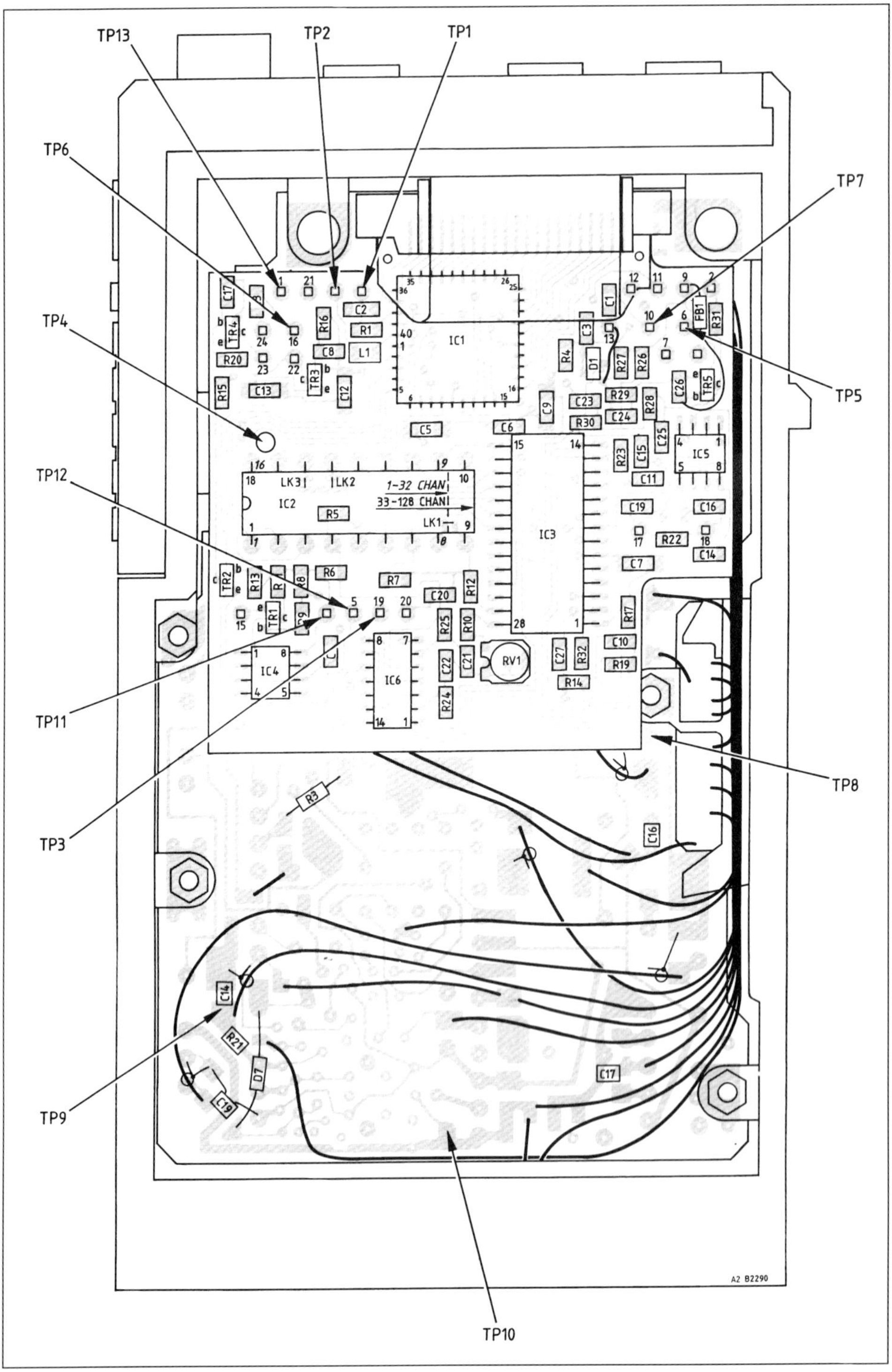

Fig 6.22. Location of PFX test points

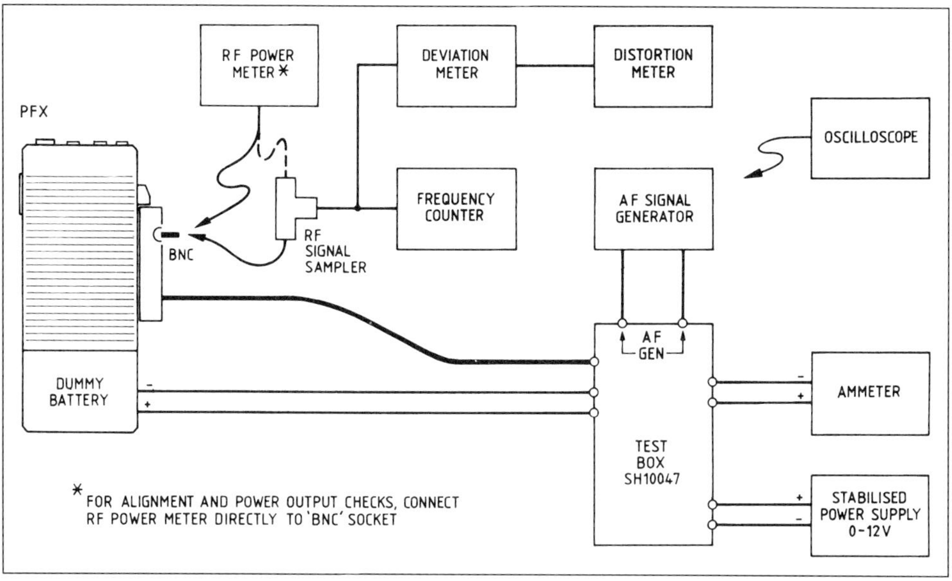

Fig 6.23. Transmitter test circuit

required peak deviation. If you've any channels programmed on the TX VCO2 range, adjust as above but with RV4 for minimum audio level and RV3 on the main board for peak deviation.

Finally, readjust RV5 if needed to set the transmit power level if you'd prefer this to be a lower level than maximum.

Receiver alignment

First rotate the squelch preset RV7 fully clockwise to defeat the receiver squelch. Select the receive channel with the highest receive frequency. Now, with your multimeter connected to test point TP4, adjust L6 on the VCO unit (module 3) for the highest possible voltage between 2.0–5.0V on this test point. Switch to the lowest receive

Fig 6.24. Receiver test circuit

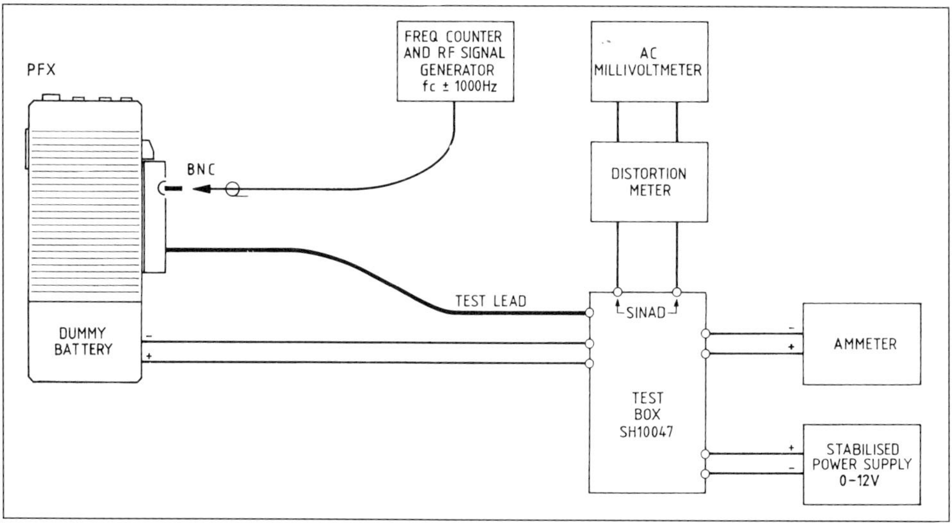

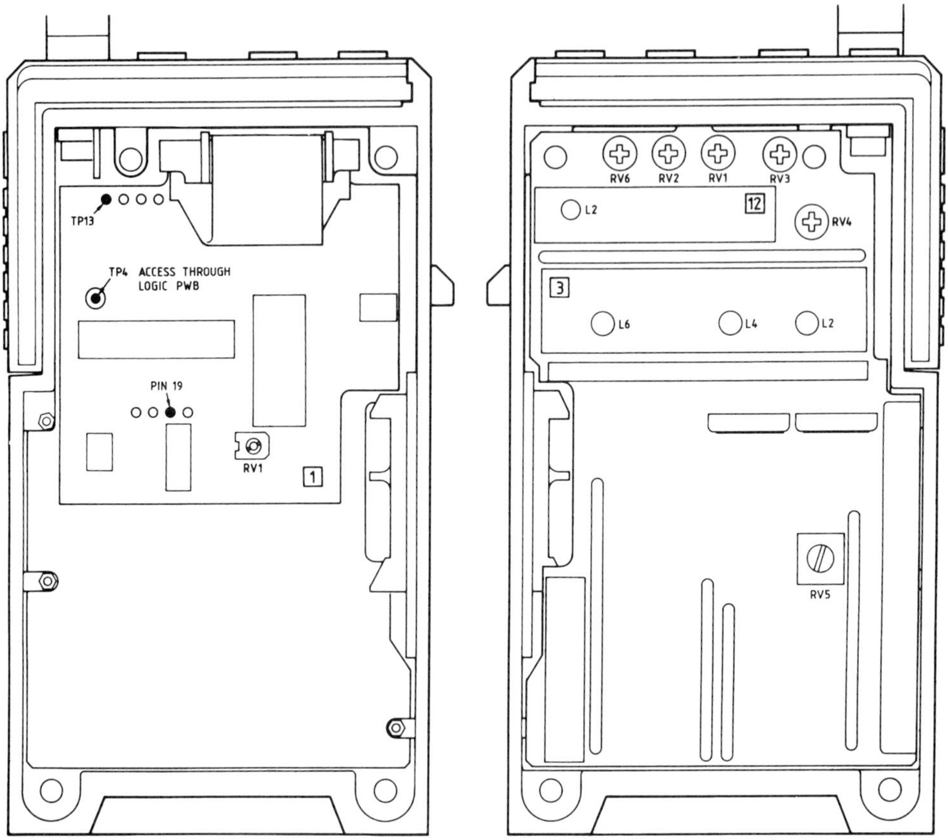

Fig 6.25. PFX transmitter alignment diagram, VHF/UHF

frequency, and check the voltage is above 2.0V, indicating the VCO is still in lock.

With a received off-air signal, on the front-end coil line-up, tune L6, L1, L2, L3 and L4 for best received signal, reducing the level of this as needed. L5 will usually already be adjusted – this is tuned for least distortion on a strong received signal. L1 is the discriminator coil, which shouldn't need adjustment, although this is set for maximum demodulated audio output.

Finally, reset RV7, the squelch preset, as needed. RV6 sets the audio level to any fitted signalling modules – this won't need adjusting.

UHF PROM code calculation

My thanks go to Tony, G4XIV, for this programming information. The method of calculation is shown here by a couple of examples, and is followed by typical codes for popular 70cm channels.

For 70cm channel RB1, ie 433.000MHz RX, 434.600MHz TX:

RX freq: *433.000*
–21.4MHz = *411.600*

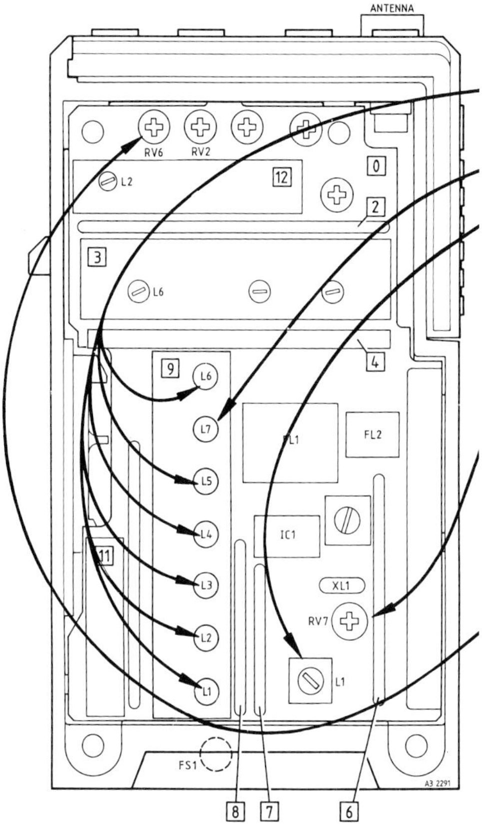

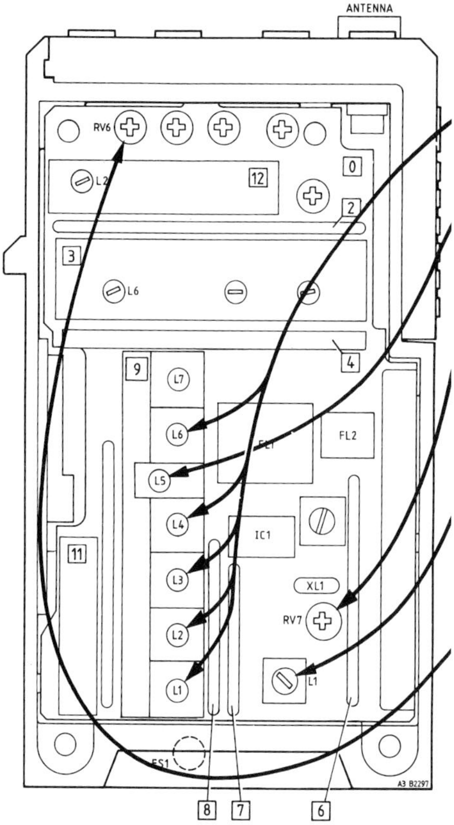

Left: **Fig 6.26. VHF PFX receiver alignment points**

Right: **Fig 6.27. UHF PFX receiver alignment points**

'MHz' – 384 = *27*
Convert to hex = *1B*
Reverse = *B1* (digit **a**)
'kHz' divided by 12.5 = *48*
Convert to hex = *30*
Reverse = *03* (digit **b**)

TX freq: *434.600*
'MHz' – 384 = *50*
Convert to hex = *32*
Reverse = *23* (digit **c**)
'kHz' divided by 12.5 = *48*
Convert to hex = *30*
Reverse = *03* (digit **d**)

Store this in PROM with the hexadecimal sequence of:

1 **b a** 3 0 B 2 **d c** 3 0 B

which for this example is 103B130B2032330B. *'1'* signifies RX, *'2'* signifies TX, with each sequence being followed with *30B* hex. Remember to prefix the string with any required address numerals for your programming software.

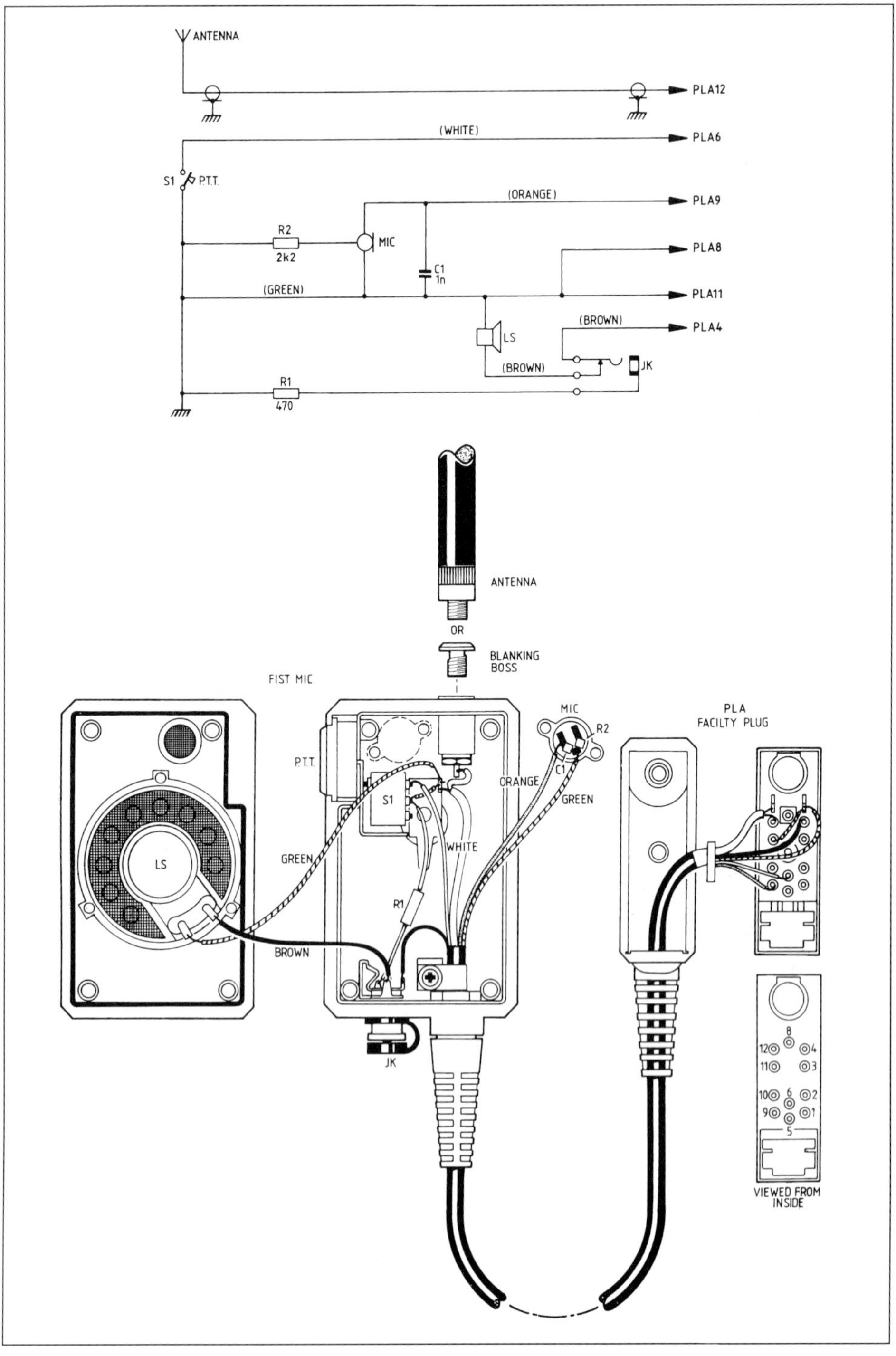

Fig 6.28. Bodyworn adapter component arrangement and circuit diagram

Here's a further example, for channel RB1, 433.025MHz receive and 434.625MHz transmit. Subtract 21.4MHz (the RX IF) from the receive frequency to give the VCO injection frequency – in this case it gives 411.625MHz. Now, take the integer of the MHz portion, ie 411, and subtract a fixed offset of 384, giving 27. Convert this to hexadecimal, giving 1B hex. Now 'reverse' this, to give B1. For the 'kHz' portion, divide by 12.5 (the minimum channel spacing), ie 625 divided by 12.5, giving 50. Convert this to hexadecimal, giving 32 hex and again 'reverse' this to give 23. Calculate the transmit code in a similar manner, remembering here to use the actual transmit frequency as the VCO frequency. For 434.625MHz, the megahertz integer (434) minus 384 is 50, which is 32 hex, reversed giving 23. The kilohertz section, 625, divided by 12.5 gives 50, ie 32 hex, and reversing this gives 23. This must be stored in the form 123B130B2232330B. Saving this in PROM address '00' will provide RB1 on the first channel, ie channel 1. Note that channel 0 is not available and is not displayed unless a fault condition occurs, so you'll need to store RB0 in a different channel, possibly channel 99 as I've done in the past.

Table 6.2. 70cm PROM codes

70cm channel	PROM address	Hexadecimal code
RB1	00	123B130B2232330B
RB2	01	143B130B2432330B
RB3	02	163B130B2632330B
RB4	03	183B130B2832330B
RB5	04	1A3B130B2A32330B
RB6	05	1C3B130B2C32330B
RB7	06	1E3B130B2E32330B
RB8	07	104B130B2042330B
RB9	08	124B130B2242330B
RB10	09	144B130B2442330B
RB11	0A	164B130B2642330B
RB12	0B	184B130B2842330B
RB13	0C	1A4B130B2A42330B
RB14	0D	1C4B130B2C42330B
RB15	0E	1E4B130B2E42330B
SU16	0F	100C130B2021330B
SU17	10	120C130B2221330B
SU18	11	130C130B2421330B
SU19	12	160C130B2621330B
SU20	13	180C130B2821330B
SU21	14	1A0C130B2A21330B
SU22	15	1C0C130B2C21330B
SU23	16	1E0C130B2E21330B

Appendix

1 CTCSS units

AS many UK repeaters become equipped for CTCSS (sub-tone) access, a simple one-IC CTCSS encoder, or encoder/decoder for advanced use, could very well be a useful 'add-on' to your rig. The circuits I've given here are both easy to build, need no frequency alignment at all (ie no frequency counter needed!), and the only setting adjustment you'll need to make is the tone level to your rig for the required frequency deviation (see Chapter 1 – 'PMR systems' for more information on this). The CTCSS frequency is determined by links to the pins of the IC, so by using a suitable multi-way switch you can have a number of CTCSS frequencies at your fingertips besides the tone used in your 'regional' area.

CTCSS ENCODER

This design (Fig A1.1) is based on a single IC from CML (Consumer Microcircuits Ltd) in Essex. It uses a 1MHz crystal, which is readily available from a number of component suppliers – you may also find that a lower-cost 1MHz ceramic resonator could also work quite well.

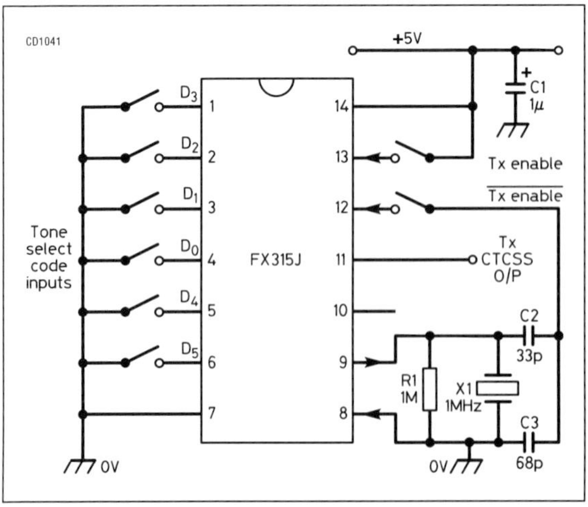

Fig A1.1. The single-IC FX315J CTCSS encoder circuit

The FX315 is a monolithic CMOS integrated circuit tone encoder for sub-audio tone squelch systems. The tone frequencies are derived from the 1MHz reference frequency, and an on-chip inverter is provided to drive an external crystal circuit. The 1MHz crystal is a parallel-resonant type – a frequency accuracy of only ±0.19% is needed to give you sufficient tone accuracy.

The tone selection is by a logic code at the D0–D5 programming inputs, and two control inputs allow either a logic '1' or logic '0' to enable the device. A low-distortion sine-wave output is generated at the TX tone output (pin 11) when the FX315 is activated. The emitter follower can source 1mW directly into a 600Ω load.

The FX315 'tone select' inputs, left open-circuit, will be programmed with logic '1's by the chip's internal pull-up resistors. This lets you use simple devices when selecting the CTCSS tone. Wire links can be fitted for permanent tone frequency, or SPST switches can allow code changes when you need them.

You'll need to feed the CTCSS tone output to your set after the microphone filtering stages, ideally at the final modulation stage, via a level-setting potentiometer and decoupling capacitor. Don't try to feed it direct to the microphone connector, as you'll undoubtedly find the subsequent filtering stages nicely remove it! The MX290 series for example have a sub-tone input pin on the facility connector which you can use.

Table A1.1. FX315 CTCSS programming table

CTCSS freq	Program inputs D0	D1	D2	D3	D4	D5
67.0	1	1	1	1	1	1
69.3	1	0	0	1	1	1
71.9	1	1	1	1	1	0
74.4	0	1	1	1	1	1
77.0	1	1	1	1	0	0
79.7	1	0	1	1	1	1
82.5	0	1	1	1	1	0
85.4	0	0	1	1	1	1
88.5	0	1	1	1	0	0
91.5	1	1	0	1	1	1
94.8	1	0	1	1	1	0
97.4	0	1	0	1	1	1
100.0	1	0	1	1	0	0
103.5	0	0	1	1	1	0
107.2	0	0	1	1	0	0
110.9	1	1	0	1	1	0
114.8	1	1	0	1	0	0
118.8	0	1	0	1	1	0
123.0	0	1	0	1	0	0
127.3	1	0	0	1	1	0
131.8	1	0	0	1	0	0
136.5	0	0	0	1	1	0
141.3	0	0	0	1	0	0
146.2	1	1	1	0	1	0
151.4	1	1	1	0	0	0
156.7	0	1	1	0	1	0
162.2	0	1	1	0	0	0
167.9	1	0	1	0	1	0
173.8	1	0	1	0	0	0
179.9	0	0	1	0	1	0
186.2	0	0	1	0	0	0
192.8	1	1	0	0	1	0
203.5	1	1	0	0	0	0
206.5	0	0	0	1	1	1
210.7	0	1	0	0	1	0
218.1	0	1	0	0	0	0
225.7	1	0	0	0	1	0
233.6	1	0	0	0	0	0
241.8	0	0	0	0	1	0
250.3	0	0	0	0	0	0

CTCSS ENCODER/DECODER

The FX365J is a CMOS LSI device in a 24-pin DIL package, and is intended for use as a CTCSS encoder/decoder. A transmit speech path filter is included, which has a cut-off frequency of 300Hz regardless of the CTCSS tone frequency selected, to remove any sub-audio elements in your rig's speech waveform before externally introducing the CTCSS tone output. A receive path audio filter is also included to allow for rejection of the CTCSS tone in your set's receiver audio after detection.

Circuitry

See Fig A1.2. The FX365 uses a 1MHz crystal reference oscillator, and is powered from a +5V supply. The tone select data lines (on the programming switches/links) are all internally pulled to the +5V supply via internal 1MΩ resistors, and thus an open link will be a logic 1, a closed link being a logic 0. Pin 24 on the IC is the received tone input line, which you should link to your receiver's discriminator or flat audio output (on the M/MX290 series for example, a suitable point for this is available on the facility connector). This line is biased to +2.5V so you'll need to use an audio coupling capacitor in-line. Pin 13 is the gated output of the tone decoder, which you can use to externally switch the receive audio path in your ex-PMR rig's receiver. This line goes to a logic 0 when a valid CTCSS tone is decoded. Pin 16 is the transmit CTCSS tone audio output, from an internal low-impedance emitter follower. Again, this line is biased to a DC level so you'll need to use an in-line audio coupling capacitor to link it to your ex-PMR rig's transmit audio stages. The tone will need to be taken via a level-setting control to feed your transmitter's modulator directly,

Fig A1.2. The FX365J CTCSS encoder/decoder circuit

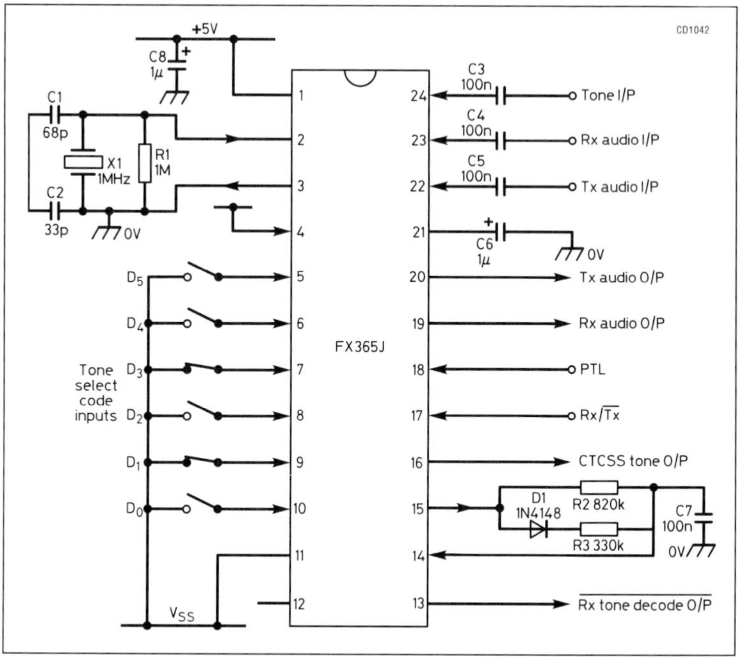

ie not the microphone input where it will probably be filtered out in your set's transmit audio shaping circuitry.

The PTL on pin 18 is a press-to-listen line which opens the RX audio path to override the tone squelch function, ie it can be used as a channel monitor button. Pin 19 is the RX audio output line, which provides an audio output when the RX tone decode (pin 13) is 0 or the PTL line (pin 18) is 1. Pin 23 is the RX audio input for use in this mode. Pins 22 and 20 are the TX audio output and input respectively, to provide the high-pass filter if needed. Finally, pin 17 selects RX or TX mode.

My thanks go to Consumer Microcircuits Ltd in Essex for help with the above application information. The FX315 and FX365J ICs are available from CML distributors around the world, which include Joseph Electronics (Steatite Group), tel 0121-643 6999, in the UK.

Fig A1.3. Simple 1750Hz piezo-ceramic toneburst circuit

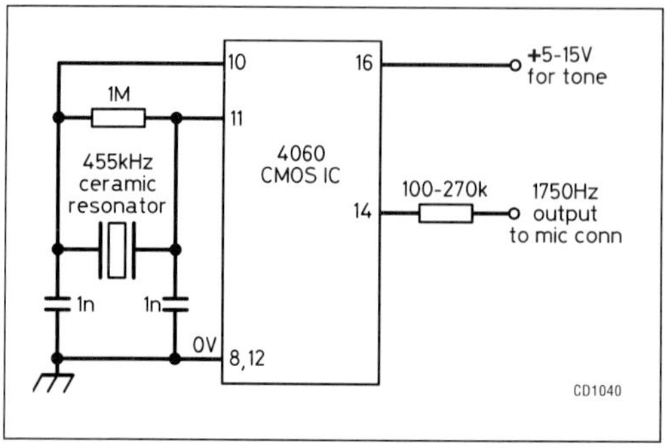

1750Hz TONEBURST

I'm often asked for a simple 1750Hz toneburst circuit, suitable for incorporation into a typical ex-PMR rig. The one shown in Fig A1.3 is a simple one-IC design, which I originally developed for use in my PF2FMB 2m handheld, and which I published in the Cambridgeshire Repeater Group newsletter over 10 years ago. It's based on a CMOS 4060 divider IC, which has its own built-in inverter gate which can be used as a simple oscillator.

A commonly available and low-cost 455kHz ceramic resonator is used for this – the resonator is available from component dealers such as Cirkit, Tandy and Maplin. It's pulled down in oscillation frequency from 455kHz slightly by the two 1nF capacitors connected to ground. The divide-by-256 line output is used from the IC, which provides a 1750Hz square wave, ie composed of 1750Hz plus lesser amounts of odd-order harmonics. If you feed this to your rig's microphone line (not direct to the transmitter's modulator circuitry), then audio frequencies above 3kHz are very effectively filtered out, leaving a drift-free 1750Hz sine wave as the resultant modulated transmitter output. The series 100kΩ resistor in the tone output line acts as a simple level control and microphone line decoupler.

Depending upon your set's audio circuitry you may need to vary the value of this (possibly use a 470kΩ preset instead) and also maybe add a DC blocking capacitor, eg 100nF, to prevent any DC voltage offset problems if a direct and non-decoupled electret microphone (rather than a normal dynamic microphone) is used.

The supply voltage may be taken directly from the +13.8V supply if required, via a momentary push-to-make button to provide a 1750Hz tone for as long as the button (together with your rig's PTT) is pressed.

I designed the circuit to be as small and simple as possible, and by soldering the components directly to the IC pins you'll find it fits into the tiniest of spaces on your rig.

Table A1.2. FX365J CTCSS programming table

CTCSS	Program inputs					
freq	D0	D1	D2	D3	D4	D5
67.0	1	1	1	1	1	1
71.9	1	1	1	1	1	0
74.4	0	1	1	1	1	1
77.0	1	1	1	1	0	0
79.7	1	0	1	1	1	1
82.5	0	1	1	1	1	0
85.4	0	0	1	1	1	1
88.5	0	1	1	1	0	0
91.5	1	1	0	1	1	1
94.8	1	0	1	1	1	0
97.4	0	1	0	1	1	1
100.0	1	0	1	1	0	0
103.5	0	0	1	1	1	0
107.2	0	0	1	1	0	0
110.9	1	1	0	1	1	0
114.8	1	1	0	1	0	0
118.8	0	1	0	1	1	0
123.0	0	1	0	1	0	0
127.3	1	0	0	1	1	0
131.8	1	0	0	1	0	0
136.5	0	0	0	1	1	0
141.3	0	0	0	1	0	0
146.2	1	1	1	0	1	0
151.4	1	1	1	0	0	0
156.7	0	1	1	0	1	0
162.2	0	1	1	0	0	0
167.9	1	0	1	0	1	0
173.8	1	0	1	0	0	0
179.9	0	0	1	0	1	0
186.2	0	0	1	0	0	0
192.8	1	1	0	0	1	0
203.5	1	1	0	0	0	0
210.7	0	1	0	0	1	0
218.1	0	1	0	0	0	0
225.7	1	0	0	0	1	0
233.6	1	0	0	0	0	0
241.8	0	0	0	0	1	0
250.3	0	0	0	0	0	0

Appendix

2 SMC PMR equipment

MANY early SMC PMR transceivers were based on equipment manufactured by Yaesu in Japan, these being made by Yaesu for SMC with appropriate modifications incorporated to suit UK-type approval requirements. Later sets included synthesised equipment which required either a dedicated handheld programmer, or later still a PC interface and suitable software. In these cases, the easiest method of 'conversion' would be to get your local PMR dealer to reprogram the equipment for you, after which you can perform any final RF tuning required by peaking up the receiver front end and transmitter power amplifier. The SMC2520, however, identified by its large LCD panel and front-panel keypad, is a dedicated Band III trunked radio transceiver, operating in the 174–225MHz band with MPT1327 signalling, and it *isn't* capable of operation on 2m without a *lot* of work.

The SMC307L1

Besides many sets coming onto the surplus market having seen PMR use in the UK, a number of equipment, particularly for 4m (the SMC 307L1 handheld) and 70cm (the SMC 545L1 and SMC 1045L2), have been sold new and boxed as surplus stock, primarily for amateur packet radio use.

Identification

The identification of frequency bands, transmitter power, and number of available channels in SMC PMR equipment is based on a fairly straightforward numbering arrangement.

The model identification sequence and meanings are given in Table A2.1.

The 307L6, 317L6 and 345L6 transceivers are 'chunky' handhelds, and for packet use the 307L6 has also been available at quite low cost as a new and boxed set without the nicad and helical.

The 2507L12 and 2515L12 are robust mobile rigs with a digital channel readout. I've used the 2507L12 myself for some time as a 4m packet node transceiver.

The 1015L1 is simple to align and comes in a reasonably compact case size, a single main board being used for the transmit and receive circuitry. The 515L1 (very rare) is basically exactly the same unit as

The SMC1015L1 looks exactly like the SMC1045L1 apart from the label

the 1015L1, but is type approved to a 5W transmitter power level. The 1015L7 is a seven-channel version of the 1015L1, the RF circuitry being the same but with the addition of a multi-channel crystal bank

Table A2.1. Identification codes for SMC PMR equipment

Format:	**SMC xx yy L zz** with the following meanings:
xx:	Identifies the transmitter power in watts, ie 3 is 3W, 10 is 10W, etc.
yy:	Identifies the frequency range of operation, eg: 07: VHF low band (ie 70MHz) 15: VHF high band, early models (ie 150MHz) 16: VHF high band, later models 17: VHF high band, later models still 45: UHF (ie 450MHz) 46: UHF, later models
L:	Identifies the set as a land mobile transceiver
zz:	Identifies the maximum number of channels that may be crystalled.

Table A2.2. Crystal information for SMC PMR equipment

Model No	Band	TX crystal	RX crystal
307L6	VHF low band (4m)	TX ÷ 12	(RX + 10.7MHz) ÷ 5
317L6	VHF high band (2m)	TX ÷ 12	(RX – 10.7MHz) ÷ 9
345L6	UHF (70cm)	TX ÷ 9	(RX – 21.4MHz) ÷ 9
515L1	VHF high band (2m)	TX ÷ 6	(RX – 21.4MHz) ÷ 3
545L1	UHF (70cm)	TX ÷ 12	(RX – 21.4MHz) ÷ 9
1015L1	VHF high band (2m)	TX ÷ 6	(RX – 21.4MHz) ÷ 3
1015L2	VHF high band (2m)	TX ÷ 6	(RX – 21.4MHz) ÷ 3
1015L7	VHF high band (2m)	TX ÷ 6	(RX – 21.4MHz) ÷ 3
1045L1	UHF (70cm)	TX ÷ 12	(RX – 21.4MHz) ÷ 9
2507L12	VHF low band (4m)	TX ÷ 6	(RX – 10.7MHz) ÷ 4
2515L12	VHF high band (2m)	TX ÷ 12	(RX – 10.7MHz) ÷ 9

and front-panel channel switch. The 545L1 and 1045L1 sets are the UHF versions of these.

The 1015L2 is a very small mobile, with the RX and TX circuits using separate boards on either side of a central chassis screen. It's capable of full-duplex operation if you fit an additional antenna socket to the rear panel and link out the antenna changeover circuit. The 1045L2 is the UHF version of this set.

Appendix

3 Crystal calculations for ex-PMR sets

THESE lists have been collated with information provided by the PMR User Group (UK). Please check that your set does indeed use these frequency formulae, eg by checking the existing crystals fitted, before spending money on ordering new crystals.

Table A4.1. Crystals for PMR equipment from various manufacturers

Model name and band	Transmit crystal	Receive crystal
AWA (Cleartone)		
2280 (68–81)	TX ÷ 2	(RX + 10.7) ÷ 2
2280 (81–97)	TX ÷ 2	(RX – 10.7) ÷ 2
2280 (97–108)	TX ÷ 2	(RX + 10.7) ÷ 2
2280 (97–108)	TX ÷ 2	(RX – 10.7) ÷ 2
2280 (118–174)	TX ÷ 4	(RX – 10.7) ÷ 3
2295A (Lo & hi)	TX ÷ 12	
2291 (Lo)		(RX + 10.7) ÷ 2
2291 (Hi)		(RX – 10.7) ÷ 3
TR265 (Lo)	TX ÷ 2	(RX + 10.7) ÷ 2
TR265 (Hi)	TX ÷ 4	(RX – 10.7) ÷ 3
TR235A (Mid)	TX ÷ 4	(RX + 10.7) ÷ 3
810 (Lo)	TX ÷ 2	(RX + 10.7) ÷ 2
25M (Hi)	TX ÷ 27	(RX + 10.7) ÷ 4
Pager (Lo)		(RX – 10.7) ÷ 2
Bosch		
HFE165	TX ÷ 4	(RX – 21.4) ÷ 2
HFG451	TX ÷ 12	(RX – 21.4) ÷ 12
Pager GRE62		(RX – 10.7) ÷ 4
Pager GRE163		(RX – 10.7) ÷ 3
Burndept		
BE357 (UHF)	TX ÷ 18	(RX + 10.7) ÷ 5
BE363 (UHF)	TX ÷ 18	(RX + 10.7) ÷ 5
BE365 (UHF)	TX ÷ 18	(RX + 10.7) ÷ 5
BE372 (UHF)	TX ÷ 18	(RX + 10.7) ÷ 5
BE373 (UHF)	TX ÷ 18	(RX + 10.7) ÷ 5
BE422 (Hi)	TX ÷ 9	(RX + 10.7) ÷ 9
BE443 (Hi)	TX ÷ 9	(RX + 10.7) ÷ 9
BE439 (Hi)	TX ÷ 9	(RX + 10.7) ÷ 9
BE471 (Hi)	TX ÷ 9	(RX + 10.7) ÷ 9
BE470 (Hi)	TX ÷ 9	(RX + 10.7) ÷ 9
BE448 (Lo)	TX ÷ 8	(RX – 10.7) ÷ 2
BE448 (Hi)	TX ÷ 16	(RX – 10.7) ÷ 4
BE448 (UHF)	TX ÷ 32	(RX – 21.4) ÷ 12
BE449 (Hi)	TX ÷ 16	(RX – 10.7) ÷ 4
BE450 (Hi)	TX ÷ 16	(RX – 10.7) ÷ 4
BE450 (Lo)	TX ÷ 8	(RX – 10.7) ÷ 2
BE451 (Hi)	TX ÷ 16	(RX – 10.7) ÷ 4

Model name and band	Transmit crystal	Receive crystal
(Burndept – continued)		
BE451 (Lo)	TX ÷ 8	(RX – 10.7) ÷ 2
BE453 (Hi)	TX ÷ 16	(RX – 10.7) ÷ 4
BE453 (Lo)	TX ÷ 8	(RX – 10.7) ÷ 2
BE452 (Hi)	TX ÷ 16	(RX – 10.7) ÷ 4
BE452 (UHF)	TX ÷ 32	(RX – 21.4) ÷ 12
BE454 (UHF)	TX ÷ 30	(RX + 21.4) ÷ 30
BE456 (Hi)	TX ÷ 16	(RX – 10.7) ÷ 4
BE457 (Hi)	TX ÷ 16	(RX – 10.7) ÷ 4
BE458 (Hi)	TX ÷ 12	(RX + 21.4) ÷ 12
BE460 (UHF)	TX ÷ 96	(RX#35 ÷ 8
BE468 (Hi)	TX ÷ 16	(RX – 10.7) ÷ 4
BE469 (Hi)	TX ÷ 16	(RX – 10.7) ÷ 4
BE473 (Hi)	TX ÷ 9	(RX – 10.7) ÷ 3
BE513 (Hi)	TX ÷ 6	(RX – 10.7) ÷ 3
BE570 (UHF)	TX ÷ 9	(RX + 10.7) ÷ 9
BE600 (Hi)	TX ÷ 6	(RX – 21.4) ÷ 3
BE600 (UHF)	TX ÷ 9	(RX + 21.4) ÷ 9
Cody		
FC1500 (134–174)	TX ÷ 12	(RX – 10.7) ÷ 3
FC720 (68–88)	TX ÷ 12	(RX + 10.7) ÷ 3
FC900 (156–163)	TX ÷ 9	(RX – 10.7) ÷ 3
FC950 (134–174)	TX ÷ 9	(RX – 10.7) ÷ 3
FC205 (134–174)	TX ÷ 12	(RX – 10.7) ÷ 3
FC1605 (134–174)	TX ÷ 9	(RX – 10.7) ÷ 3
FC885 (68–88)	TX ÷ 6	(RX – 10.7) ÷ 2
APH56/52 (148–174)	TX ÷ 9	(RX – 21.4) ÷ 3
APH26/22 (148–174)	TX ÷ 9	(RX – 21.4) ÷ 3
APU44/42 (UHF only)	TX ÷ 27	(RX – 21.4) ÷ 9
APU24/22 (UHF only)	TX ÷ 27	(RX – 21.4) ÷ 9
AMH150 (Hi)	TX ÷ 9	(RX – 21.4) ÷ 3
AMH150 (UHF only)	TX ÷ 27	(RX – 21.4) ÷ 9
T1502MX (Marine)	TX ÷ 12	(RX – 11.7) ÷ 9
T165MX (Marine)	TX ÷ 12	(RX – 11.7) ÷ 9
T165N (Marine)	TX ÷ 12	(RX – 11.7) ÷ 9
T462MX (UHF only)	TX ÷ 24	(RX – 211.4 ÷ 24
T464MX (UHF only)	TX ÷ 24	(RX – 211.4 ÷ 24
T72 MX (Marine)	TX ÷ 6	(RX – 10.7) ÷ 4
T72N (Lo)	TX ÷ 6	(RX – 10.7) ÷ 4
Communique		
C544 (Lo)	TX ÷ 6	(RX + 21.4) ÷ 3
C734 (UHF)	TX ÷ 36	(RX – 21.4) ÷ 9
C844 (Hi)	TX ÷ 12	(RX – 21.4) ÷ 3
C833 (Hi)	TX ÷ 12	(RX – 21.4) ÷ 3
C146A (Hi)	TX ÷ 12	(RX – 10.7) ÷ 9
SR146A (Hi)	TX ÷ 12	(RX – 10.7) ÷ 9
C830S (Hi)	TX ÷ 18	(RX – 11.7) ÷ 9
C832 (Hi)	TX ÷ 9	(RX – 10.7) ÷ 3
V8001 (Hi)	TX ÷ 9	(RX – 10.7) ÷ 3
V600 (Hi)	TX ÷ 9	(RX – 10.7) ÷ 3
C511 Pager (Lo)		(RX – 10.7) ÷ 2
C811 Pager (Hi)		(RX – 10.7) ÷ 3
HX507U (UHF)	TX ÷ 36	(RX – 21.4) ÷ 9
HX507V (Hi)	TX ÷ 12	(RX – 21.4) ÷ 3
GEC		
RC506	TX ÷ 2	(RX – 21.4) ÷ 2
RC508	TX ÷ 6	(RX – 21.4) ÷ 6

Model name and band	Transmit crystal	Receive crystal
(GEC – continued)		
RC516	TX ÷ 6	(RX – 21.4) ÷ 3
RC530 (Lo)	TX ÷ 12	(RX – 10.7) ÷ 6
RC530 (156–174)	TX ÷ 12	(RX – 10.7) ÷ 12
RC530 (146–156)	TX ÷ 12	(RX + 10.7) ÷ 12
RC550 (Lo)	TX ÷ 2	(RX – 10.7) ÷ 2
RC550 (Mid)	TX ÷ 2	(RX – 10.7) ÷ 3
RC550 (Hi)	TX ÷ ?	(RX – 10.7) ÷ 3
RC555 (Lo)	TX ÷ 8	(RX – 10.7) ÷ 6
RC555 (Hi)	TX ÷ 12	(RX – 10.7) ÷ 12
RC570 (80–84)	TX ÷ 2	(RX + 10.7) ÷ 2
RC570 (97–102)	TX ÷ 2	(RX – 10.7) ÷ 2
RC600 (Lo)	TX ÷ 36	RX – 10.7
RC600 (Hi)	TX ÷ 72	(RX – 10.7) ÷ 2
RC602 (Hi)	TX ÷ 72	(RX – 10.7) ÷ 2
RC602 (Lo)	TX ÷ 36	RX – 10.7
RC620 (Lo)	TX ÷ 12	(RX – 10.7) ÷ 6
RC620 (Hi)	TX ÷ 12	(RX – 10.7) ÷ 12
RC625 (Lo)	TX ÷ 12	(RX + 10.7) ÷ 6
RC625 (Air band)	TX ÷ 8	(RX + 10.7) ÷ 12
RC625 (132–160)	TX ÷ 12	(RX + 10.7) ÷ 12
RC625 (156–174)	TX ÷ 12	(RX – 10.7) ÷ 12
RC650 (Lo)	TX ÷ 12	(RX – 10.7) ÷ 6
RC650 (Mid)	TX ÷ 12	(RX – 10.7) ÷ 12
RC650 (Hi)	TX ÷ 12	(RX – 10.7) ÷ 12
RC660 (Lo)	TX ÷ 8	(RX – 10.7) ÷ 6
RC660 (Mid)	TX ÷ 8	(RX + 10.7) ÷ 12
RC660 (Hi)	TX ÷ 12	(RX – 10.7) ÷ 12
RC665 (Hi)	TX ÷ 12	(RX – 10.7) ÷ 12
RC665 (Lo)	TX ÷ 8	(RX – 10.7) ÷ 6
RC665 (Mid)	TX ÷ 8	(RX + 10.7) ÷ 12
RC666 (Lo)	TX ÷ 8	(RX – 10.7) ÷ 6
RC666 (Hi)	TX ÷ 12	(RX – 10.7) ÷ 12
RC666 (Mid)	TX ÷ 8	(RX + 10.7) ÷ 12
GEC RC680 (Mid)	TX ÷ 12	(RX + 10.7) ÷ 12
GEC RC680 (Lo)	TX ÷ 12	(RX + 10.7) ÷ 6
GEC RC680 (Hi)	TX ÷ 12	(RX – 10.7) ÷ 12
GEC RC681 (Lo)	TX ÷ 12	(RX + 10.7) ÷ 6
GEC RC681 (Mid)	TX ÷ 12	(RX + 10.7) ÷ 12
GEC RC681 (Hi)	TX ÷ 12	(RX – 10.7) ÷ 12
GEC RC700 (Hi)	TX ÷ 72	(RX – 10.7) ÷ 2
GEC RC700 (Lo)	TX ÷ 36	RX – 10.7
GEC RC710 (Lo)	TX ÷ 36	RX – 10.7
GEC RC710 (Mid)	TX ÷ 36	RX – 10.7
GEC RC710 (Hi)	TX ÷ 72	(RX – 10.7) ÷ 2
GEC RC730 (Lo)	TX ÷ 12	(RX + 10.7) ÷ 6
GEC RC730 (105–108)	TX ÷ 12	(RX – 10.7) ÷ 6
GEC RC730 (132–152)	TX ÷ 12	(RX + 10.7) ÷ 12
GEC RC730 (150–174)	TX ÷ 12	(RX – 10.7) ÷ 12
GEC RC742 (150–174)	TX ÷ 12	(RX – 10.7) ÷ 12
GEC RC742 (132–152)	TX ÷ 12	(RX + 10.7) ÷ 12
GEC RC742 (Lo)	TX ÷ 12	(RX – 10.7) ÷ 4
GEC RC750 (Lo)	TX ÷ 12	(RX – 10.7) ÷ 6
GEC RC750 (Hi)	TX ÷ 12	(RX – 10.7) ÷ 12
GEC RC751 (Hi)	TX ÷ 12	(RX – 10.7) ÷ 12
GEC RC751 (Lo)	TX ÷ 8	(RX – 10.7) ÷ 6
GEC RC751 (Mid)	TX ÷ 8	(RX + 10.7) ÷ 12
GEC RC760 (Mid)	TX ÷ 12	(RX – 10.7) ÷ 12
GEC RC760 (Hi)	TX ÷ 12	(RX – 10.7) ÷ 12

Model name and band	Transmit crystal	Receive crystal
(GEC – continued)		
RC760 (Lo)	TX ÷ 12	(RX – 10.7) ÷ 6
RC770 (Lo)	TX ÷ 8	(RX – 10.7) ÷ 6
RC770 (Hi)	TX ÷ 12	(RX – 10.7) ÷ 12
RC770 (Mid)	TX ÷ 12	(RX + 10.7) ÷ 12
RC770 (73–77)	TX ÷ 8	(RX + 10.7) ÷ 6
RC770 (118–133)	TX ÷ 8	(RX – 10.7) ÷ 12
RC770 (133–136)	TX ÷ 8	(RX + 10.7) ÷ 12
RC782 (Lo)	TX ÷ 12	(RX – 10.7) ÷ 4
RC782 (Hi)	TX ÷ 12	(RX – 10.7) ÷ 12
RC782 (Mid)	TX ÷ 12	(RX + 10.7) ÷ 12
RC800 (UHF)	TX ÷ 96	(RX – 35) ÷ 8
RC810 (UHF)	TX ÷ 72	(RX + 10.7) ÷ 10
RC826	TX ÷ 32	(RX + 10.7) ÷ 32
RC850	TX ÷ 72	(RX + 10.7) ÷ 10
Maxon		
CGX0510N (Hi)	TX ÷ 9	(RX – 10.7) ÷ 9
CGX0520S (UHF)	TX ÷ 27	(RX – 21.4) ÷ 9
CGX0511N (Hi)	TX ÷ 9	(RX – 10.7) ÷ 9
CGX0521S (UHF)	TX ÷ 27	(RX – 21.4) ÷ 9
Motorola		
Spirit Pager (VHF)	Pager	(RX – 17.9 ÷ 3
Spirit Pager (UHF)	Pager	(RX – 17.9 ÷ 9
HT220 (Hi)	TX ÷ 9	(RX – 16.8 ÷ 3
Metrix Pager (VHF)	Pager	(RX – 17.9 ÷ 3
HT220 (380–520)	TX ÷ 27	(RX – 11.7) ÷ 9
UNK1 (380–520)	TX ÷ 27	(RX – 17.9 ÷ 9
Maxar (68–104)	TX ÷ 6	(RX – 10.7) ÷ 2
Maxar (104–141)	TX ÷ 6	(RX – 10.7) ÷ 3
Maxar (142–174)	TX ÷ 9	(RX – 10.7) ÷ 3
Maxar (380–520)	TX ÷ 27	(RX – 10.7) ÷ 9
MC80 (68–88)	TX ÷ 6	(RX – 10.7) ÷ 2
MC80 (104–174)	TX ÷ 9	(RX – 10.7) ÷ 3
MC80 (380–520)	TX ÷ 27	(RX – 10.7) ÷ 9
Micro (UHF)	TX ÷ 36	(RX – 11.7) ÷ 24
CD100 (68–88)	TX ÷ 6	(RX – 10.7) ÷ 6
CD100 (105–108)	TX ÷ 8	(RX – 10.7) ÷ 6
CD100 (138–141)	TX ÷ 12	(RX – 10.7) ÷ 9
CD100 (142–174)	TX ÷ 12	(RX – 10.7) ÷ 9
CD100 (UHF)	TX ÷ 36	(RX – 10.7) ÷ 24
MT500 (68–88)	TX ÷ 3	(RX – 8.4) ÷ 2
MT500 (142–174)	TX ÷ 3	(RX – 17.9) ÷ 3
MT500 (380–520)	TX ÷ 9	(RX – 17.9 ÷ 8
MT700 (142–174)	TX ÷ 9	(RX – 17.9) ÷ 3
MT700 (380–520)	TX ÷ 24	(RX – 17.9) ÷ 8
HT440 (142–174)	TX ÷ 9	(RX – 17.9) ÷ 3
HT440 (403–430)	TX ÷ 27	(RX + 21.4) ÷ 8
HT440 (440–512)	TX ÷ 27	(RX – 21.4) ÷ 8
MX320 (VHF only)	TX ÷ 3	(RX – 21.4) ÷ 2
MX330 (VHF only)	TX ÷ 3	(RX – 21.4) ÷ 2
PT400 (VHF only)	TX ÷ 18	(RX – 11.7) ÷ 3
Pagers (others)		(RX freq – 0.455) ÷ 25
Nolton		
Nova (Hi)	TX ÷ 8	(RX – 21.4) ÷ 3
Nova (Lo)	TX ÷ 8	(RX + 21.4) ÷ 2
Nova (Mid)	TX ÷ 8	(RX – 21.4) ÷ 2
Sabre (Lo AM)	TX ÷ 2	(RX – 10.7) ÷ 2

Model name and band	Transmit crystal	Receive crystal
(Nolton – continued)		
Sabre (Hi AM)	TX ÷ 4	(RX – 10.7) ÷ 4
Sabre (Mid AM)	TX ÷ 2	(RX + 10.7) ÷ 4
Sabre (Mid FM)	TX ÷ 16	(RX + 10.7) ÷ 4
Sabre (Hi FM)	TX ÷ 16	(RX – 10.7) ÷ 4
Sabre (Lo FM)	TX ÷ 16	(RX – 10.7) ÷ 2
Sabre (Air FM)	TX ÷ 16	(RX + 10.7) ÷ 4
Miscellaneous		
Ultra Lion (Lo)	TX ÷ 8	(RX – 10.7) ÷ 2
Ultra Lion (Hi)	TX ÷ 16	(RX – 10.7) ÷ 4
MX4145 (VHF)	TX ÷ 6	
Callbuoy CB31PU (UHF)	TX ÷ 24	(RX – 21.4) ÷ 24
Callbuoy CB31PH (Hi)	TX ÷ 12	(RX – 10.7) ÷ 9
Callbuoy mobile (Hi)	TX ÷ 6	(RX – 10.7) ÷ 4
Callbuoy mobile (Lo)	TX ÷ 3	(RX + 10.7) ÷ 2
Pye		
PF85 (UHF)	TX ÷ 9	(RX – 21.4) ÷ 8
F496 (UHF)	TX ÷ 8	(RX + 21.4) ÷ 8
F9U (UHF)	TX ÷ 32	(RX + 10.7) ÷ 36
L9U (UHF)	TX ÷ 32	(RX – 10.7) ÷ 36
AM10B (68–88)	TX ÷ 8	(RX – 10.7) ÷ 2
AM10D (68–88)	TX ÷ 8	(RX – 10.7) ÷ 2
AM10B (88–108)	TX ÷ 12	(RX – 10.7) ÷ 3
AM10D (88–108)	TX ÷ 12	(RX – 10.7) ÷ 3
AM10B (148–174)	TX ÷ 18	(RX – 10.7) ÷ 3
AM10D (148–174)	TX ÷ 18	(RX – 10.7) ÷ 3
AM25T (148–174)	TX ÷ 18	(RX – 10.7) ÷ 3
AM25T (68–88)	TX ÷ 8	(RX – 10.7) ÷ 2
AM25T (88–108)	TX ÷ 12	(RX – 10.7) ÷ 3
AM25B (148–174)	TX ÷ 18	(RX + 10.7) ÷ 12
AM25B (68–88)	TX ÷ 8	(RX + 10.7) ÷ 12
AM25B (79–132)	TX ÷ 12	(RX + 10.7) ÷ 12
F100 (68–88)	TX ÷ 18	(RX – 10.7) ÷ 2
F100 (80–102)	TX ÷ 18	(RX – 10.7) ÷ 2
F100 (132–174)	TX ÷ 36	(RX – 10.7) ÷ 3
F27AM (Lo)	TX ÷ 8	(RX – 10.7) ÷ 2
F27AM (Hi)	TX ÷ 18	(RX – 10.7) ÷ 3
T30AM (Lo)	TX ÷ 3	
T30AM (Hi)	TX ÷ 6	
F25FM (Any band)	same as MF25FM	
MF25FM (Lo)	TX ÷ 16	(RX – 10.7) ÷ 8
MF25FM (Mid)	TX ÷ 16	(RX – 10.7) ÷ 12
MF25FM (Hi)	TX ÷ 16	(RX – 10.7) ÷ 12
MF25FM (132–156)	TX ÷ 16	(RX + 10.7) ÷ 12
MF25FM (380–440)	TX ÷ 32	(RX + 10.7) ÷ 36
MF25FM (440–470)	TX ÷ 32	(RX – 10.7) ÷ 36
PTC145 Monitor		(RX – 2.9) ÷ 13
FM10D (Lo)	TX ÷ 24	(RX – 10.7) ÷ 2
FM10D (Mid)	TX ÷ 24	(RX – 10.7) ÷ 3
FM10D (Hi)	TX ÷ 36	(RX – 10.7) ÷ 3
FM10B (Lo)	TX ÷ 24	(RX – 10.7) ÷ 2
FM10B (Mid)	TX ÷ 24	(RX – 10.7) ÷ 3
FM10B (Hi)	TX ÷ 36	(RX – 10.7) ÷ 3
U10B (UHF)	TX ÷ 36	(RX – 10.7) ÷ 13
HP1AM (Lo)	TX ÷ 8	(RX – 10.7) ÷ 2
HP1AM (Hi)	TX ÷ 18	(RX – 10.7) ÷ 3
HP1AM (Mid)	TX ÷ 12	(RX – 10.7) ÷ 3
HP1FM (Lo)	TX ÷ 24	(RX – 10.7) ÷ 2

Model name and band	Transmit crystal	Receive crystal
(Pye – continued)		
HP1FM (Mid)	TX ÷ 24	(RX – 10.7) ÷ 3
HP1FM (Hi)	TX ÷ 36	(RX – 10.7) ÷ 3
W15AM (Lo)	TX ÷ 2	(RX – 10.7) ÷ 2
W15AM (Mid)	TX ÷ 3	(RX – 10.7) ÷ 3
W15AM (Hi)	TX ÷ 4	(RX – 10.7) ÷ 3
W15FM (Lo)	TX ÷ 24	(RX – 10.7) ÷ 2
W25FM (Lo)	TX ÷ 24	(RX – 10.7) ÷ 2
W15FM (Mid)	TX ÷ 24	(RX – 10.7) ÷ 3
W15FM (Hi)	TX ÷ 36	(RX – 10.7) ÷ 3
W30AM (Mid)	TX ÷ 3	(RX – 10.7) ÷ 3
W30AM (Hi)	TX ÷ 4	(RX – 10.7) ÷ 3
W30AM (Lo)	TX ÷ 2	(RX – 10.7) ÷ 2
W25FM (Mid)	TX ÷ 24	(RX – 10.7) ÷ 3
W25FM (Hi)	TX ÷ 36	(RX – 10.7) ÷ 3
W15U (UHF)	TX ÷ 32	(RX – 10.7) ÷ 36
Storno		
CQF614 (146–160)	TX ÷ 12	(RX + 10.7) ÷ 3
CQF614 (156–174)	TX ÷ 12	(RX – 10.7) ÷ 3
CQF632 (Lo)	TX ÷ 6	(RX + 10.7) ÷ 2
CQF634 (Hi)	TX ÷ 12	(RX – 10.7) ÷ 3
CQF634 (Lo)	TX ÷ 6	(RX + 10.7) ÷ 2
CQF662 (UHF only)	TX ÷ 36	(RX – 10.7) ÷ 36
CQF674 (Lo)	TX ÷ 12	(RX – 10.7) ÷ 2
CQL612 (Hi)	TX ÷ 12	(RX – 10.7) ÷ 3
CQL614 (Hi)	TX ÷ 12	(RX – 10.7) ÷ 3
CQL634 (Hi)	TX ÷ 12	(RX – 10.7) ÷ 3
CQL634 (Lo)	TX ÷ 6	(RX + 10.7) ÷ 2
CQL662 (UHF only)	TX ÷ 36	(RX – 10.7) ÷ 36
CRP240 (Lo) Pager		RX – 0.455
CRP240 (Hi) Pager		(RX – 0.455) ÷ 2
MP1 (Hi)	TX ÷ 8R	(RX – 21.4) ÷ 9
CQP513 (146–160)	TX ÷ 12	(RX + 10.7) ÷ 3
CQP513 (156–174)	TX ÷ 12	(RX – 10.7) ÷ 3
CQP514 (146–160)	TX ÷ 12	(RX + 10.7) ÷ 3
CQP531 (Lo)	TX ÷ 12	(RX + 10.7) ÷ 2
CQP532 (Lo)	TX ÷ 6	(RX + 10.7) ÷ 2
CQP533 (Lo)	TX ÷ 6	(RX + 10.7) ÷ 2
CQP534 (Lo)	TX ÷ 6	(RX + 10.7) ÷ 2
CQP561 (Hi)	TX ÷ 36	(RX – 10.7) ÷ 3
CQP562 (Hi)	TX ÷ 36	(RX – 10.7) ÷ 3
CQP563 (Hi)	TX ÷ 36	(RX – 10.7) ÷ 3
CQP812 (Marine)	TX ÷ 8	RX – 21.4
CQP814 (Hi)	TX ÷ 8	RX – 21.4
CQP833 (Lo)	TX ÷ 4	RX + 21.4
CQP863 (UHF only)	TX ÷ 8	(RX – 21.4) ÷ 3
CQM5114 (Hi)	TX ÷ 3	(RX – 10.7) ÷ 3
CQM5334 (Lo)	TX ÷ 4	(RX + 10.7) ÷ 2
CQM5662 (420–440)	TX ÷ 9	(RX – 21.4) ÷ 9
CQM5662 (440–449)	TX ÷ 9	(RX + 21.4) ÷ 9
CQM5662 (450–479)	TX ÷ 9	(RX – 21.4) ÷ 9
CQM5663 (450–479)	TX ÷ 9	(RX – 21.4) ÷ 9
CQM5663 (420–440)	TX ÷ 9	(RX – 21.4) ÷ 9
CQM5663 (440–449)	TX ÷ 9	(RX + 21.4) ÷ 9
CQM19.50	TX ÷ 18	(RX – 0.455) ÷ 16
CQM19.25	TX ÷ 18	(RX – 0.455) ÷ 16
CQM19.12.5	TX ÷ 18	(RX – 0.455) ÷ 16
CQM19I	TX ÷ 18	(RX – 0.455) ÷ 14

Model name and band	**Transmit crystal**	**Receive crystal**
(Storno – continued)		
CQP511 (146–160)	TX ÷ 12	(RX + 10.7) ÷ 3
CQP511 (156–174)	TX ÷ 12	(RX – 10.7) ÷ 3
CQP512 (156–174)	TX ÷ 12	(RX – 10.7) ÷ 3
CQP512 (146–160)	TX ÷ 12	(RX + 10.7) ÷ 3
CQM612 (146–160)	TX ÷ 12	(RX + 10.7) ÷ 3
CQM612 (156–174)	TX ÷ 12	(RX – 10.7) ÷ 3
CQM614 (146–160)	TX ÷ 12	(RX + 10.7) ÷ 3
CQM614 (156–174)	TX ÷ 12	(RX – 10.7) ÷ 3
CQM614 (Lo)	TX ÷ 6	(RX + 10.7) ÷ 2
CQM634 (Lo)	TX ÷ 6	(RX + 10.7) ÷ 2
CQM644 (Mid)	TX ÷ 8	(RX + 10.7) ÷ 3
CQM662 (UHF only)	TX ÷ 36	(RX – 10.7) ÷ 36
CQM713 (VHF only)	TX ÷ 12	(RX – 10.7) ÷ 12
CQM714 (VHF only)	TX ÷ 12	(RX – 10.7) ÷ 12
CQM733 (VHF only)	TX ÷ 6	(RX – 10.7) ÷ 6
CQM734 (VHF only)	TX ÷ 6	(RX – 10.7) ÷ 6
CQM761 (UHF only)	TX ÷ 36	(RX – 10.7) ÷ 36
CQM763 (UHF only)	TX ÷ 36	(RX – 10.7) ÷ 36
Tait		
T162 (70–88)	TX ÷ 2	(RX + 10.7) ÷ 2
T162 (88–108)	TX ÷ 2	(RX – 10.7) ÷ 2
T373 (118–136)	TX ÷ 3	(RX + 10.7) ÷ 3
T172 (148–174)	TX ÷ 3	(RX – 10.7) ÷ 3
T182 (70–88)	TX ÷ 2	(RX + 10.7) ÷ 3
T182 (88–108)	TX ÷ 2	(RX – 10.7) ÷ 3
T215C (70–94)		(RX + 10.7) ÷ 2
T215C (94–108)		(RX – 10.7) ÷ 2
T199 (68–88)	TX ÷ 3	(RX – 10.7) ÷ 2
T198 (148–174)	TX ÷ 6	(RX – 10.7) ÷ 3
T196 (401–520)	TX ÷ 12	(RX – 10.7) ÷ 12
T197 (105–108)	TX ÷ 6	(RX – 10.7) ÷ 3
T266 (148–161)		(RX + 10.7) ÷ 3
T266 (161–174)		(RX – 10.7) ÷ 3
T267 (148–174)	TX ÷ 12	
T335 (Lo)		(RX – 10.7) ÷ 3
T336 (Lo)	TX ÷ 3	
T355 (Hi)		(RX – 10.7) ÷ 3
T356 (Hi)	TX ÷ 6	
T345 (UHF)		(RX – 10.7) ÷ 12
T346 (UHF)	TX ÷ 12	
T347 (UHF)	TX ÷ 12	
T293 (UHF)		(RX – 10.7) ÷ 12
T294 (UHF)	TX ÷ 12	
T215C (118–136)		(RX + 10.7) ÷ 3
T215 (148–174)		(RX – 10.7) ÷ 3
T216C (Lo)	TX ÷ 2	
T216 (Hi)	TX ÷ 3	
T307 (81–108)	TX ÷ 2	(RX + 21.4) ÷ 3
T307 (118–136)	TX ÷ 3	(RX – 21.4) ÷ 3
T315 (66–88)		(RX – 10.7) ÷ 2
T316 (66–88)	TX ÷ 2	

Appendix

4 FM simplex and repeater frequencies

HERE are the FM amateur band channels on 4m, 2m, 70cm and 23cm, commonly used throughout the UK, together with a comprehensive listing of amateur repeaters in the UK. This information was correct as of September 1996 but changes do occur and you'll find the latest information in the current edition of the *RSGB Amateur Radio Call Book.*

Important note

During the lifetime of this book, amateur VHF/UHF FM channels are planned to change, with implementation for 2m planned to be complete by January 2000. 12.5kHz channel spacing will be adopted for FM phone operation on 145MHz. Beacons will operate on 144.400–144.490MHz, and a digital sub-band has been established at 144.800–144.990MHz.

With 12.5kHz channel spacing, the old 'S' and 'R' names do not work, and a new scheme has been proposed. Likewise with 70cm, where it is likely that 12.5kHz channel spacing will be adopted at some time in the future.

For 2m, the letter 'V' is used, and the number is the channel, counting in 12.5kHz steps, above 145MHz. So 145.500MHz, channel S20, will become V40 in the new 12.5kHz system.

For 2m repeaters, the letter 'R' is used, and the number gives the channel of the repeater output. For example, R4 (144.700MHz output) becomes 'RV56'.

The same scheme is used on 6m but with 10kHz steps and the letter 'F'. So the simplex channel on 51.510MHz is 'F51'.

On 70cm, the channel is designated by 'U' followed by the channel number (counting in 12.5kHz steps) above 430MHz. So channel SU20, 433.500MHz, becomes 'U280' as it is 280 times 12.5kHz above 430MHz. For repeaters the same scheme is used, but with an 'R' in front just as on the other bands.

Table A5.1. 4m simplex frequencies

Frequency (MHz)	UK usage
4m	
70.3000	RTTY/Fax
70.3125	Packet
70.3250	Packet
70.3375	Packet
70.3500	Emergency comms priority
70.3625	
70.3750	Emergency comms priority
70.3875	
70.4000	Emergency comms priority
70.4125	
70.4250	
70.4375	
70.4500	
70.4875	

Table A5.2. 2m, 70cm and 23cm simplex frequencies

Chan	Frequency (MHz)	Chan	Frequency (MHz)	Chan	Frequency (MHz)
2m		S21	145.525	**23cm**	
S8	145.200	S22	145.550	SM20	1297.500
S9	145.225	S23	145.575	SM21	1297.525
S10	145.250			SM22	1297.550
S11	145.275			SM23	1297.575
S12	145.300	**70cm**		SM24	1297.600
S13	145.325	SU16	433.400	SM25	1297.625
S14	145.350	SU17	433.425	SM26	1297.650
S15	145.375	SU18	433.450	SM27	1297.675
S16	145.400	SU19	433.475	SM28	1297.700
S17	145.425	SU20	433.500	SM29	1297.725
S18	145.450	SU21	433.525	SM30	1297.750
S19	145.475	SU22	433.550		
S20	145.500	SU23	433.575		

Table A5.2. UK repeater frequencies

Channel	Input freq	Output freq	Channel	Input freq	Output freq
2m			RB8	434.800	433.200
R0	145.000	145.600	RB9	434.825	433.225
R1	145.025	145.625	RB10	434.850	433.250
R2	145.050	145.650	RB11	434.875	433.275
R3	145.075	145.675	RB12	434.900	433.300
R4	145.100	145.700	RB13	434.925	433.325
R5	145.125	145.725	RB14	434.950	433.350
R6	145.150	145.750	RB15	434.975	433.375
R7	145.175	145.775			
			23cm		
70cm			RM0	1291.000	1297.000
RB0	434.600	433.000	RM2	1291.050	1297.050
RB1	434.625	433.025	RM3	1291.075	1297.075
RB2	434.650	433.050	RM5	1291.125	1297.125
RB3	434.675	433.075	RM6	1291.150	1297.150
RB4	434.700	433.100	RM9	1291.225	1297.225
RB5	434.725	433.125	RM12	1291.300	1297.300
RB6	434.750	433.150	RM15	1291.375	1297.375
RB7	434.775	433.175			

Table A5.3. UK operational and proposed repeaters

Call	QTHL	Channel	Location	Zone	CTCSS	Keeper
GB3AB	IO87WD	RB14	Aberdeen	G	A	GM1LKD
GB3AE	IO71OQ	50MHz	Tenby, Dyfed	E		GW0WBQ
GB3AF	IO94EQ	RT1-2	Durham TV	A		G1FBY
GB3AG	IO86ON	R5	Angus, Scotland	G	G	GM1CMF
GB3AH	JO02JO	RB11	Swaffham	C	F	G8PON
GB3AM	IO91QP	50MHz	Amersham, Bucks	C		G0RDI
GB3AN	IO73UJ	RB8	Anglesey	E	H	GW6DOK
GB3AR	IO73UA	R4	NTL Arfon	E	H	GW4KAZ
GB3AS	IO84KS	R0	NTL Caldbeck	A	C	G0JGS
GB3AT	IO90IU	RT1-2	Southampton	D		G6HNJ
GB3AV	IO91OT	RB2	Aylesbury	D	D	G6NB
GB3AW	IO91HH	RB10	Newbury	D	B	G8DOR
GB3AY	IO75OR	R2	Dalry, Ayrshire	G	G	GM3YKE
GB3BA	IO87TA	RB1	NTL Durris	G	A	GM4NHI

Call	QTHL	Channel	Location	Zone	CTCSS	Keeper
GB3BB	IO81OE	R4	Brecon, Powys	E	G	GW0GHQ
GB3BC	IO81KO	R6	Mynydd Machen	E	F	GW8ERA
GB3BD	IO92RA	RB6	Ampthill, Beds	B	C	G1BWW
GB3BE	JO02IF	RB9	Bury St Edmunds	C	H	G8KMM
GB3BF	IO92SD	R2	Bedford	B	C	G1BWW
GB3BH	IO91TP	RM0	Watford	C	D	G7LXP
GB3BI	IO77UO	R5	NTL Mounteagle	G	A	GM0JFL
GB3BK	IO91KL	RB11	Reading	D	J	G8DOR
GB3BL	IO92SD	RB7	Bedford Central	B	C	G1BWW
GB3BM	IO92DK	R2	NEC Birmingham	B		G4YKE
GB3BN	IO91PK	RB0	Bracknell	D	D	G4DDN
GB3BR	IO90WT	RB6	Brighton	C	E	G8VEH
GB3BS	IO81RL	RB10	Bristol, Avon	D	J	G4SDR
GB3BT	IO85XS	R4	Berwick-on-Tweed	G	J	GM1JFF
GB3BV	IO91SR	RB1	Hemel Hempstead	C	D	G6NB
GB3BW	IO92SD	RM6	Bedford	B	C	G1BWW
GB3BX	IO82XP	R3	Wolverhampton	B	A	G4JLI
GB3CA	IO84OT	RB13	Carlisle, Cumbria	A	C	G0JGS
GB3CB	IO92BL	RB14	Birmingham	B	A	G8AMD
GB3CC	IO90OU	RB3	Chichester	C	E	G3UEQ
GB3CE	JO01LV	RB14	Colchester	C	H	G7BKU
GB3CF	IO92IQ	R0	Leicester	B	C	G0ORY
GB3CH	IO70SM	RB2	NTL Caradon Hill	D	C	G1NSV
GB3CI	IO92PL	RB2	Corby, Northants	B	B	G8MLA
GB3CK	JO01JF	RB0	Ashford, Kent	C	G	G0GCQ
GB3CL	JO01OT	RB9	Clacton, Essex	C	H	G7HJK
CB3CM	IO71VU	RB8	Carmarthen, Wales	E	F	GW0IVG
GB3CN	IO92NF	RM5	Northampton	B	C	G6NYH
GB3CP	IO91VD	RM3	Crawley, Sussex	C	E	G3GRO
GB3CR	IO83LC	RB6	Mold, Clwyd	E	H	GW4GTE
GB3CS	IO85BU	R6	NTL Black Hill	G	G	GM4COX
GB3CT	IO90WX	RT2	Crawley, Sussex	C	E	
GB3CV	IO92GJ	RB9	Coventry	B	A	G3ZFR
GB3CW	IO82HL	RB6	Newtown, Powys	E	G	GW4NQJ
GB3CY	IO93KY	RB13	York	A	E	G4FUO
GB3DA	JO01GR	R5	Chelmsford, Essex	C	H	G4GUJ
GB3DC	IO94JR	RB11	Sunderland City	A	J	G6LMR
GB3DD	IO86ML	RB10	Dundee, Angus	G	F	GM4UGF
GB3DG	IO74UV	R7	NTL Cambret Hill	G	G	GM4VIR
GB3DI	IO91IN	RB6	Didcot, Oxon	D		G8CUL
GB3DS	IO93KH	RB13	Worksop, Notts	B	B	G3XXN
GB3DT	IO80WU	RB0	Blandford Forum	D	B	G8BXQ
GB3DV	IO93JK	RB1	Doncaster	A	B	G4LUE
GB3DY	IO93FB	RB10	Wirksworth, Derbys	B	B	G3ZYC
GB3EA	IO90HW	RB8	Southampton	D	B	G4MYS
GB3EB	JO01DO	RB5	Brentwood, Essex	C	H	G6IFH
GB3ED	IO85JW	RB14	Edinburgh	G	F	GM3GBX
GB3EE	IO93GE	RB12	Chesterfield	B	B	G6SVZ
GB3EF	JO01MT	50MHz	Martlesham, Suffolk	C		G7OEC
GB3EH	IO92FC	RB8	Banbury	B	A	G4OHB
GB3EK	JO01QJ	RB2	Margate	C	G	G4TKR
GB3EL	JO01AM	R0	East London	C	D	G4RZZ
GB3EM	IO92OT	RB1	Waltham, Leics	B	C	G3WWJ
GB3ER	JO01GR	RB3	Chelmsford	C	H	G4GUJ
GB3ES	JO00HV	R3	Hastings, Sussex	C	G	G7LEL
GB3ET	IO93EO	RT1-2	Huddersfield	A		G8HUA
GB3EV	IO84SQ	R4	Eden Valley, Cumbria	A	C	G0IYQ
GB3EX	IO80FP	RB0	Exeter, Devon	D	F	G8UWE
GB3EY	IO93WT	RT1-3	North Humberside	A		G8EQZ
GB3FC	IO83LU	RB2	Blackpool, Lancs	A	A	G4EZM

Call	QTHL	Channel	Location	Zone	CTCSS	Keeper
GB3FF	IO86JB	R0	NTL Craigkelly	G	F	GM0GNT
GB3FM	IO91OF	RM2	Farnham, Surrey	D	J	G4EPX
GB3FN	IO91OF	RB15	Farnham, Surrey	D	J	G4EPX
GB3FR	JO03AE	R7	Spilsby, Lincs	B	B	G8LXI
GB3FX	IO91OF	50MHz	Farnham, Surrey	C		G4EPX
GB3GB	IO92BN	RB12	Great Barr, WM	B	A	G8NDT
GB3GC	IO93NQ	RB4	Goole, Humberside	A	E	G0GLZ
GB3GD	IO74SG	R1	Snaefell, Isle Of Man	A	H	GD3LSF
GB3GF	IO91RF	RB12	Guildford, Surrey	C	E	G4EML
GB3GH	IO81WU	RB5	Cheltenham	D	J	G6AWT
GB3GJ	IN89WE	R2	StHelier, Jersey	D	C	GJ0NSG
GB3GL	IO85WL	RB14	Glasgow	G	G	GM3SAN
GB3GM	allocated (Dorset)					
GB3GN	IO87TA	R7	Aberdeen	G	A	GM4NHI
GB3GR	IO92QW	RB11	Grantham, Lincs	B	B	G4WFK
GB3GT	IO75UU	RT2	Glasgow (proposed)	G		
GB3GU	IN89RL	RB13	Guernsey, CI	D	C	GU4EON
GB3GV	IO92IQ	RT1-2	Markfield, Leics	B		G8OBP
GB3GY	IO93XN	RB11	Grimsby	B	E	G1BRB
GB3HA	IO93WT	RB6	Hull, Humberside	A	E	G4YTV
GB3HB	IO70OI	RB15	St Austell	D	C	G3IGV
GB3HC	IO82PB	RB6	Hereford	B	J	G4JSN
GB3HD	IO93BP	RB9	Huddersfield	A	D	G1FYS
GB3HE	JO00HV	RB14	Hastings, Sussex	C	G	G4FET
GB3HG	IO94KI	R1	BBC Bilsdale	A	J	G0RHI
GB3HH	IO93BF	R4	Buxton, Derbys	B	B	G3RKL
GB3HI	IO76DL	R4	BBC Torosay, Mull	G	E	GM3RFA
GB3HK	IO85VN	RB2	NTL Selkirk	G	J	GM0FTJ
GB3HL	IO91SM	RB3	Uxbridge, London	C	D	G8SUG
GB3HM	IO94HB	RB12	Boroughbridge	A	J	G0RHI
GB3HN	IO91VW	RB11	Hitchin, Herts	C	D	G3ZQI
GB3HO	IO91UC	RB1	Horsham, Sussex	C	E	G7JRV
GB3HR	IO91TO	RB14	Harrow, London	C	D	G4KUJ
GB3HS	IO93RT	R2	North Humberside	A	E	G7JZD
GB3HT	IO92HM	RB11	Hinckley, Leics	B	C	G8SHH
GB3HU	IO93RT	RB3	North Humberside	A	E	G3TEU
GB3HV	IO91OO	RT1-3	High Wycombe, Bucks	D		G8LES
GB3HW	JO01CN	RB13	Romford, Essex	C	H	G4GBW
GB3HX	IO93BP	50MHz	Huddersfield	A		G0PRF
GB3HY	IO90WX	RB5	Haywards Heath	C	E	G3XTH
GB3HZ	IO91OO	RB7	High Wycombe, Bucks	D	D	G4KCX
GB3IG	IO68SF	R7	Stornoway, Lewis	G	E	GM4PTQ
GB3IH	JO02OB	RB4	Ipswich, Suffolk	C	H	G8CPH
GB3IM	IO74SG	RB5	Snaefell, Isle of Man	A	H	GD3LSF
GB3IW	IO90IP	RB4	Isle of Wight	D	B	G0ISB
GB3KA	IO75TO	RB3	Galston, Ayrshire	G	G	GM3YKE
GB3KL	JO02FS	RB4	Kings Lynn	C	F	G3ZCA
GB3KN	JO01GH	R4	Maidstone, Kent	C	G	G3YCN
GB3KR	IO82VJ	RB3	Kidderminster	B	J	G8NTU
GB3KS	JO01OC	R1	NTL Dover, Kent	C	G	G4HHX
GB3KV	IO75TW	RB8	Bearsden, Glasgow	G	G	GM7OLA
GB3LA	IO93ET	RB8	Leeds	A	D	G8ZXA
GB3LC	JO03AI	RB13	Louth, Lincs.	B	B	G6GZS
GB3LD	IO84KE	R3	Ulverston, Cumbria	A	H	G6LMW
GB3LE	IO92IQ	RB4	Leicester	B	C	G0ORY
GB3LF	IO84OA	RB14	Lancaster	E	H	G8UHO
GB3LG	IO76HD	R3	Lochgilphead, Argyll	G	G	GM4WMM
GB3LH	IO82OP	RB15	Shrewsbury	B	G	G3UQH
GB3LI	IO83LL	RB10	Liverpool	A	D	G3WIC
GB3LL	IO83BH	RB0	Llandudno	E	H	GW8WFS

Call	QTHL	Channel	Location	Zone	CTCSS	Keeper
GB3LM	IO93RF	R5	Lincoln	B	B	G8VGF
GB3LO	JO02VL	RT1-2	Lowestoft, Suffolk	C		G4TAD
GB3LR	JO00AS	RB11	Newhaven, Sussex	C	E	G0ENJ
GB3LS	IO93RF	RB2	Lincoln	B	B	G8VGF
GB3LT	IO91SV	RB10	Luton	B	C	G6OUA
GB3LU	IP90KD	R3	Lerwick, Shetland	G	C	GM4SWU
GB3LV	IO91XP	RB2	Enfield, London	C	D	G3KSW
GB3LW	IO91WM	RB6	Central London	C	D	G8AUU
GB3LY	IO65NC	R0	Limavady, N Ireland	F	H	GI3GGY
GB3MA	IO83UO	RB1	Bury, Manchester	A	D	G8NSS
GB3MB	IO83UO	R0	Bury, Manchester	A	D	G8NSS
GB3MC	IO83RO	RM0	NTL Winter Hill	A	D	G8NSS
GB3MD	IO93JD	RB3	Mansfield, Notts	B	B	G0UYQ
GB3ME	IO92JJ	RB6	Rugby, Warwicks	B	A	G8DLX
GB3MF	IO83WG	RB7	Macclesfield	A	G	G0AMU
GB3MG	IO81FO	RB7	Bridgend, S Wales	E	F	GW3RVG
GB3MH	IO82TC	R1	Malvern Hills, Worcs	B	J	G3PWJ
GB3MK	IO92OB	RB0	Milton Keynes	D	C	G4NJU
GB3ML	IO85BU	RB10	NTL Black Hill	G	G	GM3SAN
GB3MM	IO82XP	RM6	Wolverhampton	B	A	G4OKE
GB3MN	IO83XH	R2	Stockport, Cheshire	A	D	G8LZO
GB3MP	IO83IF	R6	NTL Moel-y-Parc	E	H	GW1ATZ
GB3MR	IO83XH	RB14	Stockport, Cheshire	A	D	G8LZO
GB3MS	IO82TC	RB0	Malvern Hills, Worcs	B	J	G3PWJ
GB3MT	IO83RO	RB12	NTL Winter Hill	A	D	G8NSS
GB3MV	IO92NF	RT1-2	Northampton	B		G4WIM
GB3MW	IO92FH	RB10	Leamington Spa	B	A	G6FEO
GB3MX	IO93JD	R6	Mansfield, Notts	B	B	G0UYQ
GB3NA	IO93FO	R3	Barnsley, Yorks	A	B	G4TCG
GB3NB	JO02NM	R1	Norwich, Norfolk	C	F	G8VLL
GB3NC	IO70OI	R5	StAustell, Cornwall	D	C	G3IGV
GB3ND	IO70WX	RB14	NTL Huntshaw Cross	D	F	G4JKN
GB3NF	IO90HU	RB11	Southampton	D	B	G4KCM
GB3NG	IO87XO	R1	Fraserburgh	G	A	GM8LYS
GB3NH	IO92NF	RB3	Northampton	B	C	G4IIO
GB3NI	IO74CO	R5	Belfast, Co Down	F	H	GI3USS
GB3NK	JO01DH	RB4	Wrotham, Kent	C	G	G8JNZ
GB3NL	IO91XP	R7	Enfield, London	C	D	G3TZZ
GB3NM	IO92KX	RB7	Nottingham	B	B	G2SP
GB3NN	JO02JV	RB2	Wells, Somerset	C	F	G0FVF
GB3NO	JO02PP	RM0	Norwich, Norfolk	C	F	G8VLL
GB3NP	IO92NF	50MHz	Northampton	B		G1IRG
GB3NR	JO02PP	RB0	Norwich, Norfolk	C	F	G8VLL
GB3NS	IO91VH	RB10	Reigate, Surrey	C	D	G0OLX
GB3NT	IO94FW	RB0	Newcastle-on-Tyne	A	J	G4GBF
GB3NV	IO92KX	RT1-2	Nottingham	B		G6SKO
GB3NW	IO91VO	RB5	Hendon, London	C	D	G4GRS
GB3NX	IO91XC	RB2	Crawley, Sussex	C	E	G0DSU
GB3NY	IO94SG	RB0	Scarborough	A	E	G4EEV
GB3OC	IO88LX	R2	Kirkwall, Orkney	G	C	GM4TYU
GB3OH	IO85EX	RB4	Bo'ness	G	F	GM6WQH
GB3OM	IO64JQ	RB15	Omagh, N Ireland	F	H	GI4SXV
GB3OS	IO82WL	RB2	Stourbridge	B	A	G1PKZ
GB3OV	IO92WD	RB5	Huntingdon	B	F	G8LRS
GB3OX	IO91JS	RB12	Oxford	C	J	G4WXC
GB3PA	IO75ST	R1	Paisley	G	G	GM0BFW
GB3PB	IO92UO	RB10	Peterborough	B (E)	C	G1ARV
GB3PC	IO90KT	R7	Portsmouth, Hants	D	B	G4NAO
GB3PE	IO92TN	R3	Peterborough	B	F	G1ARV
GB3PF	IO83SS	RB0	Blackburn, Lancs	A	D	G4FSD

Call	QTHL	Channel	Location	Zone	CTCSS	Keeper
GB3PG	IO75OW	RB9	Greenock, Renfrews	G	G	GM4PLM
GB3PH	IO90LU	RB2	Portsmouth	D	B	G8PGF
GB3PI	IO92XA	R6	Royston, Herts	B	C	G4NBS
GB3PK			Cambridge (proposal)	B		
GB3PL		RM15	Cambridge (proposal)	B		
GB3PM		MBX	Cambridge (proposal)			
GB3PO	JO02NB	R2	Ipswich, Suffolk	C	H	G8CPH
GB3PP	IO83PS	RB15	Preston, Lancs	A	D	G3SYA
GB3PR	IO86GI	R3	Perth	G	F	GM8KPH
GB3PS	IO92XA	RM3	Royston, Herts	C	C	G4NBS
GB3PT	IO92XA	RB12	Royston, Herts	C	H	G4NBS
GB3PU	IO86GI	RB0	Perth	G	F	GM8KPH
GB3PV	JO02AF	RT1-2	Cambridge	B		G4NBS
GB3PW	IO82HL	R7	Newtown, Powys	E	G	GW4NQJ
GB3PX	IO92XA	50MHz	Barkway	B		G4NBS
GB3PY	JO02AF	RB8	Cambridge	B	C	G4NBS
GB3RA	IO82GG	R5	Llandrindod Wells	E	G	GW0KQX
GB3RC	IO83MB	RB9	Wrexham, Clwyd	E	G	GW7TKZ
GB3RD	IO91KL	R3	Reading, Berks	D	J	G8DOR
GB3RE	JO01HH	RB11	Maidstone, Kent	C	G	G4AKQ
GB3RF	IO83US	R7	Burnley, Lancs	A	D	G4FSD
GB3RR	IO93JA	50MHz	Hucknall	B		G4TSN
GB3RT	IO92EJ	RT1-2	Coventry	B		G8EMX
GB3RU	IO91KL	RM9	Reading, Berks	D	J	G8DOR
GB3SA	IO81AO	R3	Swansea, Wales	E	F	GW6KQC
GB3SB	IO85VN	R2	NTL Selkirk	G	J	GM0FTJ
GB3SC	IO90BR	R1	Bournemouth	D	B	G0API
GB3SD	IO80SQ	RB14	Weymouth	D	B	G0EVW
GB3SE	IO83WA	RM3	Stoke on Trent	B	G	G8DZJ
GB3SF	IO93BF	R7X	Buxton,Derbys	B	D	G3RKL
GB3SG	IO81JK	RB15	Cardiff, Wales	E	F	GW7KWG
GB3SH	IO80KT	RB11	NTL Stockland Hill	D	F	G6WWY
GB3SI	IO70GE	R1	St Ives, Cornwall	D	C	G3NPB
GB3SK	JO01MH	RB6	Canterbury, Kent	C	G	G6DIK
GB3SL	IO91XK	R2	BBC Crystal Palace	C	D	G3PAQ
GB3SM	IO93AC	RB13	Leek, Staffs.	B	G	G8DZJ
GB3SN	IO91LC	R5	Alton, Hampshire	D	B	G4EPX
GB3SO	IO92XX	RB0	Boston, Lincs	B	B	G8LXI
GB3SP	IO71OQ	RB4	Pembroke, Dyfed	E	F	GW4VRO
GB3SR	IO90WT	R0	Brighton, Sussex	C	E	G8VEH
GB3SS	IO87KM	R0	NTL Knock More	G	A	GM7LSI
GB3ST	IO83WA	RB2	Stoke on Trent	B	G	G8DZJ
GB3SU	JO02JA	RB15	Sudbury, Suffolk	C	H	G8AAR
GB3SV	JO01BU	RB0	Bishops Stortford	C	H	G1NOL
GB3SW	IO91BA	RB9	Salisbury, Wilts	D	B	G3YWT
GB3SX	IO83WA	50MHz	Stoke on Trent	B		G8DZJ
GB3SY	IO93GM	RB6	Barnsley, Yorks	A	B	G4LUE
GB3SZ	IO90BR	RB15	Bournemouth	D	B	G0API
GB3TC	IO80SX	RB1	Wincanton, Somerset	D		G3ZXX
GB3TD	IO91DL	RB3	Swindon, Wilts	D	J	G4XUT
GB3TE	JO01OT	R7	Clacton, Essex	C	H	G7HJK
GB3TF	IO82SQ	RB8	Telford, Salop	B	G	G3UKV
GB3TG	IO91PX	RT10-3	Bletchley	D		G4NJU
GB3TG	IO91PX	RT2RR	Bletchley	D		G4NJU
GB3TH	IO92DP	RB15	Tamworth	B	A	G0FEO
GB3TL	IO92WS	RB14	Spalding, Lincs	B	B	G7JBA
GB3TM	IO73UJ	RT1-2	Anglesey, Wales	E		GW8PBX
GB3TN	JO02KS	RT1-2	Fakenham, Norfolk	C		G4WVU
GB3TP	IO93BV	R5	Keighley, Yorks	A	D	G3RXH
GB3TR	IO80FM	R2	Torquay	D	F	G8XST

Call	QTHL	Channel	Location	Zone	CTCSS	Keeper
GB3TS	IO94KN	RB7	Middlesborough	A	J	G8MBK
GB3TT	IO93IG	RT1-2	Chesterfield	B		G1IOR
GB3TV	IO91RU	RT1-2	Dunstable	B		G4ENB
GB3TW	IO94KS	R5	NTL Burnhope	A	J	G4GBF
GB3TY	IO85XA	R6	Stagshaw, Nrth'land	A	J	G0GXO
GB3UB	IO81UJ	RB4	Bath, Avon	D	J	G0LIB
GB3UD	IO83VC	RT1-2	Stoke on Trent	B		G0KBI
GB3UK	IO83RO	50MHz	Winter Hill, Lancs	A		G8NSS
GB3UL	IO74CO	RB2	Belfast	F	H	GI3USS
GB3UM	IO92IQ	50MHz	Markfield, Leics	B		G0ORY
GB3US	IO93GJ	RB0	Sheffield	A	G	G3RKL
GB3UT	IO81UJ	RT1-1	Bath, Avon	D		G0LIB
GB3UY	IO93LW	RM13	York	A	B	G7AUP
GB3VA	IO91LT	R4	Aylesbury, Bucks	D	J	G6NB
GB3VE	IO84SQ	RB4	EdenValley, Cumbria	A	C	G0IYQ
GB3VH	IO91VT	RB13	Welwyn Garden City	C	D	G4THF
GB3VI	JO00HV	RT1	Hastings, Sussex	C		G8CMK
GB3VR	IO90WT	RT1-2	Brighton, Sussex	C		G8KOE
GB3VS	IO80LX	RB3	Taunton, Somerset	D	F	G4UVZ
GB3VT	IO83WA	R5	Stoke on Trent	B	G	G8DZJ
GB3VX	JO00CX	RT1-2	Heathfield, Sussex	C		G0TJH
GB3WB	IO81MI	RB5	Weston Super Mare	D	F	F7KUD
GB3WC	IO93EO	RM15	Wakefield, Yorks	A	D	G0COA
GB3WD	IO70XN	R4	BBC N Hessary Tor	D	C	G6URM
GB3WF	IO93DV	RB14	Leeds, Yorks	A	D	G8ZXA
GB3WG	IO81AO	RB6	Swansea	E	F	GW3VPL
GB3WH	IO91EM	R2	Swindon, Wilts	D	J	G8HBE
GB3WI	JO02CP	RB15	Wisbech, Cambs	B	F	G4NPH
GB3WJ	IO93QN	RB5	Scunthorpe	B	B	G3TMD
GB3WK	IO92FH	R7	Leamington Spa	B	A	G6FEO
GB3WL	IO91SM	R1	Uxbridge, London	C	D	G8SUG
GB3WM	IO92DK	R2	NEC Birmingham	B		G4YKE
GB3WN	IO82XP	RB0	Wolverhampton	B	A	G4OKE
GB3WP	IO83XL	RB11	Glossop, Derbys	A	D	G6YRK
GB3WR	IO81QF	R0	BBC Mendip, Somerset	D	F	G0MBX
GB3WS	IO91WB	R6	Crawley, Sussex	C	E	G4EFO
GB3WT	IO64JQ	R7	Omagh, N Ireland	F	H	GI3NVW
GB3WU	IO93EP	RB15	Wakefield, Yorks	A	D	G0COA
GB3WV	IO70XN	RT1-2	Dartmoor, Devon	D		G6URM
GB3WW	IO71XT	R7	BBC Carmel, Dyfed	E	F	GW6ZUS
GB3WX	IO80VX	50MHz	Shaftesbury	D		G3ZXX
GB3WY	IO93BS	RB7	Halifax, Yorks	A	D	G8NWK
GB3WZ	IO83MB	R3	Wrexham, Clwyd	E	G	GW7TKZ
GB3XG	IO81QJ	RT103	Bristol, Avon	D		G6TVJ
GB3XT	IO92EU	RT103	Burton on Trent	B		G8OZP
GB3XX	IO92KG	RB13	Daventry, Northants	B	C	G1ZJK
GB3YC	IO94SH	R0	Scarborough	A	E	G0OII
GB3YL	JO02UL	RB14	Lowestoft, Suffolk	C	F	G4TAD
GB3YS	IO80YS	RB2	Yeovil	D	F	G0LHX
GB3ZI	IO82XT	RB11	Stafford	B	T	G1UDS
GB3ZZ	IO81RM	RT1-2	Bristol, Avon	D		G6TVJ

This list is correct at 1 September 1996 but all details are subject to change. The zone quoted is the RSGB Zone. My thanks go to the RSGB Repeater Management Group for the above repeater information.

Appendix

5 PMR User Group (UK)

THE PMR User Group (UK) is a packet radio based organisation, which was set up by Steve, GM7DUG, to provide a database of files and a listing of amateurs keen on PMR conversion. At the time of writing, the server at GB7DUG has been running for nearly two years and has over 300 files on PMR equipment of different makes – it's growing all the time.

Many popular conversions are available, together with calculation information for crystals required in non-synthesised sets. The database is a 'two-way' affair, and Steve is continually trying to get information, so if you have some that isn't covered, why not upload it for the benefit of others?

There are about 100 members in the PMR User Group at the moment, mainly amateurs who are experienced in converting PMR kit. The members list is to give people an idea of who has converted what and hopefully could help others not quite so knowledgeable.

The way information is exchanged within the group is by sending a bulletin to PMRUK@GBR. The reason for bulletins rather than personal messages is to keep on-air packet traffic to a minimum, and also to alert others who may be interested in the subject. So if you have a question on anything PMR related, you can send it to PMRUK. If you can answer somebody's question send it to SB PMRUK@GBR. By doing it this way the whole group benefits from your knowledge, and may be able to add to it.

OBTAINING INFORMATION

To download information from the MODBOX, you can use either the REQDIR or REQFIL commands, or the automatic 7-PLUS server for large files.

To obtain a directory of all files on a subject

SP REQDIR@GM7DUG.GB7AYR.#78.GBR.EU
Title of message:
C:\ *.* @ (Your BBS) eg GB7XJZ *[This will give you the root directory]*
Text of message:
Ctrl Z or /EX

To obtain a specific file in a known directory

SP REQFIL@GM7DUG.GB7AYR.#78.GBR.EU
Title of message:

C:\MODS\ICOM\IC32AT.1 *[This will give you one of the files for the IC32AT]*

Text of message:
Ctrl Z or /EX

To use the AUTO7P server

SP AUTO7P@GM7DUG.GB7AYR.#78.GBR.EU
Title of message:
C:\MODS\[Filename] *[This will send the file you require in 7+format]*
Text of message:
Ctrl Z or /EX

Appendix

6 Useful addresses

Bonex
12 Elder Way,
Langley Business Park,
Slough,
Berkshire,
SL3 6EP.
Tel: 01753 549502.
(Ceramic filters, visits large rallies)

Cirkit Distribution Ltd
Park Lane,
Broxbourne,
Hertfordshire,
EN10 7NQ.
Tel: 01992 444111.
(Mail-order ceramic and crystal filters and receive preamplifiers)

Garex Electronics
8 Sandpiper Court,
Harrington Lane,
Exeter,
EX4 8NS.
Tel: 01392 466899.
(Ex-PMR rigs, spare PMR rig boards, crystal filters, receive preamps)

GWM Radio Ltd
40/42 Portland Road,
Worthing,
West Sussex,
BN11 1QN.
Tel: 01903 234897.
(Ex-PMR rigs and accessories)

Ham Radio Today
Nexus House,
Boundary Way,
Hemel Hempstead,
Herts,
HP2 7ST.
Tel: 01442 66551.
(Magazine publisher of PMR conversions, lists/photocopies available)

Roll up, roll up, get your ex-PMR rig crystals here

Maplin Electronics PLC
PO Box 3,
Rayleigh,
Essex,
SS6 8LR.
Tel: 01702 554155.
(Mail-order/retail shops, toneburst components and filters)

Mainline Electronics
PO Box 235,
Leicester,
LE2 9SH.
Tel: 0116 2777648.
(Ceramic and crystal filters, visits large rallies)

McKnight Fordahl Ltd
Hardley Industrial Estate,
Hythe,
Southampton,
Hampshire,
SO4 6ZY.
Tel: 01703 848961.
(Mail-order crystals)

Panorama Antennas Ltd
Frogmore,
London,
SW18 1HF.
Tel: 0181 874 5300.
(Manufacturers of PMR antennas for replacements – ask them for the details of your local Panorama dealer)

Quartslab Marketing Ltd
PO Box 19,
Erith,
Kent,
DA8 1LH.
Tel: 01322 330830.
(Mail-order crystals, some channels ex-stock, visits many rallies)

Index